PARAGUAY: ECOLOGICAL ESSAYS

PARAGUAY: ECOLOGICAL ESSAYS

Edited by J. Richard Gorham

Introduction by Jesse D. Perkinson

CONTRIBUTORS

G. T. Bertoni	J. R. Gorham
M. S. Bertoni	F. H. Schade
R. Boettner	B. J. Susnik
L. Cadogan	P. D. de Storni
T. Fariña Sánchez	R. C. Unruh

ACADEMY OF THE ARTS AND SCIENCES OF THE AMERICAS · MIAMI, FLORIDA ·1973

107276

International Standard Book Number: 0–913570–03–6
Library of Congress Catalog Card Number: 73–185472
Published by the Academy of the Arts and Sciences of the Americas
Box 811, Coconut Grove, Miami, Florida 33133
Copyright © 1973 by J. Richard Gorham. All rights reserved
Printed in the United States of America
by Edwards Brothers, Inc., Ann Arbor, Michigan 48104
Designed and typeset by Eva Nyqvist, Palo Alto, California 94306

Contents

Foreword

This book on Paraguay is the second monograph published by the Academy, the first being *Hurricanes of the Caribbean and Adjacent Regions, 1492-1800* by Dr. José Carlos Millás, Dean of Antillean Meteorologists.

Dr. J. R. Gorham has produced an eminently readable book in association with several distinguished scholars. The result is a multifacetted study of Paraguay with particular emphasis on the land and the people.

We are pleased to include this important title under the imprint of the Academy.

Henry Field, President
Academy of the Arts and Sciences
of the Americas

December 6, 1972
Box 811
Coconut Grove
Miami, Florida
33133

Preface

This collection of essays is the unexpected result of curious inquiry about the natural history of Paraguay. In the course of my studies of the ecology of malaria vectors in Paraguay, I naturally sought information about the milieu of the mosquitoes. My search for sources of reliable ecoinformation on Paraguay was largely unsuccessful. These inquiries, however, did lead me to several scientists engaged in ecological studies. Some of these scientists agreed to set down their thoughts in writing; their work makes up the bulk of the present volume.

A thorough and well-balanced book on the ecology of Paraguay cannot yet be written—there are still too many ecological unknowns in the heart of the South American continent. Since 1945 the United States government has invested about $63,000,000 in loans and grants to Paraguay. Another $25,000,000 were made available to Paraguay through international agencies to which the United States is a major contributor. There are no data by which it may be determined what portion of this enormous investment was used to systematically collect and publish ecoinformation. But one thing will become readily apparent to anyone who attempts to acquire from the literature more than a superficial knowledge of the Paraguayan environment: Basic facts, such as those about weather and climate, soils and vegetation, disease vectors and nosogeography, population composition and distribution, and even geography, are either very difficult to find or are simply unavailable.

To remedy this situation, at least in part, is one of the objectives of this book. Much of the information included herein is requisite to the kind of thorough understanding of the Paraguayan environment that is essential for effective planning of programs in public health, agriculture, and other areas of applied science.

A second objective, and probably the more important one, is to stimulate the interest of scientists, Paraguayan and non-Paraguayan alike, in the pursuit of ecological studies in Paraguay.

The chapters on climate, geology, animal life, mollusks, ants, geography, population, and nutrition were originally written in Spanish. The first five were translated to English by the editor. The others were translated by Mr. Warren Armstrong, whose assistance is gratefully acknowledged.

Dr. Henry Field has expertly guided the editor through the final stages of the preparation and production of this book. The book was designed and set in type by Mrs. Eva Nyqvist. I cannot find adequate words to properly express my appreciation to Mrs. Nyqvist for her consummate skill and artistry, and to Dr. Field for his constant encouragement and generous assistance.

Many other persons have assisted me in various ways in the preparation of this book. In this context several people merit special mention: Mr. Francisco Gañan, Dr. Nikita Makucheff, Mr. Atilio Pereira, Dr. Jesse D. Perkinson, Dr. Harold G. Scott, and Dr. Harris G. Warren. To these, and to all others who have helped, I am most grateful.

Permission to quote from copyrighted publications was kindly granted by Alfred A. Knopf, Inc.; American Folklore Society; American Geographical Society; Georges Borchardt, Inc.; Dr. W. Junk, Publishers; and W. B. Saunders Company.

Fairbanks, Alaska
December 1972

JRG

Introduction

At the time when the Latin American countries are becoming increasingly aware of the need for understanding their ecology, the publication of any sound scientific information is of great importance. This volume is not presented as a definitive or complete work on the ecology of Paraguay. Rather it is a first attempt to put into one publication the pertinent information which exists. In addition to the useful scientific information it contains, this compilation is important because it hopefully will increase interest in the field of ecology and will inspire Paraguayan scientists to continue and to increase their efforts in understanding their country. It might serve as the first in a series of publications on the ecology of each Latin American country.

The needs for studies of this kind become more pressing as industrialization proceeds ever more rapidly and the requirements for more land and better use of the land increase as a result of the rapidly expanding populations. An understanding of ecology by economic planners, developers of industry and colonizers of new areas is critical to the future well-being of the Latin American region. A productive working relationship between the scientists interested in the ecology of their countries and the planners and developers must be encouraged and strengthened if the undesirable results of unplanned exploitation of natural resources that exist in other regions are to be avoided in Latin America.

Jesse D. Perkinson, Director
Department of Scientific Affairs
Organization of American States
Washington, D.C.

I. The History of Natural History in Paraguay

J. RICHARD GORHAM

Natural history has always been inextricably interwoven with ecology.[4]

The Guaraní Era

Spanish comes from the Paraguayan's mind; Guaraní springs from his heart. Guaraní is the Paraguayan's first language, his mother tongue, the vernacular of the family and home. Spanish is superimposed on his life later, in school. Probably some 2.5 million people in Paraguay and in the adjacent portions of Brazil, Argentina and Bolivia today speak Guaraní, a language acquired long ago from the Indian inhabitants of the region. But the present geographic distribution of the language is considerably more limited now than it was at a time long before the Discovery, when Guaraní was *lingua franca* on the watersheds of the Orinoco, Amazon, Paraná and Paraguay.[17,50]

A FOREST PEOPLE

To live in close harmony, in both a spiritual and physical way, with their environment was, of course, a requisite to racial and individual survival for the Guaranís. Besides providing them with a religion, the forests supplied the Guaranís, and their enemies, with food and shelter and all the other material necessities of life. Sickness was, no doubt, a common event. Being keen observers of the nature of things, they developed a folk medicine which apparently contained at least some rationally-based elements.[22,74] Some appreciation of their spiritual relationships to the plants and animals of the Paraguayan forests may be gained by reading Chapter 9 by León Cadogan. A proper Guaraní ethnobiology, however, remains to be written.

It may very well be true that this relationship between the Indians and their environment was not altogether, or even predominantly, one-sided. That is, the Indians probably directly and intentionally altered their environment.[96] Broad prairies abound in both the Chaco and eastern Paraguay. Islands of forest, scattered here and there over

the prairie, are a characteristic and interesting feature of Paraguayan grasslands. Of course, as one proceeds through the prairie-forest ecotone in the direction of the forest, the situation reverses: islands of prairie are scattered through the forest.

Just what the natural climax formation was—prairie, or forest, or something similar to what we see today—before the first Amerinds arrived in Paraguay is open to speculation. Ellenberg[41] suggests that the Argentine pampas, which are in some respects similar to the Paraguayan prairies and the *campos cerrados* of Brazil, really constitute a disclimax, the original forest having been burned off by the Indians, who used the fires as devices for attack or defense or for hunting game. The grasslands of Paraguay could have originated in the same way. Similar ideas with relation to the North American Great Plains have been discussed by Wells,[105] Ehrenfried,[40] and Rogers.[87]

Advancing to the present for a moment, it may be noted that the horizon in Paraguay is seldom free from a pillar of smoke rising from the burning prairies. These fires are deliberately set by the ranchers, who believe, rightly or wrongly, that burning is requisite to a good grass crop and that the cattle graze better when the old grass stalks are burned off.

I do not want to give the impression here that the Guaraní Indians preferred the prairie habitat. On the contrary, Godoy[48] (who disagrees with Ellenberg's ideas about the Indians' use of fire) has cited several lines of evidence to show that the Guaranís were forest Indians. They did, of course, burn off small tracts of forest to make space for plots of mandioca. Godoy believes that the savannahs (*campos cerrados*) of southern Brazil are natural climax formations, not the result of deforestation by fire.

Early Exploration

The discovery and early exploration of Paraguay brought "civilized" man for the first time into first-hand contact with the Guaranís and their relatives. Some of the *conquistadores* and *padres* wrote accounts of their experiences, and these, though they must always be read with a critical eye, give us some insight into the natural history of Paraguay and the life of the Indians that inhabited the heart of South America. My purpose here is not to repeat the details of the history of the discovery, exploration, and colonization of Paraguay. This has already been admirably done by Warren,[103] on whose account the subsequent historical synopsis is largely based. Rather, I wish to present a brief and cursory introduction, mainly bibliographic, to the history of the natural history of Paraguay. Little has been written on this subject *per se*. Centurión[30] included many points pertinent to the subject in his monumental monograph on the cultural history of Paraguay, but his viewpoint is literary, not scientific. The history of the naturalists and of the natural history of Paraguay is just one of several lacunae in the history of Paraguay waiting to be filled.

ALEJO GARCÍA

This history of European intervention in Paraguay begins with the intrepid conquistador Alejo García. After Juan de Solís discovered the Río de Solís (= Río de la Plata) and was murdered by some Charrua Indians on its east bank, his "decapitated" expedition set sail for Spain. Just off the coast of Brazil, one of the ships foundered near Santa Catarina Island. Alejo García was one of the few survivors. He soon heard tales of Inca treasure and promptly laid plans for a foraging expedition to the Inca Empire. Incredibly, this end was accomplished in 1524 and 1525, with the help of the Guaraní Indians. He walked across southern Brazil, discovering the magnificent Iguazú Falls on the way, and continued on across eastern Paraguay to the Río Paraguay. Then he surmounted the treacheries of the Chaco Boreal and succeeded in wresting a little silver from some Bolivian Incas. García returned to the Río Paraguay where he died at the hands of the Indians. His exploits served as a stimulating and challenging example for the many European explorers who inevitably followed.[30,103]

CABOT, MENDOZA, AYOLAS

The next expedition to Paraguay was headed by Sebastián Cabot (= Gaboto), who sailed up the Río Paraguay in 1537 and found some silver (Alejo García's?) there in the possession of some Guaraní Indians. This prompted him to change the name of the river from Río de Solís to Río de la Plata.[103]

After Cabot returned to Spain, Charles V charged Pedro de Mendoza with the task of colonizing Paraguay. In those days the term Paraguay included all of present-day Paraguay, Argentina and Uruguay, as well as parts of Bolivia, Brazil and Chile.[100] Mendoza's first effort in the New World was to establish a colony at what is now Buenos Aires.

While things were going from bad to worse at Buenos Aires, Mendoza sent Juan de Ayolas up river to look for a route to Peru. Ayolas returned shortly with a much-needed supply of food but no route. Mendoza decided to see for himself what was up river, so he and Ayolas sailed up as far as Corpus Christi. After again sending Ayolas, along with Domingo Martínez de Irala, to hunt for a route to Peru, Mendoza returned to Buenos Aires. He quickly grew impatient for word from Ayolas, so he sent Gonzalo de Mendoza and Juan de Salazar de Espinoza to look for Ayolas. Pedro de Mendoza then set sail for Spain (he died *en route*).

Ayolas in the meantime ascended the Río Paraguay past Bahía Negra to Candelaria, where he left Domingo de Irala in charge of the boats, and set out across the Chaco toward the Inca Empire. He was never again seen alive by his comrades.[37]

ASUNCIÓN

Gonzalo de Mendoza and Juan de Salazar eventually found Irala. While the latter waited in vain for word from Ayolas, Salazar and Mendoza dropped down river where they built a fort called Nuestra Señora de la Asunción. That was in 1537.

Irala was eventually confirmed as the first governor of Paraguay. As soon as it was practical, he set up an expedition to search for Ayolas. After wrestling with the Chaco for several weeks in 1540, he gave up and returned to the river. There he became convinced that Ayolas was dead.

Irala spent the next two years organizing his government and building Asunción. Buenos Aires was abandoned in 1541. Its population joined forces with Asunción, resulting in a European population of some six hundred men and a few women and children.[103] Irala continued to prepare for another assault on the Chaco.

CABEZA DE VACA

When the news of the death of Pedro de Mendoza reached Spain, Alvar Núñez Cabeza de Vaca immediately became interested in the job of governor and applied to the Council of the Indies. This body commissioned Cabeza de Vaca. He sailed from Spain with a large expedition in 1540. A year after leaving Spain, he left his ships on the Brazilian coast and set out overland across Brazil toward Asunción. The final leg of the journey was done by river—down the Paraná and up the Paraguay. Irala surrendered his authority to Cabeza de Vaca in March of 1542. Cabeza de Vaca was no stranger to walking, with its attendant hardships, through unexplored and hostile territory. During the period 1528 to 1536, as one of three survivors out of a group of 300, he hiked from Texas to Mexico City.[33]

Although the problems of colonial administration were serious and everpresent, dreams of Inca gold and silver eventually led to another Chaco expedition. Irala conducted a reconnaissance mission early in 1543. This was followed by a full scale attempt, led by Cabeza de Vaca, later in the same year. A month of tramping around in the Chaco was enough. The party returned to Puerto de los Reyes on the river. After secondary expeditions by Francisco de Ribera and Hernando de Ribera, the whole project deteriorated and everybody went back to Asunción. Governor Cabeza de Vaca was promptly deposed. Irala succeeded him by popular election in April of 1544.

IRALA

In January of 1548 we again find Irala poised on the edge of the Chaco, ready for another attempt to reach the Inca Empire. Eight months later his expedition was camped in the Andean foothills of Bolivia, waiting for the return of messengers sent to the recently-ascended Spanish rulers of the region. Impatience and discontent grew among the Paraguayan force when it was realized that none of the Paraguayans was going to get rich from Inca treasure. Obviously, that had already been monopolized by the Spaniards of the Viceroyalty of Peru.

Irala wanted to wait longer for word about how his plan to open trade relations between Peru and Paraguay had been received by the Spanish officials in Peru. His men, however, had other ideas. They deposed him in favor of Gonzalo de Mendoza and turned towards Asunción. Later on, in March of 1549, Irala was again elected governor. His position was eventually confirmed by official appointment from Charles V.[103]

EARLY CHRONICLERS

This period of exploration and colonization was described in two contemporary accounts which are readily available today. Ulrich Schmidl was on board when Pedro de Mendoza sailed from Spain in 1535. Schmidl, by his own account, took active part in the many expeditions of Domingo de Irala in the Chaco. His story overlaps in part with the commentaries of Alvar Núñez Cabeza de Vaca, which were apparently written by his scribe Pero Hernández, and first published in 1552. These descriptions by Schmidl[36,90,91] and Cabeza de Vaca[36] comprise the first impressions of Europeans confronted with the Guaranís and their natural environment.

During this early period of the history of Paraguay, three major circumstances began to influence life in Paraguay. (1) So far as the Paraguayans were concerned, El Dorado[32] was out of reach. (2) Because Paraguay was obviously not to be a source of mineral wealth, the Spanish Crown largely lost interest in it. (3) The Indians of Paraguay were increasingly sought after as a labor force.

Colonial Period

During the period 1550 on through 1767, three main developments progressively unfolded: 1) the use of Indians as laborers; 2) the Catholicization of the Indians; and 3) the formation of the Paraguayan "race." The origin of the Paraguayan race has been treated elsewhere in this book (see Chapter 11). The same subject has also been discussed by Benítez,[12] Cardozo,[29] Juste,[55] and Service.[94] The evangelization and exploitation of the Indians were often mutually exclusive objectives. This conflict between the material and the spiritual eventually fell to the

material when the Jesuits were expelled from Paraguay by royal decree in 1767.

Centurión[30] cites three works which bridge the gap between the chronicles of Schmidl and Cabeza de Vaca and those of the Jesuits. Martín del Barco Centenera traveled widely in Paraguay and Peru. He accompanied Juan de Garay (one of Irala's successors) on an expedition into northern Paraguay. His book *Argentina y conquista del río de la Plata y Tucumán y otros acontecimientos de los reinos del Perú, Tucumán y estado de Brasil* was published in Lisbon in 1502. Reginaldo de Lizárraga (= Baltasar de Obando) was appointed bishop of Asunción in 1607. He wrote *Descripción breve de toda la tierra del Perú, Tucumán, río de la Plata y Chile.* Paraguay's first native chronicler was Ruy Díaz de Guzman. According to Professor Warren,[103] Ruy "had a lot of fun writing a history of the Plata area as he wished it had happened." His book, completed in 1612, was called *Historia de descubrimiento y conquista del río de la Plata.*[30]

JESUITS

The Jesuits began their work in Paraguay in 1588 and worked steadily thereafter until the expulsion order of 1767. One of several obstacles in the path of the Jesuits in their efforts to evangelize the Indians was the Indian languages. The Jesuit priest Antonio Ruíz de Montoya dedicated his great talents to the mastery of the Guaraní language. His *Tesoro de la lengua guaraní* was published in Madrid in 1640. He also wrote a history of Jesuit activities called *Conquista espiritual hecha por los religiosos de la Compañía de Jesús en las provincias del Paraguay.*[30]

Nicolás del Techo reached Paraguay in 1649. His *Historia de la Provincia del Paraguay y de la Compañía de Jesús*[97] was originally hand lettered with such skill by Guaraní artisans that it appeared to have been mechanically printed.[30] In 1733 Pedro Lozano published a description of the terrain, rivers, animal life, Indian customs and missionary activities in the Gran Chaco.[61] Pierre François Xavier de Charlevoix[31] had a lot of experience as an explorer and missionary before he arrived in Paraguay. He had sailed up the St. Lawrence River, crossed overland to the Mississippi and sailed down it to the Gulf. He was also familiar with Japan and the Caribbean. His *Historia del Paraguay* was published in Paris in 1767.[30]

Giuseppe Jolis was primarily interested in the natural sciences and in the Indians of the Chaco. According to Centurión,[30] he wrote a book called *Saggio sulla storia naturale della provincia del Gran Chaco.* Martín Dobrizhoffer, an Austrian monk, spent eighteen years among the Guaranís and the Abipones. He provides us with one of the most entertaining accounts of old Paraguay. Here are some excerpts from his history of the Abipones.[35]

> The Jesuit priest, Thomas Falconer, an Englishman well versed in medicine and botany, frequently and openly declared that Paraguay had been enriched by the bounty of nature with so many wholesome plants, roots, gums, woods and fruits, that whosoever was skilled in the knowledge of those things would have no occasion for European druggists to cure any disease.
>
> China chinae, Peruvian bark, or the remedy for fever. The

celebrated physician Woytz tells us that this medicine was first brought to Europe, in the year 1650, by Cardinal de Lugo, a Spanish Jesuit.

Many may, with more justice, contend that Asia was the original country of the Americans, it being connected with America by some hitherto undiscovered tie; and so they may, with my free leave; nor, were I to hear it affirmed that the Americans fell from the moon, should I offer any refutation, but having experienced the inconstancy, volubility, and changefulness of the Indians, should freely coincide in that opinion.

It would take up a long time to relate all the different methods by which the mandioc is converted into meat, drink, and medicine, mixed with butter, barley, and sugar. Happy are the Americans who can deceive and appease their stomachs by so many artifices.

The Spaniards of St. Iago, who go to the woods to seek wax and honey, cut certain palms to the pith. At the end of some weeks they return to the place, and in those palms they had wounded find very large fat worms, which they fry, and eat with much satisfaction.

An enemy is never more to be feared than when he is feared the least.

José Sánchez Labrador was one of the most competent naturalist-missionaries to work in Paraguay. His *Paraguay católico* remained in manuscript form until it was published in Argentina in 1910.[30] The text describes in detail the flora and fauna of Paraguay.[59] Dobrizhoffer apparently had a lot of confidence in the pharmaceutical botany of his day. If so, it was largely due to the efforts of the Jesuit physician Pedro Montenegro, who specialized in the study of the medicinal virtues of plants.[67] In 1710 he published his *Libro primero y segundo de la propriedad y virtudes de los árboles y plantas de las misiones y provincias de Tucumán, con algunas de Brasil y Oriente.* Segismundo de Asperger apparently continued the work of Montenegro and also became famous as a botanist. His manuscript on medicinal plants was never published.[30] Centurión considers Domingo Muriel[71] (= Cyriaco Morelli) to have been one of the most important Jesuit missionaries in Paraguay. The activities of this Jesuit have been the object of study by Fúrlong.[47]

AZARA

During the final years of Spanish rule in Paraguay, a commission was organized to survey and fix the boundaries between the possessions of Spain and those of Portugal. The commission, set up by the viceroy of Río de la Plata in 1782, was composed mainly of Spanish naval personnel. Three of its officers produced manuscripts of considerable importance to the history of the natural history of Paraguay. Andrés de Oyárvide was primarily interested in the hydrography of the Plate and Paraná rivers. But Félix de Azara[6-9] and Diego de Alvear y Ponce de León touched in their voluminous writings practically every aspect of the natural history of Paraguay.[30] The value of Azara's descriptive works on the birds and mammals of Paraguay is obvious even today. Azara is probably the outstanding figure in the development of Paraguayan natural history in the 18th century.

Independence

Either instability or chaos could appropriately describe affairs in Paraguay during the 17th and 18th centuries. A bewildering array of governors and would-be governors, bishops and would-be bishops, etc., waxed and waned from year to year. The patient Jesuits succeeded only because they insisted on keeping their Indians isolated from the rest of the Paraguayans. Every breach of this isolation policy seemed to result in a major setback for the missions.

A great complex of events and circumstances, involving personal ambition, greed, inept government in Paraguay and the rest of South America and in Europe, secular and religious intrigues, snail's-pace communications, geographic isolation, and innumerable other factors led through a prolonged travail to the birth of independent Paraguay in 1811. Paraguay was the first of the Spanish colonies to declare itself independent.

FRANCIA

In the case of Paraguay, the word "independent" was singularly inappropriate, especially so far as individual Paraguayans were concerned. For 27 years (1813–1840), the national history of Paraguay was the personal history of Doctor José Gaspar Rodríguez de Francia, the first president and undisputed ruler of Paraguay.[11] Francia's role in the development of natural history was a negative one, to say the least. The influence of that personality was so overwhelming that any naturalist present in Paraguay at the time became far better known, if known at all, by whatever commentary he might have made on his experiences with Francia than for any contribution to the development of natural history.[84,85]

Francia's personal physician, Juan Vicente Estigarribia, published on the subject of medicinal botany, but this occurred long after Francia died. During the years 1838 and 1839, shortly before the death of Francia bought his release from prison, Mariano Antonio Molas wrote *Descripción histórica de la antigua provincia del Paraguay* (published posthumously in 1868).[66] The natural history of Paraguay was superficially treated by Molas. However, the book is unique because it is the only serious literary effort by a Paraguayan contemporary of Francia to survive the reign of Paraguay's first president. Johan Rudolf Rengger, a Swiss physician-mammalogist, studied and wrote about the mammals of Paraguay,[79] and left us his impressions of the Francia era.[80,81]

After completing his travels with von Humboldt,[53] Aimé Bonpland settled down on a farm in the province of Corrientes, Argentina, just across the river from Paraguay. He served as director of the short-lived Museum of Corrientes.[54] Francia was apparently piqued by Bonpland's supposed infringement of Paraguay's monopoly of the *yerba* trade with Buenos Aires. This was sufficient justification for Francia to send a military expedition to destroy the Bonpland colony and carry the French naturalist himself into captivity. During the years 1821 to 1829, Bonpland was a "guest" at Cerrito in the Misiones of Paraguay.[30,76,86,103] Another famous naturalist, Auguste de Saint-Hilaire, either visited the Misiones region of Paraguay or came very close to it sometime during the years 1816–1822.[89]

C. A. LÓPEZ

The intellectual vacuum of the Francia years had obvious effects on social, political and intellectual developments during many succeeding years. Francia had seen to it that his countrymen became primitively self-sufficient: food and clothing were by necessity locally produced. Carlos Antonio López,[11] Paraguay's second president, envisioned a different sort of Paraguay. He still maintained a "strong center," but Francia's *status quo* and isolationism gave way to progress and generally responsible participation in the community of nations.[52] Paraguayans, of course, lacked the technical capabilities necessary for progress. Carlos Antonio López sought to eliminate this deficiency by bringing qualified foreigners to Paraguay. About 100 technical and professional consultants, mostly Europeans, came to Paraguay under contract with the López government. The basic natural sciences did not benefit very much from this influx of foreigners. But the applied aspects of the sciences, such as minerology or medicine, progressed rapidly. In fact, Paraguay became one of the most progressive countries in South America under the regime of Carlos Antonio López.

Little is known about Eberhard Munck af Rosenschöld other than by way of his letters to a colleague in Sweden.[70] He arrived in Paraguay in 1843 and subsequently made important initial collections and studies of Paraguayan plants. Domingo Parodi, an Italian chemist-physician, began studying the flora of Paraguay soon after his arrival there in 1856.[30] A great deal of descriptive natural history is contained in Page's[73] record of experiences on the rivers of Paraguay. Demersay[34] and Du Graty[38,39] wrote general descriptive accounts of Paraguay, including certain aspects of the natural history.

F. S. LÓPEZ

Francisco Solano López, Paraguay's third president, followed, at least during the first two years of his rule, the practice of his father regarding the import of technical and professional people. A few of these contracted consultants later became fairly well known for one reason or another. Dr. William Stewart, a British physician, arrived in Paraguay in 1857, contracted by the elder López. Dr. Stewart was one of the first professors in the School of Medicine at Asunción. He served as chief of military sanitation during the Triple Alliance War.[30] He stayed on in Paraguay after the war and played an influential role in the reconstruction of the nation. George Thompson[98] and Robert von Fischer-Treuenfeld,[45] both engineers, and George Masterman,[63] a pharmacist, all wrote of their experiences in Paraguay.

Francisco López pursued as president a diplomatic course[104] that eventually led to the Triple Alliance War in which Paraguay was defeated by Brazil, Argentine and Uruguay.[58]

Reconstruction Period

Political chaos during the sixty years between wars impeded but did not stop social and educational progress. This was possibly the most intellectually productive period in the history of the country. The natural history of Paraguay attracted considerable interest, both on the part of the foreigners as well as native Paraguayans. Centurión[30] has cited most of these scientists and some of their scientific contributions. At least some of these workers should be mentioned again here, either because they wrote valuable general descriptions of Paraguay or because they made important, or at least interesting, contributions to the sciences closely associated with the field of ecology. No effort is made here to make this list complete nor, with one exception, to comment on the relative merits of these scientists or their published works.

DESCRIPTIONS OF PARAGUAY

Some of those who wrote general accounts of Paraguay were Fontana,[46] Kerr,[56] Bourgade la Dardye,[26] Mulhall,[69] Bruyssel,[27] Mangels,[62] Schuster,[93] Peterman,[77] Koebel,[57] Miller,[65] and Zahm.[107] The plant life of Paraguay* was studied by Balanza,[30,60] Morong,[68] Hassler,[30,49,75] Rojas,[82,88] and Fiebrig.[30] The fascinating and abundant animals were described by A. de W. Bertoni,[13] Agar,[2] Fiebrig,[42-44] Schrottky,[92] Wetmore,[106] Rehn,[78] and Kaempfer.[28] Anisitz[5] and Rivas[83] wrote about the climate of Paraguay.

ANTHROPOLOGY

Anthropology has long been a popular subject in Paraguay, especially as it relates to Paraguayan Indian groups and their languages. This is especially true of the Guaraní. Besides having considerable intrinsic interest both as a language and a tribe, Guaraní is a nationalistic symbol that conveniently bears a certain amount of propaganda value and is a major source of national pride and cohesiveness. Some of the students of anthropology were Hermann,[51] G. T. Bertoni,[14] Boggiani,[24,25] Nordenskiöld,[72] Alacron and Pittini,[3] Manuel Dominguez, Manuel Gondra, and Cecilio Baéz.[30]

This period also saw the founding of several organizations, institutions and journals directly related to the development of natural history. Andrés Barbero[30] founded the Museo de Historia Natural. The Universidad National de la Asunción was established in 1889, and the health department was organized the same year by Dr. Stewart.[67] Two important journals were founded: the Revista del Instituto Paraguayo in 1896 and, much later, the Sociedad Científica del Paraguay began publishing its official journal. The Jardín Botánico became an important focal point of activities in the fields of biology and geology.

---

*For a bibliography of Paraguayan botany, see Blake, S. F., and A. C. Atwood, 1942, Geographical guide to the floras of the world: an annotated list with special reference to useful plants and common plant names. Pt. 1. Africa, Australia, North America, South America and islands of the Atlantic, Pacific, and Indian Oceans. U.S. Dept. Agricultural Misc. Publication 401: 1–336.

BERTONI AND ECOLOGY

So far as ecology *per se* is concerned, the studies of Sosa Escalada[95] and Migone[64] could easily be termed ecological. But Paraguay's first and foremost ecologist, surely the outstanding scientific personage of the between-the-wars period, was Moisés Santiago Bertoni. He came to Paraguay in 1882, shortly after graduating with a doctorate in natural science from the University of Zürich. By that time natural history was a going concern, many of its basic ideas having been formulated even before Alfred Russel Wallace's "wonderful century"[102] was three-quarters over. Ecology was well on the way to becoming a separate science.[4] The Darwin-Wallace theory had come out in 1858 and 1859. In his study of the geographical distribution of animals, Wallace placed Paraguay in the Brazilian sub-region of tropical South America.[101] Bertoni was, no doubt, well grounded then in the ecological principles of that day and age when he arrived in Paraguay. His prodigious talent and enthusiasm combined to produce a multitude of studies on malaria,[15] economic botany,[16] philology,[17] ecology,[18] climatology,[19] anthropology,[20,23] agriculture,[21] and many other subjects. A chapter of his best ecological work,[18] *Condiciones generales de la vida orgánica,* is reproduced in translation in this book (Chapter 6).

Contemporary Paraguayan scientists are mentioned by Centurión[30] and by the UNESCO study.[99]

Paraguay: Politicosystem or Ecosystem?

Ever since the Triple Alliance War, politics of a very provincial and short-sighted sort has been the dominant feature of Paraguayan society and government. The first concern of each succeeding government was to stay in power. Maintenance of an appropriate "defense posture" consumed the lion's share of the national budget. *Cuartelazos* were favorite diversions of the military. This was hardly the sort of environment in which interest in the natural sciences could be expected to flourish. Nevertheless, as we have seen, considerable progress was made.

There are even encouraging signs of a more enlightened attitude on the part of the present government of Paraguay toward the promotion of scientific enterprises. Indeed, in this respect the present government seems to parallel that of Carlos Antonio López. This is as it should be, since—after all—the economic development of Paraguay must be based on the intelligent use of the natural endowments and products of the country. Obviously a great deal remains to be done.

Conservation is practically an unknown concept in Paraguay. On the other hand, reckless exploitation of natural resources is the order of the day. At least two national parks have been established, but they are not mentioned in the list of South American national parks given by Acosta-Solis.[1] Several more representative areas of Paraguay should be set aside and preserved. For example, the Misiones prairies along the Río Tebicuary, the Guayakí-inhabited forests of Caaguazú and Alto Paraná, the forested hills of Cerro Corá along the Río Aquidabán, the wet chaco *palmeras* near the Río Pilcomayo, and the *quebracho* parklands of the dry chaco near Gabino Mendoza.

The active road-building campaign of the present government is, of course, an essential part of economic development. But at the same time, the new roads facilitate the exposure of these relatively untouched areas to exploitation and destruction. Modern methods of forest and grassland management, animal husbandry, and crop production must be adapted to Paraguay and quickly put into practice.

There is, obviously, nothing new in these recommendations. Small starts have been made in all these programs in Paraguay, with both foreign and local interests playing significant roles. It is simply a matter of emphasis, or rather a shifting of emphasis from political self-preservation and exaggerated militarism to education, conservation (in the best sense of the word), and disinterested democratic government. As I said before, this shift seems to be taking place. Should it continue in this direction, not just on the part of the present national leadership, but with the devoted participation of all citizens, including the loyal opposition, then Paraguay will once again enjoy political and economic stability and an important and influential position in the community of nations.

Literature Cited

1. Acosta-Solis, M. 1969. Protección y conservación de la naturaleza en Sudamérica. *In* Fittkau, E. J., J. Illies, H. Klinge, G. H. Schwabe, and H. Sioli. (Eds.). Biogeography and ecology in South America. Vol. 1. Dr. W. Junk, The Hague.

2. Agar, W. E. 1911. A zoological expedition to South America. *In* Grubb, W. B. An unknown people in an unknown land. An account of the life and customs of the Lengua Indians of the Paraguayan Chaco, with adventures and experiences met with during twenty years' pioneering and exploration amongst them. Lippincott, Philadelphia.

3. Alacron y Cañedo, J., and R. Pittini. n.d. (circa 1925). El Chaco paraguayo y sus tribus. Sociedad Editora Internacional, Turin.

4. Allee, W. C., A. E. Emerson, O. Park, T. Park, and K. P. Schmidt. 1949. Principles of animal ecology. Saunders, Philadelphia. Quoted by permission of the publisher.

5. Anisitz, D. 1902. Observaciones meteorológicas. Rev. Inst. Paraguayo 4 (33): 260–265.

6. Azara, F. de. 1904. Geografía física y esférica de las provincias del Paraguay y misiones guaraníes. Vol. 1. Anales del Museo Nacional, Montevideo.

7. Azara, F. de. 1906. Los pájaros del Paraguay. Rev. Inst. Paraguayo 8 (53): 149–178.

8. Azara, F. de. 1941. Viajes por la América meridional. Espasa-Calpe, Madrid.

9. Azara, F. de. 1943. Descripción e historia del Paraguay y del Río de la Plata. Editorial Bajel, Buenos Aires.

10. Becu, T., and J. T. Revello. 1941. La colección de documentos de Pedro de Angelis y el diario de Diego de Alvear. Peuser, Buenos Aires.

11. Benítez, J. P. 1949. Carlos Antonio López. Editorial Ayacucho, Buenos Aires.

12. Benítez, J. P. 1955. Formación social del pueblo paraguayo. Editorial América-Sapucai, Buenos Aires.

13 Bertoni, A. de W. 1939. Catálogos sistemáticos de los vertebrados del Paraguay. Rev. Soc. Cien. Paraguay 4 (4): 1–58.

14. Bertoni, G. T. 1927. El indio guayakí. La Colmena, Asunción.

15. Bertoni, M. S. 1900. Contribución al estudio de la malaria (chucho) y su tratamiento, observaciones hechas en el Alto Paraná, Misiones y Paraguay. Kraus, Asunción.

16. Bertoni, M. S. 1914. Las plantas usuales del Paraguay y países limítrofes. Introducción, nomenclatura y diccionario de los géneros botánicos latino-guaraní. Brossa, Asunción.

17. Bertoni, M. S. 1916. Influencia de la lengua guaraní en Sudamérica y Antillas. Kraus, Asunción.

18. Bertoni, M. S. 1918. Condiciones generales de la vida orgánica y división territorial. Descripción física y económica del Paraguay. Imprenta "Ex Sylvis," Puerto Bertoni, Paraguay.

19. Bertoni, M. S. 1918. Estudio de las periodicidades diarias aparentes o reales de las lluvias y tempestades. Imprenta "Ex Sylvis," Puerto Bertoni, Paraguay.

20. Bertoni, M. S. 1922. La civilización guaraní. Parte 1. Origen, extensión y cultura de la raza Karaí-Guaraní y protohistoria de los Guaraníes. Imprenta "Ex Sylvis," Puerto Bertoni, Paraguay.

21. Bertoni, M. S. 1926. Agenda y mentor agrícola. Imprenta "Ex Sylvis," Puerto Bertoni, Paraguay.

22. Bertoni, M. S. 1927. La civilización guaraní. Parte 3. La higiene guaraní. La medicina guaraní. Imprenta "Ex Sylvis," Puerto Bertoni, Paraguay.

23. Bertoni, M. S. 1941. Los Guayakíes. Imprenta Guaraní, Asunción.

24. Boggiani, G. 1895. Viaggi d'un artista nell'America Meridionale. Loescher, Rome.

25. Boggiani, G. 1899. Cartografía lingüística del Chaco por el Dr. Daniel G. Brinton. Rev. Inst. Paraguayo 2 (16): 106–137.

26. Bourgade la Dardye, E. de. 1889. Le Paraguay. Plon, Nourrit, Paris. Also: 1892. Paraguay: The land and the people, natural wealth and commercial capabilities. Philip, London.

27. Bruyssel, E. van. 1893. La République du Paraguay. Muquardt, Brussels.

28. Camargo, H. F. de A. 1962. Sôbre a viagem de Emil Kaempfer ao Brasil. Papéis Avulsos Dpto. Zool. (São Paulo) 15 (8): 79–80.

29. Cardozo, E. 1959. Historiografía paraguaya. Vol. 1. Paraguay indígena, español y jesuita. Comisión de Historia del Instituto Panamericano de Geografía e Historia, México, D.F.

30. Centurión, C. R. 1961. Historia de la cultura paraguaya. 2 vol. Biblioteca "Ortiz Guerrero," Asunción.

31. Charlevoix, P. F. X. de. 1769. The history of Paraguay. Lockyer Davis, London.

32. Clark, L. 1954. The rivers ran east. Hutchinson, London.

33. Covey, C. (Ed.). 1961. Cabeza de Vaca's adventures in the unknown interior of America. Collier, New York.

34. Demersay, A. 1860–1865. Histoire physique, économique et politique du Paraguay et des établissements de Jésuites. 2 vol. Librarie Hachette, Paris.

35. Dobrizhoffer, M. 1822. An account of the Abipones, an equestrian people of Paraguay. 3 vol. Murray, London.

36. Dominguez, L. L. 1891. The conquest of the River Plate (1535–1555). I. Voyage of Ulrich Schmidt to the rivers La Plata and Paraguai. II. The commentaries of Alvar Núñez Cabeza de Vaca. Hakluyt Society, London.

37. Dominguez, M. 1899. Viajes y muerte de Ayolas. Rev. Inst. Paraguayo 2 (16): 146–156.

38. Du Graty, A. 1865. La République du Paraguay. Muquardt, Brussels.

39. Du Graty, A. 1902. Minerales del Paraguay. Rev. Inst. Paraguayo 4 (33): 266–282.

40. Ehrenfried, G. 1965. Grassland vegetation: Historical note. Science 148 (3674): 1173.

41. Ellenberg, H. 1962. Wald in der Pampas Argentiniens? Veröffentl. Geobot. Inst. Eidg. Techn. Hochschule, Stiftung Rübel (Zurich) 37: 39–56.

42. Fiebrig, K. 1907. Eine Wespen zerstörende Ameise aus Paraguay. *Eciton vagans* Olivier. Z. wiss. Insektenbiologie 3: 83–87.

43. Fiebrig, K. 1907. Eine Ameisen änliche Grillide aus Paraguay. Z. wiss. Insektenbiologie 3: 101–106.

44. Fiebrig, C. 1935. 1. Hormigas. *In* Apuntes zoológicos. Rev. Jardín Bot. Mus. Hist. Nat. Paraguay 4: 119–126.

45. Fischer-Treuenfeld, R. von. 1906. Le Paraguay. Guyot, Brussels.

46. Fontana, L. J. 1881. El Gran Chaco. Imprenta de Ostwald y Martínez, Buenos Aires.

47. Fúrlong, G. 1955. Domingo Muriel, S. J., y su relación de las misiones (1766). Librería del Plata, Buenos Aires.

48. Godoy, M.O. de. 1963. Antique forest, and primitive and civilized man at Pirassununga County, S. Paulo State, Brasil. Anais Acad. Brasil. Ciên. 35 (1): 83–101.

49. Hassler, E. 1901. Enumeración preliminar de las plantas usuales del Paraguay. Rev. Inst. Paraguayo 3 (29): 161–170.

50. Heredia, J. R. 1962. Caribes y Guaraníes una sola y misma raza. La Tribuna (Asunción) 37 (18984, Supl. Dom.): 1.

51. Hermann, W. 1908. Die ethnographischen Ergebnisse der Deutschen Pilcomayo Expedition. Z. Ethnol. 40 (1): 120–137.

52. Hopkins, E. A., R. E. Crist, and W. D. Snow. 1968. Paraguay 1852 and 1968. American Geographical Society, New York.

53. Humboldt, A. von, and A. Bonpland. 1900. Personal narrative of travels to the equinoctial regions of America, during the years 1799–1804. 3 vol. Thomasina Ross, London.

54. Hutchinson, T. J. 1868. The Paraná; with incidents of the Paraguayan War, and South American recollections, from 1861–1868. Edward Stanford, London.

55. Juste Martell, R. 1957. Antropogénesis del hombre guaraní. Pontificia Universidad Católica Javeriana, Bogotá.

56. Kerr, J. G. 1911. Geological structure, climate, fauna and flora of the Chaco. *In* (see Agar, 1911).

57. Koebel, W. H. 1917. Paraguay. T. Fisher Unwin, London.

58. Kolinski, C. J. 1965. Independence or death! The story of the Paraguayan War. University of Florida Press, Gainesville.

59. Labrador, J. S. 1910. El Paraguay católico. Coni Hermanos, Buenos Aires.

60. Lanjouw, J. 1945. On the location of botanical collections from Central and South America. *In* Verdoorn, F. Plants and plant science in Latin America. Chronica Botanica, Waltham, Massachussets.

61. Lozano, P. 1941. Descripción corográfica del Gran Chaco Gualamba. Instituto de Antropología, Tucumán.

62. Mangels, H. 1919. Paraguay. Wirtschaftliche, naturgeschichtliche, und klimatologische Abhandlungen. F. P. Datterer, München-Freising.

63. Masterman, G. F. 1870. Seven eventful years in Paraguay. Sampson Low, Son, and Marston, London.

64. Migone, L. E. 1929. Apuntes de climatología y nosografía médica del Paraguay. Rev. Soc. Cien. Paraguay 2 (5): 203–222.

65. Miller, L. E. 1918. In the wilds of South America. Scribner's, New York.

66. Molas, M. A. 1957. Descripción histórica de la antigua provincia del Paraguay. Ediciones Nizza, Buenos Aires.

67. Moll, A. A. 1944. Aesculapius in Latin America. Saunders, Philadelphia.

68. Morong, T., and N. L. Britton. 1892–93. An enumeration of the plants collected by Dr. Thomas Morong in Paraguay, 1888–1890. Ann. New York Acad. Sci. 7: 45–280.

69. Mulhall, M. G., and E. T. Mulhall. (Eds.). 1885. Handbook of the River Plate, comprising the Argentine Republic, Uruguay and Paraguay. 5th ed. Mulhall, Buenos Aires.

70. Munck af Rosenschöld, E. 1955. Algunas cartas del naturalista sueco don Eberhard Munck af Rosenschöld escritas durante su estadía en el Paraguay, 1843–1869. Biblioteca e Instituto de Estudios Ibero-Americanos de la Escuela de Ciencias Económicas, Stockholm.

71. Muriel, D. 1918. Historia del Paraguay desde 1747 hasta 1767. Victoriano Suárez, Madrid.

72. Nordenskiöld, E. 1912. Les Indiens du Chaco. Rev. Geog. Ann. (Paris) 6: 1–278. Also: Indianerleben. El Gran Chaco (Südamerika). Bonnier, Leipzig.

73. Page, T. J. 1859. La Plata, the Argentine Confederation, and Paraguay. Being a narrative of the exploration of the tributaries of the River La Plata and adjacent during the years 1853, '54, '55, and '56, under the orders of the United States Government. Harper, New York.

74. Pardal. R. 1938. Medicina aborigen americana. José Anesi, Buenos Aires.

75. Pennel, F. W. 1945. Historical sketch. In (see Lanjouw 1945).

76. Pérez Acosta, J. F. 1942. Francia y Bonpland. Peuser, Buenos Aires.

77. Peterman, A. 1875. Südamerikanischen Republiken Argentina, Chile, Paraguay und Uruguay in 1875. Ergänzungsband 9 (30): 1–22.

78. Rehn, J. A. G. 1934. Zoologist in the pantanal of the upper Paraguay. Sci. Mon. 39 (1): 20–39.

79. Rengger, J. R. 1830. Naturgeschichte der Säugethiere von Paraguay. Schweighausersche Buchhandlung, Basel.

80. Rengger, J. R. 1835. Reise nach Paraguay in den Jahren 1818 bis 1826. Jauerlaender, Aarau.

81. Rengger, J. R., and R. de Longchamps. 1827. The reign of doctor Joseph Gaspard Roderick De Francia, in Paraguay; being an account of a six years' residence in that republic, from July, 1819–to May, 1825. T. Hurst, E. Chance, London.

82. Riquelme García, B. 1962. Teodoro Rojas: el insigne botánico paraguayo. La Tribuna (Asunción) 37 (LB754, Supl. Dom.): 1.

83. Rivas, S. 1890. Contribución al estudio del clima del Paraguay. Tipografía de "El Paraguayo," Asunción.

84. Robertson, J. P., and W. P. Robertson. 1838. Letters on Paraguay: comprising an account of a four years' residence in that Republic, under the government of the dictator Francia. 2 vol. Murray, London.

85. Robertson, J. P., and W. P. Robertson. 1838. Four years in Paraguay. 2 vol. Carey and Hart, Philadelphia.

86. Robertson, J. P. and W. P. Robertson. 1839. Francia's reign of terror, being a sequel to Letters on Paraguay. 2 vol. Carey and Hart, Philadelphia.

87. Rogers, D. J. 1966. Woodlands in the Great Plains. Science 151 (3717): 1483.

88. Rojas, T., and J. P. Carabia. 1945. Breve reseña de la vegetación paraguaya. In (see Lanjouw 1945).

89. Saint-Hilaire, A. 1946. Esquisse de mes voyages au Brésil et Paraguay considérés principalement sous le rapport de la botanique. Chronica Botanica 10 (1): 1–61.

90. Schmidel, U. 1889. Ulrich Schmidels Reise nach Süd-Amerika in den Jahren 1534 bis 1554. Gedrückt für den Litterärischen Verein in Stuttgart, Tübingen.

91. Schmidl, U. 1942. Viaje al río de la Plata. Emecé-Editores, Buenos Aires.

92. Schrottky, C. 1907. Blumen und Insekten in Paraguay. Z. wiss. Insektenbiologie 3: 47–53, 73–78.

93. Schuster, A. N. 1929. Paraguay. Land, Volk, Geschichte, Wirtschaftsleben und Kolonisation. Strecher und Schröder, Stuttgart.

94. Service, E. R. 1954. Spanish-Guaraní relations in early colonial Paraguay. University of Michigan Press, Ann Arbor.

95. Sosa Escalada, E. 1909. Influencia de desmontes en el régimen de las aguas. Rev. Inst. Paraguayo 10 (61): 778–788; 10 (63): 968–977.

96. Sternberg, H. O. 1969. Man and environmental change in South America. In (see Acosta-Solis 1969).

97. Techo, N. del. 1897. Historia de la provincia del Paraguay y de la Compañía de Jesús. 5 vol. Uribe, Asunción.

98. Thompson, G. 1869. The war in Paraguay. Longmans, Green, London.

99. UNESCO. 1959. Scientific institutions and scientists in Latin America. Centro de Cooperación Científica para América Latina, Montevideo.

100. Vasconsellos, V. N. 1962. Lecciones de historia paraguaya. 2nd ed. Published by the author, Asunción.

101. Wallace, A. R. 1876. The geographical distribution of animals. Harper, New York.

102. Wallace, A. R. 1908. The wonderful century. 7th ed. Swan, Sonnenschein, London.

103. Warren, H. G. 1949. Paraguay. An informal history. University of Oklahoma Press, Norman.

104. Warren, H. G. 1962. The Paraguayan image of the War of the Triple Alliance. The Americas 19 (1): 3–20.

105. Wells, P. V. 1965. Scarp woodlands, transported grassland soils, and concept of grassland climate in the Great Plains region. Science 148 (3667): 246–249.

106. Wetmore, A. 1926. Observations on the birds of Argentina, Paraguay, Uruguay, and Chile. U.S. Nat. Mus. Bull. 133: 1–448.

107. Zahm, J. A. 1916. Through South America's southland. Appleton, New York.

Author's address: Dr. J. Richard Gorham
Department of Biological Sciences
University of Alaska
Fairbanks, Alaska 99701

II. The Geography of Paraguay*

GUILLERMO TELL BERTONI AND J. RICHARD GORHAM

Unlike all other lands with which I am familiar, it seems destined especially for the habitation of man.

Hopkins[19]

A fertile soil, a generally pleasant climate, and an industrious people do not add up to a prosperous nation in the case of Paraguay, where centuries of isolation, war, and revolution have spelled stagnation.

Crist[19]

Paraguay today is not a "stagnant" nation.

Snow[19]

Physiographic Zones

The first person to divide Paraguay into natural zones and regions on the basis of agricultural, physiographic and climatic considerations was Dr. Moisés Bertoni. His "Mapa agrológico, fisiográfico, y climatológico" was published in 1918.[7] These various regions were described in another Bertoni work[6] published the same year under the title "Introducción y gea—Condiciones generales de la vida orgánica." This was the introductory volume in a proposed exhaustive study, the "Descripción física y económica del Paraguay." Dr. Bertoni completed two volumes and a dozen monographs in this series before his death in 1921.

There are several other older but useful works on this general subject: Azara,[1,2] Bourgade,[9] Du Graty,[15] and others.[10,21,28,33] More recent information may be found in the geographic encyclopedias,[3,13] texts on Latin American and Paraguayan geography,[17,19,24,26,27] and in several specialized publications.[11,14,20,23,29,31,32]

In his general discussion of South American ecosystems, Mann[22] included the Paraguayan Chaco in the Savannah Biome (specifically, tropical thorn savannah), and eastern Paraguay in the Forest Biome (specifically, tropical macrothermal evergreen rain forest), and he lists the characteristic flora and fauna of each biome.

---

*During the many years that the senior author served as Professor of Economic Geography at the National University of Asunción, he developed a lengthy set of mimeographed notes on the general subject of economic geography, with special reference to Paraguay. In 1952 he gathered these notes together in a mimeographed volume[5] for use by his students. These notes included much information on the descriptive and physical geography of Paraguay. It was this material which Bertoni planned to rewrite and update for use in this volume of ecological essays. His death in 1963 thwarted that plan. The junior author has therefore assumed the task of revising the original manuscript and making many additions to it. The result, I trust, will fulfill the primary objective of this chapter, namely, to provide the reader with a brief but reasonably detailed overview of the Paraguayan environment—physical, biotic, economic, and political.

Figures 2.1 and 2.8 show the location of many of the geographic entities mentioned in this book. The provinces *(departamentos)* and physiographic zones in Paraguay are shown in Figures 2.2 and 2.3.

Western Paraguay: Chaco Boreal

The great plain that extends westward from the Río Paraguay within the national territory of Paraguay is called the Chaco Boreal. This portion of the chaco merges with the Chaco Austral, which pertains to Argentina. The Chaco Boreal is referred to in Spanish as Paraguay Occidental; the eastern half of the nation is called Paraguay Oriental.

The Chaco Boreal constitutes the northeastern section of the Plate Basin, which, in the Tertiary Era, after the uplifting of the Andes, was covered by the sea. The Chaco Boreal is bordered on the east by the Río Paraguay, on the south by the Río Pilcomayo and on the north and west by the international frontier with Bolivia. Throughout the centuries the Chaco Boreal has been the scene of dramatic episodes in the political history of Paraguay and in its struggle for economic stability. Even before the Conquest, the Guaraní people of Paraguay initiated commercial intercourse with the Incas of the Altiplano. The Guaranís sought markets for their products which they exchanged for the precious metals lacking in their own territory.

The artificial political boundary through the Chaco Boreal separates two distinct and unrelated economic zones: the Plate Basin and the Central Altiplano. There are only two natural boundaries—the Río Paraguay and the Río Pilcomayo. The international boundary between Paraguay and Bolivia runs north and south parallel to but well-separated from the foothills of the Andes. The frontier then curves eastward toward the Río Paraguay in a line more-or-less parallel to but also well-separated from the edge of the Chiquitos Plateau of Bolivia.

SURFACE AREA AND POPULATION

The Chaco Boreal has a surface area of 246,925 km². A cursory census in 1950 showed a population of 54,277, and a much more complete census in 1962 revealed a population of 74,814 (Table 2.1). The latest figure—94,111—was compiled by the Servicio Nacional para la Erradicación de Paludismo (SENEPA, National Malaria Eradication Service) in 1970.

The Chaco comprises 60.7 percent of the total area of Paraguay, but only 3.9 percent of the population lives there. The population is slowly increasing, but its potential in this regard is certainly much less than that of eastern Paraguay. Probably the major portion of the population growth over the years can be attributed to immigration and to a more thorough enumeration of the Indians already there.

Potable water is the principal limiting factor in the Chaco, but the limiting influence of natural rainfall might be modified by the introduction of irrigation waters from any of the three nearest rivers (Paraguay, Pilcomayo, Parapetí) or from underground aquifers.

PHYSICAL FEATURES

The Chaco is quite distinct geographically from the rest of the country. It differs from the Chaco Austral of Argentina in the following ways. The land is somewhat more elevated and not so flat as the Chaco Austral. The soil is different, being more fertile around the mouth of the Río Pilcomayo and more sandy toward the west. The biota is more varied. The greatest difference is that the Tertiary strata are nearer the surface in the Chaco Boreal. There are outcrops of even older rocks in the northern region of the Chaco Boreal.

The climate is drier. Both precipitation and humidity decrease progressively from east to west. The average annual rainfall on the Río Paraguay is 1,450 mm. This decreases to about 300 mm at the Bolivian border. The southwestern portion of the Chaco Boreal has the characteristic features of the "Chaco Basin," namely, great fluctuations of temperature from summer to winter, very low atmospheric humidity, frequent and severe droughts, all of which may be typical of a continental climate (see Chapters 3 & 4).

The littoral of the Río Paraguay forms a transition zone between the humid tropical climate of eastern Paraguay and the dry tropical climate of the Chaco. The geologic features are more varied in the Chaco Boreal than in the part of the Chaco Basin which belongs to Argentina. The plains of the Pilcomayo delta and the Río Paraguay littoral resemble the "Entre Rios Formation" of Argentina, which is characterized by sedimentary strata of the Upper Tertiary (Miocene and Pliocene), partly covered by Quaternary alluvial deposits.

In the higher parts of the Chaco Boreal, the oldest geologic formations either occur as outcrops or lie very close to the surface. These same strata in the Argentine Chaco form the substrata of the ancient marine limestone that is now covered by Tertiary deposits to a depth of 2,500 meters in some places. In the Chaco Boreal these oldest outcrops take the shape of isolated hills, such as those near Ingavi, that bear fossils characteristic of the Silurian Period.

The topographic profile of the Chaco is flat. A small gradual increase in elevation begins in the province of Presidente Hayes, which is located on the Pilcomayo Delta (the rivers Pilcomayo, Confuso, Aguary Guazú, Negro, and Montelindo). The elevation continues to increase gradually in the province of Boquerón (southwestern, central and northwestern Chaco), with low hills in places, right up to the Andean foothills.

The soil, topography and vegetation vary considerably in the three provinces of the Chaco Boreal. The delta of the Río Pilcomayo (Presidente Hayes province) and the littoral of the Río Paraguay (up to 50 km inland in the provinces of Boquerón and Olimpo) are essentially flat. The topsoil, characteristic of the Entre Rios Formation of the Chaco-Pampean Plains, is derived from alluvial deposits[4] of the Quaternary and overlays older strata of loess and marl. Two different plant communities appear in this portion of the Chaco. There are extensive grasslands, with or without the caranday palms (*Copernicia* spp.). The palms may be scattered or concentrated in dense groves. The grasslands surround islands of forest. These islands, elevated just a few inches above the grassland, are composed of dense thorny thickets and several types of trees of considerable commercial value, such as the *quebracho (Schinopsis* spp.), guayacana (Diospyrus hispida), palo santo (Bulnesia sarmienti), palo blanco* (several genera), and *palo de trebol (Amburana cearensis).*

The second recognizable belt of the Chaco lies between 50 and 200 km inland from the Río Paraguay. The topsoil improves in both thickness and friability. In most places it is composed of sandy alluvial deposits. The grasslands are more extensive and provide better pasturage for cattle than those of the littoral belt. The forests, though less extensive, contain a higher percentage of valuable timber.

In the third belt parallel to the river, from 200–300 km inland, the vegetation varies from north to south. Forests predominate in the north and grasslands in the south. The alluvial sandy topsoil is fertile and reaches a depth of 80 cm in some places. The extreme northwest Chaco has an undulating topography, the highest points reaching 350 meters above sea level. The weather is much drier and there are considerable stretches of semiarid sandy soils. Vegetation is comparatively sparse; neither the grasslands nor the forests reach the level of development seen in other parts of the Chaco.

HYDROGRAPHY

The Río Paraguay is the main line of north-south communication in Paraguay. New roads, both under construction and planned, will no doubt change this picture somewhat. This is already happening in eastern Paraguay, but certainly several more years will pass before any appreciable north-south road building is done in the Chaco. The only other "navigable" Chaco river is the Río Pilcomayo. And it is only seasonably navigable and only for very small vessels. The Pilcomayo is the only river that completely traverses the Paraguayan Chaco. About halfway across the Chaco it breaks up into distributaries in a region called Estero Patiño. As the snow melts off the high Andes, the river, both above and below Estero Patiño, carries enough water for small vessels. Dredging would, of course, drastically enhance its commercial importance and might even provide Bolivia with an outlet to the Atlantic, but this project would require international money and coordination. The Guaraní name of the Río Pilcomayo—Araguay—means "river coming from the heights," and, of course, refers to the origin of the river in the Andes. About the level of Estero Patiño, several main distributaries branch off successively, forming the "delta" of the Pilcomayo.

In the greater portion of the Chaco, mainly in the northern part, but also in the central and western parts, there are no surface rivers, only some isolated lakes and some ephemeral streams carrying rain water. The system of potable subsurface waters is poor and irregular. The majority of the subterranean waters of the Chaco are saline.[4] In the province of Presidente Hayes and in the littoral of Boquerón and Olimpo, the first sandy stratum in which water can be found is about 10 or 15 meters below the surface. This water is usually salty. There are many small freshwater ponds and beneath these ponds are pockets of water in the sand. The ponds dry up in the dry season but the subterranean pockets often hold water throughout the year, serving then as emergency sources of fresh water. Potable underground water has been found at 20 meters near Mariscal Estigarribia and Filadelfia. Other details concerning underground water are given by Putzer.[26]

NATURAL RESOURCES AND ECONOMIC POTENTIAL
A complete estimate of the natural resources and of the economic potential of the Chaco will be possible only after a methodical investigation of the physiography, geologic strata, underground water, and the topsoil and its suitability for agriculture. The chance of finding petroleum deposits has diminished with the termination of explorations by the Union Oil Company, although at least three of the bore holes yielded "showings." Important petroleum deposits are currently being exploited in the Andean foothills of Bolivia, just beyond the western edge of the Chaco.

There are salt deposits in the extreme northern part of the Chaco. These need to be assessed to determine their quality and suitability for exploitation.

The principal economic resources of the Chaco Boreal consist of the forest reserves of the central area and the northern littoral and the grasslands of Presidente Hayes province. The latter is the best cattle-raising region of the country. Pasturage is very good and the health of the cattle is generally better than in eastern Paraguay. The province of Boquerón also has some grasslands suitable for cattle-raising in the littoral of the Río Paraguay and on the upper Río Pilcomayo.

Forest industries and cattle production are the most important commercial enterprises of the Chaco. Agriculture is becoming increasingly important due to the activities of the Mennonite farmers around Filadelfia (see Chapter 10). The Chaco Boreal and the Chaco Austral have most of the world's supply of *quebracho,* from which tannin is extracted. Paraguay is the world's leading supplier of tannin. The Chaco forests are characterized by the abundance of very hard and durable woods, some of them practically unaffected by rot and unexcelled for certain uses, such as utility poles and railroad ties. The caranday palm (*Copernicia cerifera,* wax palm) is very common along the Río Paraguay and in the delta of the Río Pilcomayo. In that region, palm wood is the principal material for house construction, the "heart" is edible, the leaves yield carnauba wax and are sources of thatch and basket-weaving materials.

Eastern Paraguay
The eastern region, if not by its size then by virtue of its natural endowments and its privileged position in history and geography, is the more important part of Paraguay. Its total area is 159,827 km². It has 39.3 percent of the national territory and 96.1 percent of the population. It differs fundamentally from the Chaco Boreal in the following ways. The climatic types are semihumid subtropical and tropical, respectively, in the southern and northern ends of the Paraguay Valley, and humid tropical in the Paraná Valley. The topography is distinctly undulating in places. There are many rivers, providing routes of communication and potential sources of hydroelectricity. And, most important, eastern Paraguay has a great variety of fertile soils suitable for a multiplicity of agricultural activities.

HISTORICAL REVIEW
The eastern part of Paraguay was the main center of Guaraní population and culture in the River Plate region. The Paraguay River was a clear line of demarcation between two distinct Indian cultures. To the west in the Chaco were the "wild" tribes belonging to the Chaco-pampean ethnic family. The Guaranís referred to these Chaco tribes as the "Guaycurú." The few that remain in the "wild" state are still nomadic hunters and fishermen. These would be the Moro (= Ayoreo) Indians of the northern Chaco. The "civilized" Indians of the Chaco endure a subsistence living as indifferent agriculturalists around the military posts, ranches and Mennonite colonies. To the east of the Río Paraguay there were two cultural types of Guaranís: A sedentary agricultural people of the Paraguay Valley and Central Plateau, and a forest people who gathered around temporary villages and engaged in some farming in Caaguazú and the Paraná Valley.

The Payaguá or Agaces were a river people of Chaco-pampean origin, who lived in harmony with the Guaranís and were their allies against the Chaco tribes. The Payaguás dominated traffic on the Paraguay River. The

Guaranís controlled the Paraná River. The Guaraní confederation of eastern Paraguay was made up of three tribes: the Carios in the Central area, the Itatines in the north, and the Tapes in the south. The Paraguayan Guaranís were linked politically and economically with the Guaranís of the Uruguay River Basin and coastal Brazil.

The Guaranís of Paraguay enjoyed the advantages of strategic geographic position, convenient routes of communication, and comparatively advanced economic and cultural levels. The Spaniards apparently recognized these advantages since they chose Asunción as their base of operations for the conquest and colonization of the La Plata Region. No doubt the friendliness of the Indians was also a significant factor. The Spaniards somehow persuaded the Indians to accompany them on their several forays into the Chaco in search of the Inca gold.

GEOLOGY

Eastern Paraguay is very old geologically. Bedrock is quite close to the surface and even crops out in places. It is composed of ancient crystalline rocks (gneiss, granite, schists). In northeastern Paraguay the oldest rocks correspond to a very ancient formation known as the Brazilian Shield or Central Plateau of Brazil. In most of the rest of eastern Paraguay this Brazilian Shield stratum is covered by deposits of the Permian-Triassic period. From these deposits are derived the red soils characteristic of the high parts of the provinces Central, Misiones, Cordillera, Caaguazú, Guairá, Caazapá, Itapua, Alto Paraná, and Amambay.[4,31] In the northern part of the province of Concepción there are outcrops of the more ancient strata of the Silurian period. In the Piribebuy Valley there are also Silurian strata.

The Mesozoic formations (Secondary Era) appear in various parts of the valleys of the Manduvirá and Tebicuary rivers. They may be seen in greater abundance and more characteristic structure near the Yvyturusú hills in the Paraná Valley. Along the Alto Paraná River these formations are covered by effusive strata of volcanic rocks (melaphyres and basalts) from which originate the typical red soils of that region.

The central hills, *e.g.,* Cordillera de los Altos, Cerro Yvyturusú, Sierra de Monte Rosario, and a few isolated hills more to the south, are of Permian age.

In various parts of Paraguay and the adjacent Argentinian provinces of Corrientes, Entre Ríos, and Misiones, there is the Gondwana formation (upper Carboniferous to Cretaceous or Jurassic), characterized by sands or sandstones with outcroppings of melaphyres. This type of soil was named the "Guaranitic Formation" by d'Orbigny because it occupies the greater part of the territory that was dwelt in by the agricultural Guaranís of La Plata. It refers to a characteristic type of Permian-Triassic soil of Paraguay and adjacent Argentina and differentiates it from the latter in being older and poorer in melaphyres and volcanic rocks. This Permian-Triassic stratum is covered in some places with Tertiary deposits and in other places with Quaternary deposits.

CLIMATE

The climate of eastern Paraguay presents remarkable variations in view of the small geographical space that the country occupies (see Chapter 3). In the southern part (provinces of Ñeembucú, Misiones and Itapua), the climate is semihumid subtropical, with 1300 to 1500 mm of precipitation on the average per year, and variations of temperature from winter to summer of 0 to 38 C. In the central and northern part of the Paraguay River Valley the climate is semihumid tropical, with 1300 to 1700 mm of rainfall annually, 22 to 25 C average temperature, and variations of temperature from winter to summer of from 1 to 40 C. The Central Plateau zone also has a semihumid tropical climate with 22 to 23 C average temperature and 1400 to 1600 mm of rainfall. But the climate is more regular, with only moderate variations of temperature, due to the greater altitude (300 to 500 meters above sea level) and to being protected against the cold winds from the south and the dry winds from the east. The Paraná Valley has a climate that varies from subtropical to tropical humid, with an average annual rainfall of 1700 to 1800 mm and a high percentage of atmospheric humidity (average 80 to 86 percent).

The main reasons for this diversity of climate do not depend on the latitude as much as on the height above sea level and the increasing density of the forest from west to east. The plains of the Paraguay River Valley are exposed to cold winds from the south and to the influence of the climatic variability of the Chaco Basin. The Central Plateau and the Paraná River Valley are protected from these winds and their climates are more influenced by southern Brazil, where the climate is more humid and less variable.

RÍO PARAGUAY VALLEY

The valley of Río Paraguay is essentially a plain, slightly tilted from north to south, the lower edge being on the south. Most of the plain is covered by grasses utilized in cattle production. There are considerable stretches of forests and marshes. There are a few isolated hills or strings of hills, between which run many rivers and streams. Tillable soils are quite varied, permitting a wide range of agricultural activities. There are some deposits of metallic ores (iron and manganese), which are not now being utilized, and considerable deposits of industrial and construction materials such as kaolin, limestone, granite, volcanic rock, tufa and sand.

CENTRAL PLATEAU

The topography of the Central Plateau is much more varied than that of the Paraguay Valley. The many low hills are covered with forests containing considerable merchantable timber. The surrounding valleys and plains are clothed with grasses. Toward the north and east the land becomes increasingly covered with forests, so that along the Río Alto Paraná there are only isolated patches of grassland.

ALTO PARANÁ VALLEY
From the agricultural colonies near Encarnación north to Guairá Falls, the Alto Paraná Valley is densely forested. Most of this is virgin forest, but the lumber industry is rapidly expanding. Lumber and forest products accounted for 20 percent of the total exports of Paraguay in 1965. The many falls along the valley are potential sources of hydroelectric power. A hydroelectric power station has been constructed on the falls of the Río Acaray.

BIOTIC ENVIRONMENT
The abundant natural biotic productions of eastern Paraguay, as expressed in the forests, the grasslands, and the animal life, indicate that eastern Paraguay is admirably suited for a wide variety of agricultural activities.

The Paraguay River Valley
LOCATION, SIZE AND POPULATION
This zone occupies a wide belt along the Río Paraguay, from the confluence of the Paraguay and Alto Paraná Rivers north to the Apa River. The eastern boundary of this zone runs north and south along the mountain ranges known as Yvyturusú, Caaguazú and Amambay. The sizes, populations and population densities are given in Table 2.1 for the zone and each of the provinces making up the zone. The Paraguay Valley occupies 18.6 percent of the national territory, 47.5 percent of eastern Paraguay, and in 1950 had 68 percent of the total national population. The latter figure was 62.8 percent in 1970.

Except for the commercial and industrial enterprises of the cities—Asunción (population 305,160), Concepción (population 33,282), and Pilar (population 10,909)—the zone is predominantly agricultural. The Río Paraguay is still the main line of north-south communication. The railroad and highway also run north and south between Asunción and Encarnación, passing through portions of all three zones (Paraguay Valley, Central Plateau, Alto Paraná Valley) of eastern Paraguay.

Ever since its founding in 1537, Asunción has been the focal point of Paraguay. Commerical, industrial and political activities are centered there. All lines of communication—roads, rivers, railroads, airways—radiate from Asunción. According to the 1962 census, 1,210,419 people (two-thirds of the entire population of the country) live within 160 km (100 miles) of Asunción. The capital has grown rapidly during the past several years, the result of country people migrating to the big city. But there is now a government-sponsored program which encourages and assists people to move into the sparsely populated hinterlands. The hinterlands have obvious potential in the areas of agriculture and forestry, but until just a very few years ago, these regions were virtually inaccessible. This picture is rapidly and drastically changing due to the construction of main highways and farm-to-market roads in and across formerly isolated areas.

GEOLOGY
Much of eastern Paraguay was covered by the sea during part of the Paleozoic Era. At this time the Silurian strata

of Concepción and San Pedro provinces were formed, along the basins of the Manduvirá and Caañabé rivers. In like fashion were formed the Silurian deposits in the Piribebuy Basin, the Permian-Triassic strata of the Central Plateau, and the Triassic formations of the Paraná Valley and Ñeembucú province. There was a general uplifting of the land during the Cretaceous Period, culminating in the formation of the Andes. The sea apparently advanced and receded several times and the wave action at various levels eroded away some of the Permian-Triassic strata. These strata persisted where there was no wave action. Much later, the Chaco Basin was formed as a result of the active movements of the earth's surface during the Eocene Period. The Chaco Basin, along with a part of eastern Paraguay, was covered by a sea, the sediments from which formed the strata that are now characteristic of that region. In other words, the geology of eastern Paraguay is complicated and the outcrops are quite diverse in origin.

PHYSICAL ENVIRONMENT
The physical environments of the Paraguay Valley zone are highly varied. These variations are derived from the differences in altitude, geologic origin, and topography. The northern part of the zone, comprised of Concepción province, is north of the Tropic of Capricorn and therefore lies within the "tropics." The topography is undulating. A chain of hills runs east-west, culminating in the Tacurú Pytá Mountains in the northeastern corner of the country. This range is the highest in Paraguay, reaching 800 meters above sea level. This is the "continental divide" between the Río Alto Paraná and the Río Paraguay. In the northernmost section of the Paraguay Valley there are grasslands suitable for cattle production. The extensive deposits of limestone in this area are being exploited for the manufacture of cement.

The province of San Pedro comprises another sector of this zone. The slope of the sector is east to west, with two principal rivers flowing east-west across the sector and into the Río Paraguay. These are the Ypané and the Jejuí, the latter being navigable for small freighters. Forests predominate and are exploited to some extent, the logs being floated out as rafts to the Río Paraguay. There are also some grasslands. The soils are fertile and there is plenty of surface and subsurface water.

In the southern part of the province there is an extensive area of marshy, flat, poorly drained ground which forms the basin of Lake Vera and Arroyo Tobatiry. There are some forested areas, but grasslands and marshes predominate. This region is more suitable for farms than for cattle production. It could be greatly improved for both by establishing systems for drainage and irrigation. It is flooded during the rains, but water for livestock becomes quite scarce during droughts. There are some deposits of limestone and kaolin.

The provinces Cordillera, Central, and Paraguarí comprise another sector of the Paraguay Valley zone. This sector is quite hilly, with a series of hills and plateaus. These are separated by broad valleys through which run permanent streams. The sandy soils on the heights are of Permian origin and support dense forests. These soils are rocky but fertile. The valleys are dominated by grasslands. These could be converted to rice culture if an irrigation system was installed. In some places the older geological strata are covered by Tertiary sediments or Quaternary alluvials, but in the basins of Laka Ypoá and Arroyo Caañabé the older strata are exposed. This sector has some important mineral deposits: manganese in Cordillera (Emboscada, Escobar, Ybytimí); iron, oligist and limonite in Caapucú, Ybycuí and San Miguel; a little sulfur (marcasite) in Valenzuela, and copper in Caapucú; kaolin in several places. This sector is particularly suited for farming.

The southermost section of the Paraguay Valley is located near the confluence of the Río Paraguay and the Río Alto Paraná and is composed of the provinces of Misiones and Ñeembucú. The economy of Misiones province is divided between farming and cattle production. There are extensive grasslands surrounding islands of forest. The sandy soils are very fertile. There are a few hills of Permian origin.

Ñeembucú province is devoted to cattle production. The land is quite flat. There are extensive grasslands and marshes. There is practically no natural drainage. The small elevations of terrain suitable for farming are few and far between. That situation could obviously be improved by construction of a drainage system. The Ñeembucú Plain is basically of Permian-Triassic origin, but in places there are overlays of Tertiary sediments and Quaternary alluvial deposits.

RIVERS AND LAKES

The Paraguay and Alto Paraná Rivers are the main routes for both local and international transportation. Other rivers—Tebicuary, Manduvirá, Jejuí, Ypané—are navigable for vessels of small tonnage during the rainy season. Dredging would, of course, greatly increase their utility as routes of communication. Installation of drainage systems in the marshes of Ñeembucú and around the lakes Ypoá, Ypacaraí and Vera (= Aguaracatí) would enhance the agricultural potentialities of these regions.

The Central Plateau

The Central Plateau lies on either side of the "continental divide" between the watersheds of the Río Paraguay and the Río Alto Paraná in the provinces of Amambay, Caaguazú, Guairá and Caazapá. The boundary lines of the Central Plateau zone follow the provincial boundaries on the east, south and west, the Cordillera de Amambay on the northwest, and the upper course of the Río Apa on the north.

AREA AND POPULATION

This zone comprises 11.6 percent of the total national territory, 29.5 percent of eastern Paraguay, and in 1950 contained 19 percent of the total population of the country. The latter figure was 22.2 percent in 1970. Other details are given in Table 2.1.

PHYSICAL ENVIRONMENT

The climate of the Central Plateau is semitropical humid. The zone is protected from climatic extremes by virtue of its elevation and by being shielded from cold winds from the south. The zone is also influenced by the same climatic determinants that produce the mild humid climate of southern Brazil. Because of the moderate climate, the production of certain tropical crops (coffee, cacao, vanilla, rubber) is unrestricted in the Central Plateau zone. These crops can be grown only in sheltered places in other parts of the country.

The Central Plateau is not flat as the name might imply, but it is definitely elevated with respect to the surrounding plains and basins of the Río Alto Paraná and the Río Paraguay. The Cordillera de Villarrica (= Yvyturusú) in the southern part of this zone is a northward extension of a chain of hills beginning in the Argentine province of Misiones and crossing the Alto Paraná River in the district of Jesús y Trinidad. The Villarrica Range has peaks almost as high as the Tacurú Pytá Range in the northeastern corner of the country.

Forests, rich in quality and variety of hardwood species, cover most of the Central Plateau. Besides timber species, there are the *yerba mate (Ilex paraguariensis)*, rubber trees *(Hancornia speciosa),* and *mbokayá (Acrocomia spp.).* The latter are palms which provide oils and fibers. The *yerba mate* trees are the source of Paraguayan tea, also called *yerba mate,* a drink universally used in Paraguay and exported to Argentina. The large stands *(yerbales)* of *yerba mate* trees provided the inspiration for the Guaraní name of one province, Caaguazú (Ka'a = *yerba mate;* guazú = big). In the higher parts of the watersheds of the Tobatiry, Tebicuary, and Acaray Rivers, there are meadows which could be converted to rice culture.

The principal natural products of the Central Plateau are derived from the plant kingdom. The most important and extensive deposits of kaolin in Paraguay are located in the bed of the Río Tobatiry near Tobatí. There are some iron ores in the district of Yuty. The hydroelectric potentialities of the zone are great.

The Alto Paraná River Valley

AREA AND POPULATION

Table 2.1 gives the figures of size and population for the two provinces—Itapua and Alto Paraná—which make up this zone.

The zone of the Alto Paraná Valley comprises 9 percent of the total national territory, 23 percent of eastern Paraguay. In 1950 it contained 9 percent and in 1970, 11 percent of the total population of Paraguay. Most of the population of the zone is concentrated into five districts—Encarnación, Coronel Bogado, Fram, General Artigas, San Pedro del Paraná—of Itapua province. This zone has great potential for economic and agricultural development. The soils, the forests, the waterfalls, all connected by the great Alto Paraná River, provide the ideal physical basis for economic development. Only roads, people and money are lacking.

Colonization of the area is being encouraged by the government. Private firms are investing increasing amounts of money in the area, principally in connection with agricultural colonies and timber harvesting. The northern portion of the zone is connected by a paved highway to Asunción, and by the international bridge to Brazil. Encarnación is connected to Asunción by railroad and paved highway. Highway traffic now crosses the Río Tebicuary by ferry, but a bridge is in the planning stage.

PHYSICAL ENVIRONMENT

The climate varies from humid tropical in the north to humid subtropical in the southern part of the zone. The relative humidity is commonly quite high (78.86 percent on the average) and rainfall averages about 1700–1800 mm annually. The average annual temperature is about 21 or 22 C. This zone is subject to fewer climatic extremes than any other part of the nation. This moderation of the climate of the zone stems on the one hand from the large expanses of forest which clothe it, and on the other from the combined influences of the three geographic regions which surround it, namely, the Chaco Basin, the Central Plateau of Paraguay, and southern Brazil. In the littoral of the Alto Paraná River, and to some extent inland, nights are comfortably cool even in the summer. On winter nights fog settles in the Valley and forms a protective blanket over cold-sensitive plants such as oranges and bananas.

The Alto Paraná River runs through a deep gorge (see Chapter 6). With this exception, the topography of the zone is fairly level. It is in effect an undulating plain, ascending in elevation toward the west, where it merges with the Villarrica Mountains. The zone is abundantly supplied with many large and small watercourses. The Río Alto Paraná is the main trunk of the system. There are at least 50 major and minor tributaries of the Río Alto Paraná in the provinces of Alto Paraná and Itapua. Four of the largest tributaries are the Río Tacuarí, Río Ñacunday, Río Monday, and Río Acaray. A hydroelectrical power facility has been constructed at the falls of the Río Acaray. There is a falls about 20 to 30 meters high at the mouth of most of the Paraguayan tributaries of the Río Alto Paraná, above Encarnación (Itapua). The Alto Paraná is navigable up to the Guairá Falls. The hydroelectric potential of Guairá Falls is also being developed.[8] The Alto Paraná Valley may eventually become one of the richest regions of Paraguay.

Contemporary Paraguay

Paraguay is admittedly one of the more backward countries of Latin America. Its remoteness, its tragic history of war and dictatorships, its endless military coups and revolutions have all sapped energies that could have been better used in serving the best interests of the people of Paraguay. Any objective survey of present-day Paraguay (or any other country) would reveal much to criticize in the realms of politics, government, economics, etc. On the other hand, this same objective look would also reveal some very encouraging signs of progress in many areas of national life. Paraguay may have difficult problems to solve, but compared to many other nations of the world, Paraguay's future looks very bright.

ECONOMIC IMPEDIMENTS

In a list of causes of Paraguay's lethargic economic development, the following items could be included: past political instability, lack of domestic purchasing power, shortage of domestic skills, poor roads (especially farm-to-market roads), distance from foreign markets, and the poor health of many of the people.

POLITICS AND GOVERNMENT

The Constitution of 1940 provided for a strong central government. The three major political parties—Febreristas, Liberals, and Colorados—have all held the reigns of government at one time or another. Each in its day of glory was quite as intolerant of opposition as its predecessors had been.

The Colorado Party has been in power since the civil war of 1947; the current president has been in office since the coup of 1954. President Stroessner was elected, without opposition, for a five-year term in 1958, and re-elected, with opposition, for additional five year terms in 1963 and 1968. These were the second and third times in the history of Paraguay that there were opposition candidates for the presidency. A new constitution, adopted in 1967, made it legal for a Paraguayan president to hold office for three consecutive five-year terms. The 1963 opposition candidate, provided by a Liberal party splinter group, polled about 47,000 votes against President Stroessner's 557,000 votes. There were four presidential candidates in 1968; President Stroessner received 77 percent of the votes.

The 1940 Constitution guaranteed the opposition party one-third of the 60 seats in the unicameral legislature. In 1963, for the first time in 30 years, opposition legislators claimed their 20 seats. Each of the 60 congressmen then represented about 30,000 constituents. Women voted for the first time in 1963. The 1967 Constitution created a bicameral legislature. Paraguay has a long tradition of pro-Western, anti-communist sentiments.

Political situations in Latin America tend to change with such frequency and rapidity that only the periodical journals and annual reviews of political science can provide the interested reader with up-to-date descriptions of current political trends and events.

EDUCATION

There are no accurate measures of literacy but estimates vary from 50 to 75 percent. In any case, the need for education is very great. About 25 percent of primary-school-age children are not in school. Only nine percent of the high-school-age population goes to high school. Paraguay is a bilingual nation. Ninety-four percent of the the people speak the Guaraní language, 60 percent speak Spanish, and about 40 percent speak only Guaraní or some other Indian language. Often a Paraguayan child's first exposure to Spanish occurs in the first grade.

The educational programs of the United States Agency for International Development emphasize school construction, elementary teacher education, production of educational materials, and vocational education, especially in the areas of electricity, plumbing, leathercraft, iron working, radio, refrigeration, carpentry, automobile mechanics, machine shop, graphic arts and service station operation. The Rural Education Development Program is constructing and organizing six rural education centers designed to train teachers for Paraguay.

TRANSPORTATION

Road and bridge construction have received a great deal of emphasis by the Paraguayan government in recent years (Fig. 2.4). There are about 8,000 miles of roads of all types. The five major roads, all products of the present administration, are producing a definite salutary effect on the national economy. One of the roads connects Concepción (on the Río Paraguay) and Pedro Juan Caballero (on the Brazilian frontier). This highway intersects a recently-completed north-south route that runs between Coronel Oviedo (Caaguazú) and the new international bridge (completed 1971) across the Apa River. The other three roads radiate from Asunción. The Trans-Chaco Highway runs diagonally across the Chaco from the Río Paraguay to the Bolivian border. There is no counterpart to the Trans-Chaco Highway in Bolivia. Another highway, now paved in its entirety, connects Asunción with Puerto Presidente Stroessner on the Río Alto Paraná. The international bridge across the river at this point gives Paraguay direct and convenient access to Brazil and the Atlantic Coast. The fourth road runs from Asunción south to Encarnación. This road is now entirely paved. Many miles of farm-to-market roads are under construction. Other roads and bridges are in the planning stage. In 1965 there were approximately 12,500 automobiles and microbuses, 2,500 buses and 3,000 trucks.

Paraguay has about 1,800 miles of navigable waterways. The government owns and operates some 40 freight vessels of various sizes. Most of the navigable mileage is provided by the Paraguay and Alto Paraná rivers. The Río Jejuí can also take small river steamers in its lower reaches. Ferry service for cars and trucks is available on the Río Paraguay between Piquetecué and Villa Hayes (connection for Trans-Chaco Highway), between Itá Enramada and Puerto Pilcomayo, Argentina, and on the Río Tebicary at Villa Florida.

A government-owned railway, originally built and operated by the British, provides freight and passenger service between Asunción and Encarnación via Villarrica. A railcar ferry, operating on the Río Alto Paraná between Encarnación and Posadas, Argentina, connects the Paraguayan line with the railway to Buenos Aires.

The international airport at Asunción handles commercial jet aircraft. At present, the rest of the country's airports are of the cow-pasture variety, handling DC3s or smaller aircraft. Domestic air freight and passenger services are available.

AGRICULTURE

Paraguay is a predominantly agricultural country. About 50 percent of all employed persons have jobs related to agriculture and 64 percent of the population lives in rural areas. But only about 4 percent of the total land area of the nation is classified as farms (Figs. 2.5 and 2.6) and only about 2 percent of the total land area is under cultivation. Fifty-four percent of the land is classified as forests and 40 percent as ranches.

Some 500,000 hectares are under cultivation. About 30 percent of this area is devoted to corn production, the largest acreage of any crop in Paraguay. An estimated 20 to 30 percent of all farm crops are destroyed by leaf-cutting ants (see Chapter 8). Thirty-five percent of all farms are tilled by hand, without animal or mechanical power. Production of the ten leading crops increased only 2.7 percent during the period 1950–1963. Some of the crops regularly produced in Paraguay are corn, wheat, cotton, tobacco, oranges, grapefruit, tangerines, grapes, rice, sugar cane, mandioca, beans, bananas, peanuts, coffee, tung, and various other fruits and vegetables. Mandioca, a staple and ubiquitous item of Paraguayan diet, is produced in greater quantity than any other crop.

Livestock production is one of the principal industries of Paraguay. There are an estimated seven to nine million cattle. Meat products and hides account for about 30 percent of the annual value of exports.

One of the goals of the United States Agency for International Development is the expansion and modernization of food production. The Servicio Técnico Interamericano de Cooperación Agrícola provides technical assistance in agriculture, forestry and animal husbandry.

FORESTRY

During each of the past few years, forest products have accounted for about 20 percent of the total value of Paraguayan exports. About 50 percent of Paraguay's land area is forested. There are large stands of merchantable timber in both eastern and western Paraguay (Figs. 2.5 and 2.6).[18] About 66 percent of the forested lands remain unexploited. Wood is a major source of fuel for heating, steam and electric power. Paraguay is the world's leading supplier of *quebracho* extract (for tannin) and petitgrain oil (from orange-tree leaves).

ECONOMICS

In 1967 the gross national product was about $415 million or $192 per capita. The gross national product has increased on the average about four percent annually since 1962. Agriculture, forestry and livestock accounted for 37 percent of the gross national product in 1965, 34 percent in 1967. Annual income per capita has been variously estimated at $127, $194, and $240. Rural per capita income, much lower than the national average, is estimated to be about $80 annually.

The national budget was approximately $40 million in 1965. Agriculture contributed 50 percent of the income and manufacturing, 17 percent. Some of the expenditures were for defense (20%), police (9%), and education (14%).

Total government expenditures grew to $56.4 million in 1967, exceeding total revenus by $2.4 million.

Total annual imports averaged $40.8 million during the period 1961 to 1928. Argentina, the United States, West Germany, and the United Kingdom are the principal suppliers of imports to Paraguay.[25,30,34] Details of imports are given in Tables 2.2 and 2.4.

The annual average value of exports during the period 1953 to 1962 was $32.6 million; this figure was $43.4 million from 1963 to 1967. Export values comprise an average of 11.3 percent of the gross national product (the contribution of exports to the gross national product of the Latin American countries is shown in Fig. 2.7). The principal exported commodities are canned meat, lumber (usually unsawed), *quebracho* extract, *yerba mate*, and animal hides. The main foreign buyers are the United States (*quebracho* extract, canned meats), Argentina (lumber, *yerba mate*), and the United Kingdom (canned meats). Other details of exports are given in Tables 2.3 and 2.5. The value of Paraguayan exports is compared with those of the other Latin American countries in Table 2.6.

INTERNATIONAL ASSISTANCE

No effort is made here to give a complete list of international assistance programs in Paraguay. The object is to give some indication of the variety of programs and sponsors. UNICEF has been very active in Paraguay, with programs mainly in the area of education, such as new schools with associated gardens and chicken farms, carpentry shops, nutrition education, elementary and vocational teacher education. UNICEF's contributions have amounted to nearly $2,000,000.

The Export-Import Bank has loaned $10.4 million for construction of the Asunción waterworks, airport improvement, and textile plant expansion. The Development Loan Fund made $16 million available for the Asunción waterworks, road construction, expansion of telecommunications, agricultural credit, and expansion of the facilities of International Products Corporation, a meat packing plant. The International Development Association and the World Bank loaned $8.2 million for paving of the highway from Asunción to Encarnación. The International Development Bank loaned $4 million for the development of medium industry and another $7 million to the Paraguayan National Development Bank. In 1963 the International Development Association granted a $3.6 million loan for a livestock improvement program The Inter-American Development Bank has loaned $2.9 million for small farmer credit and $3.4 million for housing construction to the Paraguayan National Development Bank. Another loan of $14.2 million was granted by the Inter-American Development Bank to cover the initial costs of the Acaray Hydroelectric Project (total estimated cost, $30 million).

UNITED STATES ASSISTANCE PROGRAMS

In addition to being heavily involved financially in the international assistance programs to Paraguay, the United States has on its own invested more than $65 million in loans and grants to Paraguay since 1945. During 1962–64 the value of wheat and other surplus commodities shipped to Paraguay under Title I PL 480 was $10.9 million. Some of the goals of the United States programs in Paraguay are outlined below.

Improve Investment Climate. The government of Paraguay is actively seeking foreign private investments. The necessary laws and agreements for protecting and encouraging private investment are now in effect. Several private United States companies have considerable investments in Paraguay. Americans own and operate several large coffee plantations in northeastern Paraguay. International Products Corporation is involved in ranching, meat canning, and production of *quebracho* extract. The First National City Bank of New York has a large branch in Asunción. ESSO Standard Paraguay refines and distributes petroleum products. Morrison-Knudsen Corporation and Williams Brothers Corporation are involved in road building. Pan Western Enterprises does cattle ranching. Kaiser & Company built the Asunción water system. Rader & Company are consulting engineers in Paraguay.

Expand and Modernize Food Production. This program dates back to 1942. Activities include projects in crop development, livestock improvement, agricultural extension services, including youth clubs, agricultural education, forestry, and agricultural economics. Much of the developmental and demonstration work is done at two experimental farms at Caacupé and Encarnación.

Development, Improvement and Maintenance of Land, Water, and Air Transport Facilities. United States programs have included road building and maintenance, construction of the jet runway at the international airport, expansion and improvement of the merchant marine fleet, and the Acaray River hydroelectric power project.

Improve Health. The Rockefeller Foundation was involved in public health projects in Paraguay as far back as the 1920s but the United States government began its official programs in 1942. These programs have emphasized improvement of health facilities (health centers, tuberculosis sanitorium, leper hospital, health ministry headquarters), medical education (the University of Buffalo provides technical advice on the improvement of training for physicians and nurses), and malaria eradication. The government of Paraguay recently accepted a grant of $2 million from the United States to finance the completion of the malaria eradication program that was started with an initial grant of $250,000 several years ago.

Improve Education. These programs have emphasized school construction, production of educational materials, and training of teachers in the vocational and elementary fields.

Improve Government Organization and Management. The United States has provided technical personnel as advisers in many areas of public administration. The School of Public Administration, a part of the National University of Asunción, was planned and organized with the aid of U.S. advisers. Other programs include the improvement of procedures in customs, tariffs, banking, government budget and organization, and personnel management.

Literature Cited

1. Azara, F. de. 1941. Viajes por la América meridional. Espasa-Calpe, Madrid. (Report of observations made between 1781 and 1801.)

2. Azara, F. de. 1943. Descripción e historia del Paraguay y del Río de la Plata. Editorial Bajel, Buenos Aires.

3. Barron, L. (Ed.). 1963. Americas. Worldmark encyclopedia of the nations. Worldmark Press, New York.

4. Beek, K. J., and D. L. Bramao. 1969. Nature and geography of South American soils. *In* Fittkau, E. J., J. Illies, H. Klinge, H. G. Schwabe, and H. Sioli. (Eds.). Biogeography and ecology in South America. Vol. 1. Dr. W. Junk, The Hague.

5. Bertoni, G. T. 1952. Geografía económica nacional y comparada de Paraguay y América. Editorial Cultura Guaraní, Asunción. (Mimeographed.)

6. Bertoni, M. S. 1918. Condiciones generales de la vida orgánica y división territorial. Descripción física y económica del Paraguay. Imprenta "Ex Sylvis," Puerto Bertoni, Paraguay.

7. Bertoni, M. S. 1918. Mapa agrológico, fisiográfico, y climatológico. Imprenta "Ex Sylvis," Puerto Bertoni, Paraguay.

8. Blanco Sánchez, J. L. 1968. El Paraguay como fuente energética. El Kanendiyú Guasú o Gran Salto del Guayrá. Su aprovechamiento hidroeléctrico según los Proyectos Brasileños. Asunción.

9. Bourgade la Dardye, E. de. 1892. Paraguay: The land and the people, natural wealth and commercial capabilities. George Philip, London.

10. Bruyssel, E. van. 1893. La République du Paraguay. Librarie Européenne de C. Muquardt, Brussels.

11. Canese, A. 1966. Algunos aspectos sobre el nivel social, económico, sanitario y cultural del campesino paraguayo. Rev. Paraguaya Microbiol. 9 (1): 105-109.

12. Da Ponte, A. 1946. Atlas de la República del Paraguay por departamentos. Estudio Cartográfico Da Ponte, Asunción.

13. Deffontaines, P. (Ed.). 1965. Larousse encyclopedia of world geography. Odyssey Press, New York.

14. Department of Public Information. 1965. Paraguay. American Republics Series no. 17. Pan American Union, Washington, D.C.

15. Du Graty, A. 1862. La République du Paraguay. Librarie Européenne de C. Muquardt, Brussels.

16. Ferrell, D. M. 1967. Paraguay: Site of budding promises. Industrial Development, July/August 1967.

17. González, J. N. 1964. Geografía del Paraguay. Editorial Guarania, México, D.F.

18. Hamill, E. B. 1955. Pulping possibilities of the Alto Paraná forest. Institute of Inter-American Affairs, and Servicio Técnico Interamericano de Cooperación Agrícola, Asunción. (Mimeographed.)

19. Hopkins, E. A., R. E. Crist, and W. P. Snow. 1968. Paraguay 1852 and 1968. American Geographical Society, New York. Quoted by permission of the publisher.

20. Inter-American Committee for Agricultural Development. 1963. Inventory of information basic to the planning of agricultural development in Latin America. Paraguay. Pan American Union, Washington, D.C.

21. Koebel, W. H. 1917. Paraguay. T. Fisher Unwin, London.

22. Mann, G. 1969. Die Ökosysteme Südamerikas. *In* (see Beek and Bramao 1969).

23. Natural Resources Unit, Department of Economic Affairs. 1964. Paraguay: Annotated index of aerial photographic coverage and mapping of topography and natural resources. Pan American Union, Washington, D.C.

24. Pendle, G. 1967. Paraguay. A riverside nation. 3rd ed. Oxford University Press, London.

25. Pincus, J. 1968. Economy of Paraguay. Praeger, New York.

26. Putzer, H. 1962. Geologie von Paraguay. Gebrüder Borntraeger, Berlin.

27. Raine, P. 1956. Paraguay. Scarecrow Press, New Brunswick.

28. Schuster, A. N. 1929. Paraguay. Land, Volk, Geschichte, Wirtschaftsleben und Kolonisation. Strecher und Schröder, Stuttgart.

29. Servin, R. H. (Ed.). 1964. Población y vivienda. Bol. Estad. Paraguay (Dirección General de Estadística y Censos, Ministerio de Hacienda, Asunción) 7 (19-21): 17-26.

30. Spruce, W. E. 1964. Basic data on the economy of Paraguay. Overseas Business Reports 64-135: 1-12.

31. Stewart, N. R. 1967. Japanese colonization in eastern Paraguay. National Academy of Sciences, National Research Council, Washington, D.C.

32. United States Board on Geographic Names. 1957. Paraguay. Official standard names. Gazetteer no. 35. Office of Geography, Department of the Interior, Washington, D.C.

33. Von Fischer-Treuenfeld, R. 1906. Le Paraguay. Guyot, Brussels.

34. Werner, E. 1968. Basic data on the economy of Paraguay. Overseas Business Reports 68-57: 1-12.

Author's address: Dr. J. Richard Gorham
Department of Biological Sciences
University of Alaska
Fairbanks, Alaska 99701

Table 2.1. Paraguay: Surface Area and Population

Zone / Departamento	Size km²	% of National Territory	Population			% Increase in Population		Annual Growth Rate			Density (People/km²)			% of Total Population		
			1950	1962	1970	1950-62	1962-70	1950-62	1962-70	1950-70	1950	1962	1970	1950	1962	1970
Central and Capital	2,852	0.07	374,439	517,955	693,594	38.3	33.9	2.7	3.6	3.0	131.2	181.6	243.2	28.5	28.5	28.9
Concepción	18,051	4.4	62,326	85,690	110,555	37.5	29.0	2.6	3.2	2.8	3.4	4.7	6.1	4.7	4.7	4.6
Cordillera	4,948	1.2	145,232	188,313	199,621	29.7	6.0	2.2	0.7	1.6	29.4	38.1	40.3	10.4	10.4	8.3
Misiones	7,836	1.9	43,449	59,441	74,023	36.8	24.5	2.6	2.7	2.6	5.5	7.6	9.4	3.3	3.3	3.1
Ñeembucú	13,868	3.4	50,861	57,878	69,639	13.8	20.3	1.1	2.3	1.6	3.7	4.2	5.0	3.8	3.2	2.9
Paraguarí	8,255	2.0	159,161	203,012	228,192	27.6	12.4	2.0	1.4	1.8	19.3	24.6	27.6	12.0	11.2	9.5
San Pedro	20,002	4.9	64,534	91,804	127,767	42.2	39.2	2.9	4.1	3.3	3.2	4.6	6.4	4.8	5.0	5.3
Paraguay Valley	*75,811*	*18.6*	*900,002*	*1,204,093*	*1,503,391*	*33.8*	*24.9*	*2.4*	*2.8*	*2.5*	*11.9*	*15.9*	*19.8*	*67.7*	*66.2*	*62.8*
Amambay	12,933	3.2	18.160	34,505	67.917	90.0	96.8	5.2	8.2	5.8	1.4	2.7	5.2	1.4	1.9	2.8
Caaguazú	21,613	5.3	71,699	125,138	226,675	74.5	81.1	4.5	7.2	5.2	3.3	5.8	10.5	5.4	6.9	9.5
Guairá	3,202	0.08	90,308	114,949	132,772	27.3	15.5	2.0	1.8	1.9	28.2	35.9	41.5	6.8	6.3	5.5
Caazapá	9,496	2.3	73,051	92,401	105,578	26.5	14.2	1.9	1.7	1.8	7.7	9.7	11.1	5.5	5.1	4.4
Central Plateau	*47,244*	*11.6*	*253,218*	*366,993*	*532,942*	*44.9*	*45.2*	*3.0*	*4.6*	*3.6*	*5.4*	*7.8*	*11.3*	*19.1*	*20.2*	*22.2*
Alto Paraná	20,247	5.0	9,531	24,067	63,497	152.5	163.8	7.2	11.2	7.4	0.47	1.2	3.1	0.7	1.3	2.7
Itapua	16,525	4.1	111,424	149,821	201,670	34.5	34.6	2.4	3.7	2.9	6.7	9.1	12.2	8.4	8.2	8.4
Alto Paraná Valley	*36,772*	*9.0*	*120,955*	*173,888*	*265,167*	*43.8*	*52.5*	*3.0*	*5.2*	*3.7*	*3.3*	*4.7*	*7.2*	*9.1*	*9.6*	*11.1*
Eastern Paraguay	*159,827*	*39.3*	*1,274,175*	*1,744,974*	*2,301,500*	*37.0*	*31.9*	*2.6*	*3.4*	*2.9*	*8.0*	*10.9*	*14.4*	*95.9*	*95.9*	*96.1*
Presidente Hayes	58,480	14.4	23,490	29,870	42,141	27.2	41.1	2.0	4.3	2.8	0.40	0.51	0.7	1.8	1.6	1.8
Boquerón	168,030	41.3	28,082	40,405	47,033	43.9	16.4	3.0	1.9	2.5	0.17	0.24	0.28	2.1	2.2	2.0
Olimpo	20,415	5.0	2,705	3,854	4,940	42.5	28.2	2.9	3.1	2.9	0.13	0.19	0.2	0.20	0.21	0.21
Western Paraguay (Chaco)	*246,925*	*60.7*	*54,277*	*74,129*	*94,114*	*36.6*	*27.0*	*2.6*	*3.0*	*2.7*	*0.22*	*0.30*	*0.4*	*4.1*	*4.1*	*3.9*
Total	406,752	100.0	1,328,452	1,819,103	2,395,614	36.9	31.7	2.6	3.4	2.9	3.3	4.5	5.9	100.0	100.0	100.0

Based on data from da Ponte,[12] and Servin,[29] and census figures compiled by the Servicio Nacional para la Erradicación de Paludismo and supplied through the courtesy of Sr. José Díaz de Bedoya, Director General, Dirección General de Estadística y Censos, Asunción, Paraguay.

Table 2.2. Imports by Principal Commodities, 1967
(In metric tons and thousands of U.S. dollars)

	Volume	Value (f.o.b.)
Foodstuffs	108,959	7,278
Machinery, motors, etc.	7,073	12,570
Combustibles and lubricants	160,695	3,750
Transportation material and vehicles	5,441	7,787
Textiles and manufactures	2,115	3,002
Nonferrous metals and manufactures	4,966	2,495
Chemicals and pharmaceutical products	6,007	2,524
Iron and manufactures	22,664	5,907
Paper, cartons and manufactures	5,802	1,662
Beverages and tobacco	1,247	657
Agricultural implements and accessories	675	690
Miscellaneous	79,546	9,031
Total	**405,189**	**57,355**

Table 2.3. Exports by Principal Commodities, 1967
(In metric tons and thousands of U.S. dollars)

	Volume	Value (f.o.b.)
Meat and by-products	28,590	17,524
Vegetable oils	20,675	4,572
Logs	182,065	6,168
Coffee	2,384	1,458
Tobacco	11,561	3,370
Cotton	6,271	2,290
Quebracho extract	16,812	1,985
Hides	7,766	1,442
Essential oils	446	1,485
Lumber	20,582	1,531
Yerba mate	4,971	633
Castor beans	5,349	412
Cakes	12,314	525
Fruits	6,052	386
Corn	9,431	283
Wild animal hides	147	535
Other	14,440	4,660
Total	**349,856**	**48,259**

Source: Banco Central del Paraguay, *Boletín Estadístico Mensual.*

Table 2.4. Imports by Principal Commodities, Paraguay, 1961–1967
(in thousands of U.S. dollars)*

Commodity	1961	1962	% Change 1961-62	1963	% Change 1962-63	1964	% Change 1963-64	1965	% Change 1964-65	1966	% Change 1965-66	1967	% Change 1966-67	% Change 1961-67
Foodstuffs	7,058	7,130	1.0	7,348	3.0	6,374	-13.2	5,666.7	-11.1	5,564.9	-1.8	7,278	30.8	3.1
Tobacco, Beverages	346	382	10.4	412	7.6	437	6.1	652.0	49.2	681.1	4.5	657	-3.5	89.9
Fuel oil & lubricants	3,494	3,536	1.2	4,008	13.3	4,147	3.5	4,883.4	17.8	4,495.0	-7.9	3,750	-16.6	7.3
Paper & mfg.	931	818	-12.1	1,024	25.2	1,113	8.7	1,365.3	22.7	1,306.2	-4.3	1,662	27.2	78.5
Chemicals & pharmaceuticals	1,498	1,626	8.5	1,660	2.1	1,927	16.1	2,107.9	9.4	2,307.9	9.5	2,524	9.4	68.5
Automobiles & accessories	8,114	1,962	-75.8	3,764	91.8	4,635	23.1	6,356.4	37.1	7,613.7	19.8	7,787	2.3	106.9 (1963-67)
Textiles & mfg.	2,695	3,096	14.9	2,297	-25.8	2,656	15.6	3,336.5	25.6	3,175.2	-4.8	3,002	-5.4	11.4
Agricultural implements	384	326	-15.1	316	-3.1	491	55.4	980.0	84.9	641.4	-29.4	690	7.6	79.7
Metals, metal tools & mfg.	2,701	2,615	-3.2	3,271	25.1	3,629	10.9	4,820.6	32.8	5,497.4	14.0	5,907	7.4	118.7
Motors & equipment	3,882	5,457	40.6	4,060	-25.6	4,929	21.4	9,648.7	95.8	11,136.8	15.4	12,570	12.9	223.8
Others	3,631	4,227		4,444		3,428		4,263.4		7,032.0		13,997		
Total	34,734	31,175	10.2	32,604	1.4	33,766	3.6	44,008.9	30.3	49,451.6	12.4	59,824	21.0	72.2

*From Ferrell[16] and Werner,[34] based on data compiled by the Banco Central del Paraguay, Asunción.

Table 2.5. Exports by Principal Commodities, Paraguay, 1961–1967
(in thousands of U.S. dollars)*

Commodity	1961	1962	% Change 1961-62	1963	% Change 1962-63	1964	% Change 1963-64	1965	% Change 1964-65	1966	% Change 1965-66	1967	% Change 1966-67	% Change 1961-67
Meat & by-products	8,751	7,634	-12.8	10,682	39.9	15,062	41.0	19,025	26.3	14,230	-25.2	17,524	23.1	100.25
Seeds and oils for industry	2,572	3,152	22.6	5,199	64.9	4,965	-4.5	4,379	-11.8	4,969	13.5	4,984	0.3	93.8
Logs	4,557	4,841	6.2	3,718	-23.2	5,424	45.9	7,363	35.7	8,529	15.8	6,168	-27.7	35.4
Coffee	933	2,835	203.8	3,306	16.6	3,180	-3.8	3,644	14.6	1,959	-46.2	1,458	-25.6	56.8
Tobacco	1,528	3,019	97.6	3,156	4.5	3,741	18.5	4,293	14.8	2,475	-42.5	3,370	36.2	120.5
Cotton	1,598	2,469	54.5	3,199	29.6	4,197	31.2	4,687	11.7	1,988	-57.6	2,290	15.2	43.3
Quebracho extract	2,469	2,530	2.5	2,805	10.9	3,976	41.7	3,465	-12.9	3,086	-10.9	1,985	-35.7	-19.6
Hides (livestock)	2,052	1,687	-17.8	1,518	-10.0	1,307	-13.9	1,362	4.2	2,573	88.9	1,442	-44.0	-29.7
Essential oils	1,054	1,078	2.3	1,283	19.0	1,456	13.5	1,123	-22.9	1,398	24.5	1,485	6.2	40.9
Sawed lumber	1,905	1,819	-4.5	1,025	-43.6	1,725	68.3	2,403	39.3	2,234	-7.0	1,531	-31.5	-19.6
Yerba mate	1,487	920	-38.0	1,878	104.1	1,348	-28.2	1,603	18.9	1,647	3.4	633	-61.6	-57.4
Fruits	224	309	37.9	340	10.0	406	19.4	561	38.2	609	8.6	386	-36.6	72.3
Corn	321	250	-22.1	145	-42.0	288	98.6	246	-14.6	47	-80.9	283	502.1	-11.8
Hides (wild)	116	161	38.8	134	-16.8	247	84.3	435	76.1	481	10.6	535	11.2	361.2
Other agr. products	777	551	-29.1	1,256	127.0	1,146	-8.8	905	-20.0	694	-23.3	525	-24.4	-32.4
Other	45	320		1,542		1,298		1,737		2,556		4,660		
Totals	30,389	33,575	10.5	41,186	22.7	49,766	20.8	57,231	15.0	49,475	-13.6	49,259	-0.4	62.1

*From Ferrell[16] and Werner,[34] based on data compiled by the Banco Central del Paraguay, Asunción.

Table 2.6. Value of Exports of the Latin American Countries, 1950 to 1967*
(Millions of U.S. Dollars)

Countries	1950	1953	1956	1959	1962	1965	1966	1967
Argentina	1,361	1,125	944	1,009	1,216	1,493	1,593	1,464
Bolivia	75	84	81	59	59	110	126	146
Brazil	1,347	1,539	1,482	1,282	1,214	1,595	1,741	1,654
Chile	281	408	542	495	530	685	877	887
Colombia	396	596	599	474	463	537	510	510
Costa Rica	56	80	67	77	93	112	136	143
Dominican Republic	87	105	125	130	172	126	137	157
Ecuador	74	92	116	142	143	178	185	200
El Salvador	68	89	113	113	136	189	192	207
Guatemala	79	99	123	107	118	187	228	199
Haiti	39	38	42	28	43	36	34	33
Honduras	55	68	73	69	81	127	143	151
Mexico	521	585	880	750	930	1,146	1,228	1,145
Nicaragua	27	46	58	65	82	144	138	146
Panama	24	26	31	35	48	79	89	91
Paraguay	33	31	37	31	33	57	49	50
Peru	189	219	308	312	538	666	763	774
Trinidad and Tobago	104	150	193	260	345	404	429	438
Uruguay	254	270	211	98	153	191	186	159
Venezuela	1,161	1,445	2,116	2,369	2,594	2,744	2,713	2,850**
Total	6,231	7,095	8,141	7,905	8,991	10,806	11,497	11,404

Source: International Monetary Fund, International Financial Statistics. *All values FOB. **Estimate, Inter-American Development Bank.

FIGURE 2.1

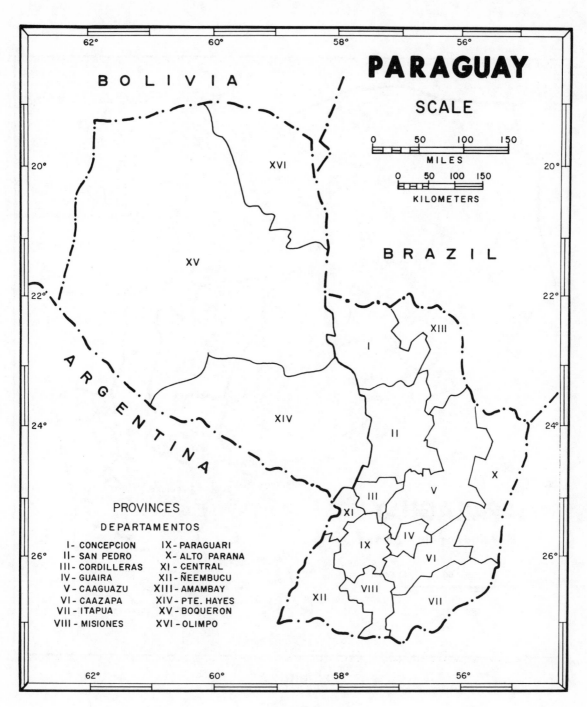

PARAGUAY

SCALE

0   50   100   150
MILES

0   50 100 150
KILOMETERS

B O L I V I A

B R A Z I L

A R G E N T I N A

XVI

XV

XVI

I

XIII

XIV

II

X

III

V

XI

IX

IV

VI

XII

VIII

VII

PROVINCES

DEPARTAMENTOS

I- CONCEPCION   IX- PARAGUARI
II- SAN PEDRO   X- ALTO PARANA
III- CORDILLERAS   XI- CENTRAL
IV- GUAIRA   XII- ÑEEMBUCU
V- CAAGUAZU   XIII- AMAMBAY
VI- CAAZAPA   XIV- PTE. HAYES
VII- ITAPUA   XV- BOQUERON
VIII- MISIONES   XVI- OLIMPO

FIGURE 2.2

PARAGUAY

Physiographic Zones

CHACO

Pedro Juan Caballero

Concepción

San Pedro

Villa Hayes

ASUNCION

Coronel
Oviedo

Hernandarias

Villarrica

San Juan Bautista

Pilar

Encarnación

VALLEY

CENTRAL PLATEAU

PARAGUAY

ALTO PARANA VALLEY

0   25   50   100 KMS.

FIGURE 2.3

FIGURE 2.4

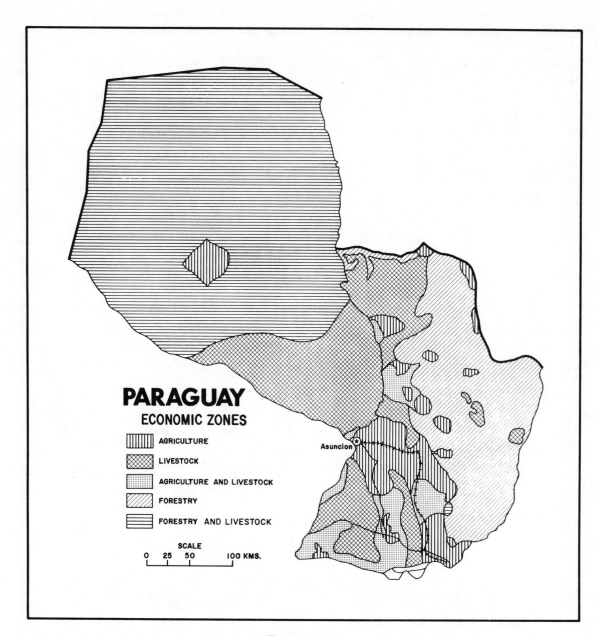

PARAGUAY

ECONOMIC ZONES

- AGRICULTURE
- LIVESTOCK
- AGRICULTURE AND LIVESTOCK
- FORESTRY
- FORESTRY AND LIVESTOCK

SCALE

0   25   50   100 KMS.

Asuncion

FIGURE 2.5

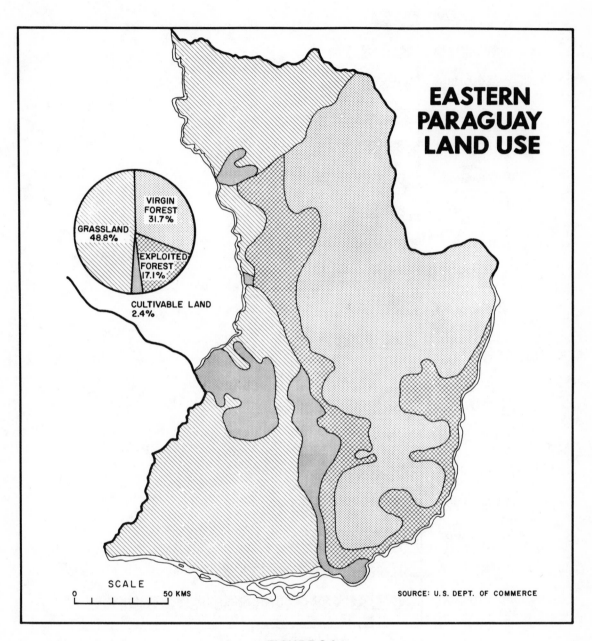

EASTERN PARAGUAY LAND USE

VIRGIN FOREST 31.7%

GRASSLAND 48.8%

EXPLOITED FOREST 17.1%

CULTIVABLE LAND 2.4%

SCALE

0   50 KMS

SOURCE: U.S. DEPT. OF COMMERCE

FIGURE 2.6

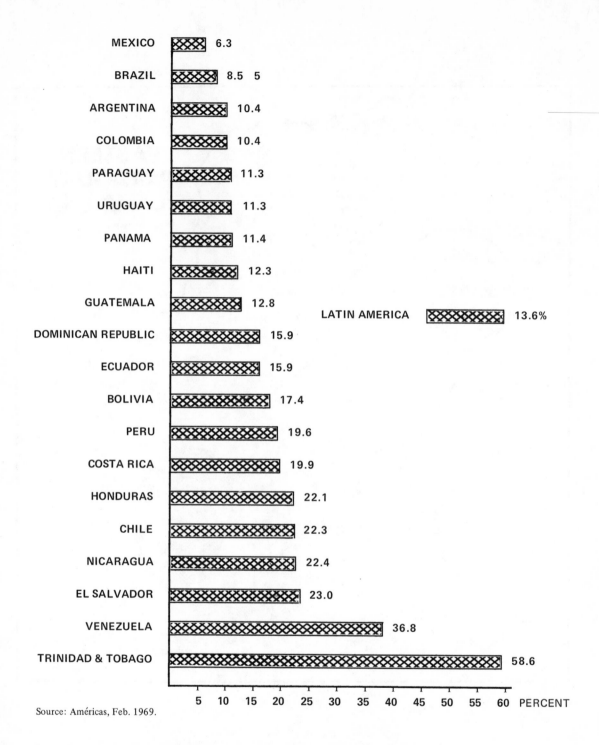

Source: Américas, Feb. 1969.

**FIG. 2.7. THE CONTRIBUTION OF EXPORTS TO THE NATIONAL PRODUCT
OF THE INDIVIDUAL LATIN AMERICAN ECONOMIES
AVERAGE PERCENT FOR 1962–1966**

EASTERN PARAGUAY

FIGURE 2.8

III. The Climate of Paraguay

TEÓFILO FARIÑA SÁNCHEZ

In the tropics lies the future of the race, and much of the past as well . . . the bad old days when the equatorial regions were considered the white man's grave have passed away, and the eyes of the world to-day are turned with expectancy towards the fair lands of sunshine, where Nature is seen at her best.

Macdonald*

Introduction

This paper has as its objective the realization of the first synopsis of the climate of Paraguay, that is, to present the average picture of the prevailing meteorological conditions. The basic data were recorded at weather stations, which were located so as to represent each of the major areas of the country (Fig. 3.1). The analysis of the collected data shows that even though Paraguay is a relatively small country (406,752 km²), there are nevertheless six different climatic types represented.

Two principal problems were encountered during the preparation of this paper: 1) the several meteorological stations have each been operating for varying periods of time, and 2) there are several gaps in the records of some stations occasioned by periods of internal strife in Paraguay. In most cases, however, the record extends over nearly two decades (Fig. 3.1).

Tropical Continental Climate

Paraguay is located in the heart of South America, far from the influence of any large body of water, and consequently has in general a tropical continental climate. The Atlantic Ocean lies some 600 km to the east of Paraguay, and the Pacific Ocean some 800 km to the west, with the Cordillera de los Andes in between it and Paraguay.

The various meteorological stations are located at altitudes ranging from 55 meters at Pilar (Ñeembucú) to 645 meters at Pedro Juan Caballero (Amambay) (Fig. 3.1). The meteorological observations were made three times each day, namely at 1200, 1800, and 2400 hours, Greenwich Mean Time. This corresponds respectively to Paraguay time as follows: 0800, 1400, and 2000 hours. Some 1,095 observations are made each year.

---

*Macdonald, A. K. 1911. Picturesque Paraguay. Kelly, London.

By applying the climate criteria of Thornthwaite (1931, 1933) to the data thus obtained, six regional climates can be demonstrated within the territorial limits of Paraguay:

1. Tropical, semiarid, with deficient rainfall throughout the year—Mariscal Estigarribia (Boquerón).
2. Tropical, subhumid, with deficient rainfall throughout the year—Bahía Negra (Olimpo).
3. Tropical, subhumid, with rainfall deficient in the winter—Puerto Casado (Boquerón), Horqueta (Concepción), and Asunción (Central).
4. Mesothermal, humid, with winter-deficient rainfall—Pedro Juan Caballero (Amambay), Puerto Presidente Franco (Alto Paraná), San Juan Bautista (Misiones), and Pilar (Ñeembucú).
5. Mesothermal, humid, with sufficient rainfall throughout the year—Villarrica (Guairá).
6. Mesothermal, subhumid, with sufficient rainfall year round—Encarnación (Itapua).

Paraguay falls within the C climates of Köppen, with Asunción being typical of Köppen's Cwa classification (Eidt 1969).

Insolation

At Asunción the sun shines an average of 65 per cent of the time (2,898 hours out of a possible 4,423 hours). Monthly data, based on averaged observations from 1941 to 1960, are given below.

The shortest days of the year fall between 20 and 26 June, with 10 hours 35 minutes being the maximum possible amount of sunshine (sunrise—0634 hours; sunset—1709 hours). The longest days of the year occur between 22 and 28 December, with 13 hours 45 minutes being the possible duration of insolation (sunrise at approximately 0500 hours; sunset at approximately 1843 hours).

Month	Maximum Possible Hours of Sunshine	Actual Hours of Sunshine	%
January	418.8	290.4	69
February	365.3	252.0	69
March	380.3	247.2	65
April	346.0	233.0	68
May	338.7	204.1	60
June	318.5	168.3	53
July	333.4	192.2	57
August	349.1	218.7	63
September	358.1	209.6	58
October	393.1	252.2	64
November	399.1	254.0	68
December	424.1	306.0	72

Temperature

The mean annual temperature varies from 25.9 in the north of Paraguay (Bahía Negra, Olimpo) to 21.4 at Pedro Juan Caballero, Amambay, in the northeastern corner of eastern Paraguay (Fig. 3.2). Daily variations are often marked, commonly changing 15 or 20 degrees in a few hours with the onset of a storm. For example, at Puerto Presidente Franco, Alto Paraná, on 23 November 1951, the temperature dropped from 35.2 to 4.2 due to the sudden arrival of a cold front from the south.

The mean annual temperature at Asunción is 24.2, based on some 36,000 observations. December, January, and February are the warmest months, the absolute maximum often exceeding 40. Specific examples follow.

Locality	Absolute Minimum	Absolute Maximum
Horqueta, Concepción	−2.5	44.0
Fortín Pedro P. Peña, Boquerón	−4.0	44.0
Mariscal Estigarribia, Boquerón	−5.1	43.6
Pilar, Ñeembucú	−	42.5
Asunción, Central	−2.2	41.8
Fortín Nueva Asunción, Boquerón	−5.0	41.7
Puerto Casado, Boquerón	0.9	41.7
Villarrica, Guairá	−3.0	41.6
Bahía Negra, Olimpo	−	41.2
Encarnación, Itapua	−6.0	41.0
San Juan Bautista, Misiones	−	40.8
Puerto Presidente Franco, Alto Paraná	−3.0	−
San Lorenzo, Central	−1.6	−
Pedro Juan Caballero, Amambay	0.0	−

Rainfall

The rainy season begins in October and lasts through February or March. The amount of rainfall then progressively diminishes from March to August, which is the driest month. On the average it rains on about 80 days each year. Mariscal Estigarribia (Boquerón) has the fewest rainy days per year (59), while Encarnación has the most (96).

The spatial distribution of rainfall over the country appears roughly to be in successive belts arranged diagonally northeast-southwest across Paraguay. Starting from the northwest corner of the Chaco where the least rain falls, the precipitation increases gradually in a southeasterly direction, being about 500 mm per year at Mariscal Estigarribia (Boquerón), around 1200 mm near the Río Paraguay, 1500 mm in central Paraguay (Guairá), and about 1700 mm in the most southeasterly corner of Paraguay Oriental (Fig. 3.3).

On one occasion, 100.5 mm of rain fell on Asunción in 1.25 hours. The average annual rainfall at Asunción is 1348 mm (Fariña Sánchez 1946). Villarrica (Guairá) holds the record for the greatest amount of rainfall during a 24-hour period: 270 mm. The record for maximum rainfall during one month is 614 mm (Encarnación, Itapua), and for one year, 2265.4 mm (Puerto Presidente Franco, Alto Paraná). Other rainfall data from the 1941–1960 period are given below (all data are maxima expressed in millimeters).

Locality	In 24 Hours	In One Month	In One Year
Bahía Negra, Olimpo	150.0	334.8–Feb.	1417.4–1958
Mariscal Estigarribia, Boquerón	150.0	265.7–Feb.	1123.7–1958
Puerto Casado, Boquerón	210.0	390.1–Sept.	1565.4–1958
Horqueta, Concepción	130.0	418.9–Jan.	2482.4–1946
Pedro Juan Caballero, Amambay	120.0	353.2–Nov.	1719.7–1960
Asunción, Central	202.1	426.5–May	1898.1–1959
Puerto Presidente Franco, Alto Paraná	160.0	392.0–Nov.	2265.4–1946
Villarrica, Guairá	270.0	420.6–June	2115.5–1954
Pilar, Ñeembucú	190.0	417.0–Dec.	1784.8–1959
Encarnación, Itapua	240.0	614.0–Feb.	2493.8–1959

Winds

Northeasterly winds are most frequent, then south and east winds; westerly winds are least frequent. The average wind velocity varies from 4 to 7 miles per hour. Winds of 60 miles per hour are not uncommon during the passage of warm or cold fronts. These high winds often cause considerable property damage. On 22 September 1925, a hurricane struck Encarnación, Itapua. The port facilities and the lower portions of the city were demolished by wind and flood, with considerable loss of life. In October of 1962 a hurricane caused widespread property damage in many parts of the country and especially in the capital.

Summers in Paraguay are hot, even very hot, depending on the location. However, the humidity of the air is usually low enough to make the heat bearable. There are some days though which are exceedingly uncomfortable due to a conjunction of both high temperature and humidity. In the summer evenings a cooling northeast breeze sometimes brings relief from the heat of the day. This air has its origin in the South Atlantic and reaches Paraguay by rotating counter-clockwise around a stable high-pressure area located over Uruguay and southern Brazil.

Some data on the annual frequency and direction of windstorms for several stations are given below.

Locality	Number of Windstorms	Velocity km/hour	Direction
Mariscal Estigarribia, Boquerón	40	65–104	N,S,SE
Asunción, Central	13	65–84	S,SE,NE,NW
Horqueta, Concepción	12	65–77	N,S,SE
Encarnación, Itapua	11	65–104	S,SE
Pedro Juan Caballero, Amambay	9	65–77	S,SE
Puerto Presidente Franco, Alto Paraná	8	65–77	SE,W
Villarrica, Guairá	7	65–77	S,SE
Pilar, Ñeembucú	6	65–90	S,SE
Puerto Casado, Boquerón	5	65–77	S,SE,N
San Juan Bautista, Misiones	4	65–77	S,SE

Thunderstorms

Since Paraguay is a low country in both altitude and latitude and a tropical country as well (the Tropic of Capricorn bisects Paraguay), thunderstorms are well known. Lightning strikes cause property damage and injury or death to people and animals. A thunderstorm raging for hours over the Paraguayan prairies is indeed a magnificent spectacle. The following figures indicate the average annual frequency of thunderstorms at various stations: Encarnación, Itapua—40; Horqueta, Concepción—39; Pedro Juan Caballero, Amambay—38; Pilar, Ñeembucu—25; Puerto Casado, Boquerón—19; Bahía Negra, Olimpo—18; Asunción, Central—18; Villarrica, Guairá—16; San Juan Bautista, Misiones—16; Puerto Presidente Franco, Alto Paraná—15; and Mariscal Estigarribia, Boquerón—13.

Fog

Fog occurs fairly frequently, especially in winter and spring, but its occurrence varies considerably from place to place. The average number of foggy days per year for several stations follows: Puerto Presidente Franco, Alto Paraná—80; Pedro Juan Caballero, Amambay—43; Encarnación, Itapua—34; Horqueta, Concepción—33; San Juan Bautista, Misiones—21; San Lorenzo, Central—12; Asunción, Central—9; Villarrica, Guairá—9; Bahía Negra, Olimpo—7; Mariscal Estigarribia, Boquerón—7; Puerto Casado, Boquerón—7; and Pilar, Ñeembucú—7.

Haze

Hazy days are certainly known in Paraguay, especially in August, September, and October. The haze sometimes covers all of Paraguay plus adjacent parts of Argentina and Brazil. Air traffic over Paraguay must occasionally be curtailed due to haze.

Frost

This is not rare in Paraguay; in fact, it may be observed in all parts of the country except the region around Bahía Negra. Two types of frosts are seen here: the common or "white" frost that is not particularly injurious to crops, and the "black" frost that freezes the sap and damages the tissues of plants. The distribution of frost through the year at several stations is given below.

Locality	May	June	July	Aug.	Sept.
Mariscal Estigarribia	x	x	x	x	x
Puerto Casado		x	x	x	x
Horqueta		x	x	x	
Asunción	x	x	x	x	x
Puerto Presidente Franco		x	x	x	
Pilar		x	x	x	x
Encarnación	x	x	x	x	x
Villarrica		x	x	x	

The writer wishes to acknowledge the fine work of the many weather station operators who have with unstinting regularity and dedication made and recorded the observations on which this paper is based.

Bibliography

Eidt, R. C. 1969. The climatology of South America. *In* Fittkau, E. J., J. Illies, H. Klinge, G. H. Schwabe, and H. Sioli. (Eds.). Biogeography and ecology of South America. Vol. 1. Dr. W. Junk, The Hague.

Fariña Sánchez, T. 1946. Investigación estadística de las precipitaciones pluviométricas en Asunción del Paraguay. Rev. Meteorol. (Montevideo) 5 (18): 78–88.

Thornthwaite, C. W. 1931. The climates of North America according to a new classification. Geog. Rev. 21 (4): 633–655. Map.

Thornthwaite, C. W. 1933. The climates of the earth. Geog. Rev. 23 (3): 433–440. Map.

Author's address: Capitán Teófilo Fariña Sánchez
                   Servicio de Meteorología
                   Ministerio de Defensa Nacional
                   Asunción, Paraguay

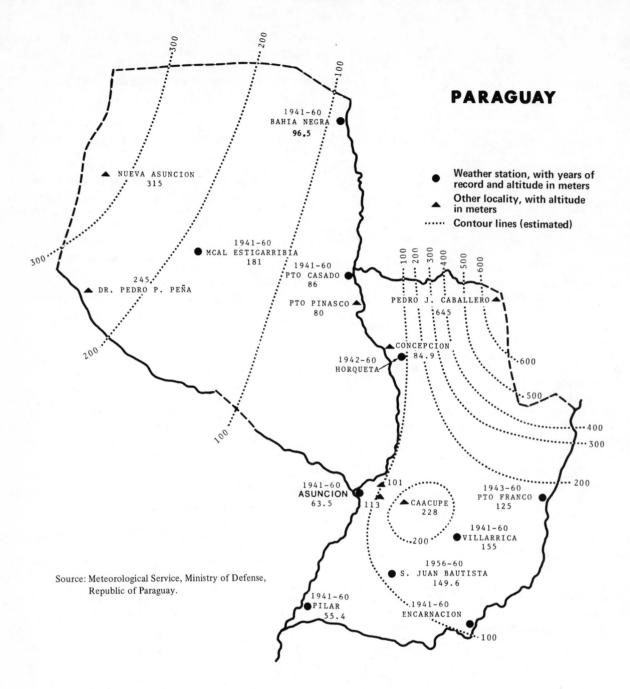

FIG. 3.1. LOCATION AND ALTITUDE OF WEATHER STATIONS

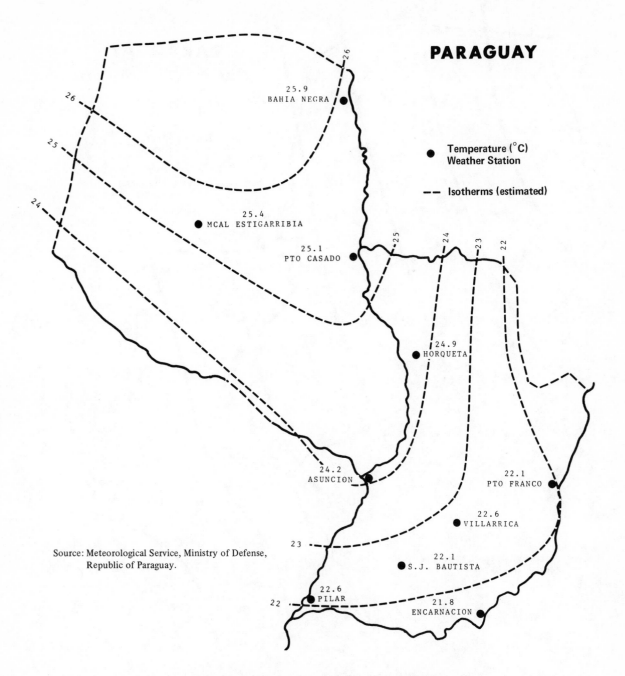

PARAGUAY

Source: Meteorological Service, Ministry of Defense,
Republic of Paraguay.

FIG. 3.2. AVERAGE ANNUAL TEMPERATURE

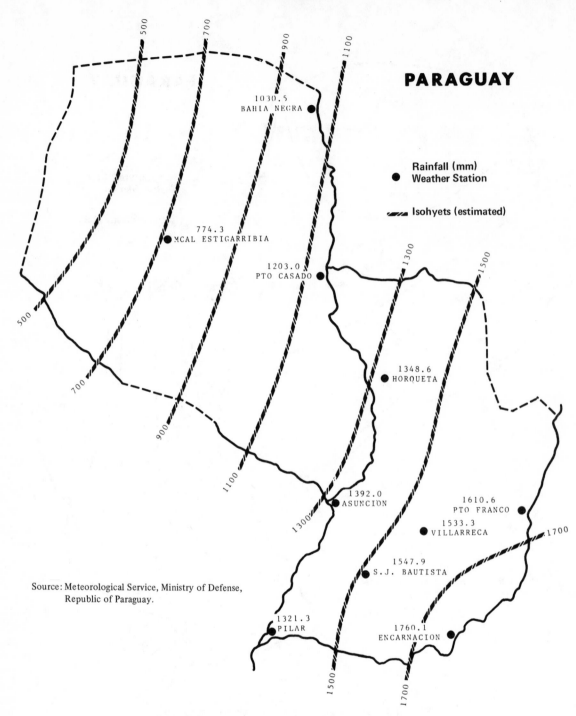

Fig. 3.3. ANNUAL RAINFALL

IV. The Paraguayan Chaco and Its Rainfall

J. RICHARD GORHAM

This is the face of the province called Chaco! which the Spanish soldiers look upon as a theatre of misery, and the savages as their Palestine and Elysium.

Dobrizhoffer[6]

Physiography

The Chaco Boreal is a great alluvial plain, the product of erosion from the Andes. It extends to the south at least as far as the Río Bermejo, to the north as far as the Serranías de Santiago and San José. The eastern boundary is plainly marked by the Río Paraguay, the western, by the foothills of the Andes. The surface is essentially flat and slightly tilted from west to east, the lowest portions being adjacent to the Río Paraguay. The gradient is very gradual, about 2.3 meters per kilometer. The altitude of Nueva Asunción, near the Bolivian border, is 315 meters; that of Asunción, about 575 kilometers to the southeast, is 63 meters. Naturally, under these circumstances, rainwater tends to stand rather than run off. One visitor to the Chaco, in the early 1900s, reported that "For nine months of the year the interior of the Chaco is one vast swamp, so far as it is known at present. During a 200-mile ride, including the return journey, over a tract chosen by the Indians as being the highest and driest, I can safely say that 180 miles lay through water, and this in the middle of November, with the sun almost vertical."[13]

This report, of course, represents only one of the many and greatly variable moods of the Chaco. Variability, from place to place and time to time, seems to be the principal characteristic of the Chaco. This variability is all the more noteworthy in view of the relatively small size of the Chaco and the absence of any prominent topographic features. The location of the Chaco, that is, its remoteness from ocean influences, is in itself sufficient explanation for a good deal of the variability, especially as it relates to weather and climate. The climate, of course, is typically continental.

In spite of the intrinsic variability, certain patterns of distribution of rainfall are clearly evident. As will be shown in detail later, there is a northwest-to-southeast gradient of rainfall, lesser on the west, greater on the east.

This phenomenon alone affects a great variety of Chaco features.

Vegetation

Vegetation throughout the Chaco tends to be mostly of the xerophytic sort.[10] This is probably a reflection of the frequent droughts which affect all parts of the Chaco, except perhaps the narrow riverine section. This riverine strip normally gets more rainfall than any other section of the Chaco. Much of the littoral is inundated annually when the river rises. The region thus enjoys considerable protection against the occasional short periods of drought. Actually, the littoral does not differ markedly from the corresponding parts of eastern Paraguay.

The southeastern region of the Chaco is covered by *palmeras,* marshes, grasslands and thorny scrub *(monte).* The caranday palms sometimes occur in groves, but more typically are widely scattered over the grassland. These *palmeras* constitute one of the most characteristic features of this section of the Chaco. However, they do occur in eastern Paraguay, particularly in the regions near the Río Paraguay. As the observer quoted above noted on his Chaco trip, a good rainy season may convert the Chaco grasslands into a huge marsh. On the other hand, a prolonged dry spell may have the opposite effect, reducing surface waters to the very few more-or-less permanent water holes and working considerable hardship on both man and beast.

The grasslands are composed principally of bunch grasses which grow on hummocks rising several inches above the ground. This feature is no doubt related to the frequent and prolonged inundations to which the grasslands are subject. The dense thorny scrub occurs as islands of varying size and shape, surrounded by grassland and *palmera*. These islands of thorny scrub are elevated a few inches above the level of the surrounding grassland and therefore remain relatively dry even when the adjacent grassland is covered with water.

A very serious problem related to the expansion of the thorny scrub islands and consequent loss of grass-producing lands, is developing in the Chaco and is posing a grave threat to the ranching economy. Apparently, the cows browse on the seed pods of certain scrub legumes and subsequently deposit the still-viable seeds on the grassland where they sprout and eventually replace the grass. As one proceeds north and west from the southeast Chaco, the thorny scrub is seen to occupy increasingly greater expanses of land. There are islands of grassland and groves of the larger trees, such as *palo boracho, palo santo* and *quebracho*.

Hydrography

Only one river, Río Pilcomayo, traverses the entire Paraguayan Chaco. It forms, in fact, the international boundary between Paraguay and Argentina. The Pilcomayo, like the Río Bermejo, breaks up into distributaries which farther along anastamose, forming again the main stream. Most of the Chaco rivers are concentrated in the southeastern section. Perhaps this is a function of the relatively higher rainfall of that section and the overall slope toward the east. These rivers might also represent remnants of formerly larger rivers which, like the Pilcomayo, had their origin in Andean snows.

The Pilcomayo is the northernmost river of that portion of the Paraguay drainage basin which originates in the Andes. All of the other more northerly rivers which emerge from the eastern side of the Andes flow into the Amazon basin. The next Andean river to the north of the Pilcomayo is the Río Parapetí. It originates in the subranges of the Andes to the west of Camiri, Bolivia. After forming distribuatries in the Bañados de Izozog of the extreme northwest Chaco near Santa Cruz de la Sierra, the river, now greatly reduced in size, joins those tributaries of the Río Guaporé which drain the Chiquitos Plateau.

At some remote time in the past, the Río Parapetí, and perhaps even the Río Grande (Guapay), probably flowed across the Chaco to the Río Paraguay. What is now called Río Tímane could be a remnant of the Parapetí of an earlier day. The Tímane passes near Ingavi (Mayor Lagarenza) in the northwestern Paraguayan Chaco. This river is only a few miles long, yet, in the manner of an intermittent stream, the water level apparently rises and falls, fluctuating from dry to overflowing in relation to local rains and possibly in relation to the melting of Andean snows. All of the Chaco rivers are slow-moving, meandering and muddy, and tend to be brackish.

Subsurface waters are often too salty for irrigation or for human consumption. There are aquifers of fresh water, especially in the region of Filadelfia. The search for good water has, of course, been more intense in the Mennonite colonies than any other place in the Chaco. In those places where good well water has either not been found or not looked for, the local residents often obtain "potable" water by collecting runoff from the thatched roofs. The rain water is carried by palm log spouting to an open, earthwall storage pit.

Indians

All the principal Chaco ingredients—rainfall, vegetation, surface water, soils, topography, etc.—interact and affect other factors as well. Every Chaco marsh and pool is graced by a remarkably large number of aquatic birds. The bird population falls off toward the north and west in relation to the decreasing amount of surface water.

Nothing definite is known of the distribution of the aboriginal human population of the Chaco in terms of population density. However, one may suppose that the greater natural productivity of the southeast supported Indian populations of comparatively greater density than that of the north and west. These latter regions were certainly inhabited by the resourceful Indians. The northwest still has its nomadic Moros who can subsist solely on the meagre natural products (e.g., honey, tubers, tortoises) of the dry Chaco, but who also accept hand-outs whenever it suits their purposes.

Cattle and Forests

The first non-Indian visitors to the Chaco soon became primarily interested in escaping from it, with life and limb intact. The intractable Chaco tribes and the inhospitable nature of the land discouraged permanent settlement. Eventually though, two important enterprises became established on the western banks of the Río Paraguay: ranching and logging (for the tannin-bearing *quebracho*). These industries soon proliferated toward the west, but not very far to the west. The distance between ranch and market and between *quebracho* forest and river was definitely a limiting factor. But not so much the distance itself as the difficult nature of the Chaco terrain, and this in spite of the fact that the land is virtually flat.

Travel and transport were then (and off the main road, still are) extremely difficult. The *quebracho* industry built narrow-gauge railroads, the longest of which penetrates 160 kilometers into the Chaco due west from Puerto Casado. Cattle, however, had to be driven to market (trucks have only recently been introduced). The non-Indian population was therefore concentrated in the southeast section and the littoral. Even there the density was not particularly great (neither ranching nor logging, at least as it is done in the Chaco, requires large numbers of workers) and it dropped off to practically zero in the north and west.

Colonization

Two events changed this picture of human population and the effects of a third event are still to be fully felt. These three events are intimately associated with the recent history and the future development and exploitation of the Chaco. The first Mennonite colony was founded in 1927 right in the middle of the Chaco. Colonization continued over the years and the Mennonite population now exceeds 10,000. The Mennonites introduced crop production, cattle production and horticulture to the central Chaco. Success has been remarkable, especially in view of the uncertain rainfall.

Roads

The Chaco War (1933–35), between Bolivia and Paraguay, really introduced Paraguayans to that great unknown western half of their country and aroused in them an awareness of its potential. It also resulted in the construction of a network of dirt roads throughout the Chaco. These roads fell into disrepair after the war. Finally, the war established the tradition of military rule for the Chaco. The military government is still in force and has its seat in Mariscal Estigarribia. Both the Mennonite colonizations and the military occupation have caused a great increase in the population of the central Chaco. Some of the old roads were repaired and some new roads were constructed in connection with oil explorations in the western Chaco.

Trans-Chaco Highway

The third event is directly related to the preceding two and is probably the most important happening in the recent history of the Chaco. The economic development of the Mennonite colonies was seriously hindered by the lack of a market outlet. The combination of oxcart, railroad and river boat required to transport products to Asunción prevented profitable exports. The military population of Mariscal Estigarribia was similarly hampered because the same combination, in reverse, had to be utilized for the importation of supplies. All of this was remedied by the construction of the Trans-Chaco Highway, completed in 1964. This road in effect opened up the Chaco. By following this transect through the Chaco, one can observe all the vicissitudes of the land, from the *palmeras* of the southeast through the Mennonite farms of the middle Chaco to the Moro-inhabited *quebracho* parklands and sandy hills of the northwest. The highway intersects with roads left over from the oil explorations. The secondary roads are now being maintained and improved by the Paraguayan army.

Roads, however, often lead to reckless exploitation of a newly opened region rather than to planned development. The future of the Chaco is charged with grave questions, the answers to which should be based on the best of applied ecology and conservation. Excessive population pressures, either of cattle or people, may quickly destroy all that is unique and remarkable about the Chaco. I have elsewhere suggested that large tracts of the Chaco should be set aside as natural areas, preserved and protected in their present state. No doubt irrigation will eventually be employed on a large scale in the Chaco. The source of irrigation water is conjectural: perhaps from stored rainwater, or from as yet undiscovered subsurface aquifers, or from the Río Paraguay or Río Pilcomayo. The best source might be the Río Parapetí across the border in Bolivia, less than 100 kilometers from Gabino Mendoza. The Mennonites have proved that the dry Chaco soils can produce, but scarcely anything is known of the stability of these soils under intensive cultivation.

Chaco Descriptions

Some of the older descriptions of the Chaco—by the conquistadores, Jesuits, and early colonists—are mentioned elsewhere in this book. Domínguez[7] reviewed the salient features of 14 early Chaco expeditions, and Mendoza[17] traced the history of the Chaco during the periods of Exploration and Conquest. Several books intended for mainly non-scientific readers provide interesting insight into Chaco life and conditions: Attenborough,[3] Durrell,[8,9] Gibson,[12] Grubb,[13,14,15] Kerr,[16] Ray,[22] Thompson,[23] and Tolten.[24] A team of experts from the United States Operations Mission to Paraguay compiled a book that touches on virtually every aspect of the Chaco.[5] The geology of the Chaco has been described in detail by Putzer.[21] Surveys of the Indian life of the region were done by Alacron and Pittini,[1] Belaieff,[4] Métraux,[18] Nordenskiöld,[19] and Zerries.[25]

Meteorology

The oldest known rainfall data pertaining to the Chaco were collected at Misión Central, located 130 km due west of Concepción. During the late 1800s, Misión Central was an official observatory of the Argentine weather service. A book by Fontana,[11] published in 1881, contains the results of meteorological observations made at Villa Occidental (now Villa Hayes) in 1878. Rainfall records from Puerto Casado date from 1927; those of Bahía Negra, from 1933. In the early 1940s, a network of weather stations was organized by the Paraguayan government. These stations were located at some of the many *fortines* left over from the Chaco War. More than 20 years of data are now available in the records of these stations.

The Paraguayan meteorological service has established ten first-class official weather observatories throughout the country. Three of these are Chaco stations: Bahía Negra, Puerto Casado and Mariscal Estigarribia. All three of these have more than 20 years of records. These three official stations plus the *fortines* cover the Chaco fairly well and their records constitute a reasonably complete picture of the rainfall. These records are supplemented by unofficial observations made at several ranches, most of which are in the southeastern section. The Paraguayan meteorological service serves as a repository for all of these records, both official and unofficial.

Rainfall

Twenty-nine stations, each with five or more years of records, are included in this study. The salient features of each station are presented in Table 4.1 and their locations are mapped in Figure 4.1. Three basic concepts readily emerge from a study of the records: 1) The seasonal distribution of rainfall follows the pattern of the rest of Paraguay, i.e., a wet summer and a dry winter. 2) There is a west-to-east gradient of rainfall. 3) There is a great deal of variability in rainfall from place to place, from month to month, and from year to year.

SEASONAL RAINFALL

Figure 4.2 shows the annual distribution of rainfall, based on the annual mean of each station. The annual picture may be compared to similar maps (Figures 4.3 and 4.4) based on the summer (October–May) and winter (June–September) means (for other maps of rainfall distribution see Figures 3.3, 4.8, and 4.9).

August is the driest month of the year. About 75 percent of the entries for August show rainfall of less than 20 millimeters (Table 4.2). No rainfall at all is recorded in 38 percent of the entries for August (Figure 4.5). When the stations are segregated as "wet" stations (more than 900 mm per year) and "dry" stations (less than 900 mm per year), the percentages of zero rainfall entries for August are 24 and 49, respectively. Taking all months together, the percentages of zero observations are 6 for the wet stations, 17 for the dry stations, and 12 for all stations.

Regardless of the season, the riverine strip gets more rain than any other section of the Chaco. The western frontier region, on the other hand, receives less rainfall than any other section. The gradient of increasing rainfall from west to east is fairly clear and regular. However, the Filadelfia-Mariscal Estigarribia area is for some reason exceptional in that it receives a little more rain, at least in the summer, than the region immediately adjacent to it on the east (Figure 4.3).

VARIABILITY

Mention was previously made of the variability of Chaco rainfall. Simple perusal of the raw data is sufficient to give one the impression that variability of rainfall, as regards time and place, is a very common phenomenon. In order to more precisely define this impression of variability, standard deviations of the monthly means were computed and tabulated (Table 4.3). A standard deviation of 1 indicates the least possible amount of variation in data. Therefore, the larger the standard deviation, the more variable and less predictable are the data. Conversely, the more closely the standard deviation approaches one, the less variable the rainfall has been and the more predictable it will be in the future.

The predictability and variability of rainfall are related to place and to season. The most predictable (least variable) month is August; the most variable (least predictable), November. Months in order of predictability from least to greatest are November, February, January, March, April, December, October, May, June, September, July and August. Normally, the drier western stations are more predictable than the wetter eastern stations (Figure 4.6). Some of the more important stations, in ascending order of predictability, are 3, 7, 12, 10, 19, 1, 18, 20, 22, 21, 16, 23, 24 and 25. Apparently, one is fairly safe in predicting scant rainfall for those stations normally having scant rainfall, especially if the prediction applies to one of the winter months. Such cannot be done with equal chance of success with regard to the wetter eastern stations. The relationships among the variables of month, monthly mean, and standard deviation of the mean are shown in Table 4.4.

Puerto Sastre on the Río Paraguay apparently holds all the records for variability of rainfall. In 1961, the difference between the amount of rain in September and that of October was 605 mm. October of 1961 had 617 mm more rainfall than October 1962. The total annual rainfall for 1957 was 1,673 mm greater than that of 1958. Other examples of the same sort are given in Table 4.5.

DISTRIBUTION

Two stations located near one another and presumably existing under similar environmental conditions may, in fact, have rather dissimilar rainfall records. This difference may be a function of the relatively short period of time over which observations have been made. It may also indicate that the distribution of rainfall is often spotty and local in nature, rather than general over a wide area. Thus Station A may get a good shower while nearby Station B stays dry. There is nothing especially unusual about this. But when A continues to get significantly more rain than B during an entire month, the phenomenon is worthy of some attention. Specific examples are given in Table 4.6.

This localized distribution may not be completely random. There are cases in which Station A over a long period often gets a little more rain than Station B, its close neighbor. The rainfall at Soledad (11) has been 5.4 percent greater than at San Sebastián (10); Puerto Sastre 14 percent greater than Puerto Casado; Garay (24) 16 percent greater than Oruro (25).

CYCLES

Twenty years is really too short a period to expect to see any sort of long-term periodicity of rainfall. Nevertheless, the available data (Table 4.7) present an interesting picture. When data for 14 of the more important stations are averaged together and plotted, the resulting curve shows remarkably regular fluctuations, with peaks every three or four years (Figure 4.7).

DROUGHT

Palmer[20] defines drought as prolonged and abnormal moisture deficiency. Leaving out the word abnormal, it would appear that much of the Chaco climate is in a perennial state of drought. Taking the average number of consecutive months without rain (3.8 months) as an arbitrary measure of normal, then 4 months or more might be considered abnormal. Obviously, insufficient rainfall can produce drought almost as well as no rainfall at all. The data were therefore searched for cases in which periods of zero rainfall were preceded and/or followed by months in which the rainfall was less than half the monthly mean. For those stations with 7 or more years of record, most of the periods of zero rainfall lasting 4 or more months were preceded and/or followed by one or more months of devicient rainfall, that is, amounts less than half the monthly mean. These data, summarized in Table 4.8, indicate that the western two-thirds of Boquerón province falls within the drought-prone region of the Chaco.

Acknowledgements

The raw data were given to me by Capitán de Navío Fariña Sánchez and Mayor Ososky of the Paraguayan meteorological service. The facilities of the computer center of the Division of Epidemiology, Institute of International Medicine, University of Maryland School of Medicine, were made available to me by Dr. Christian Klimt, Division Director. The computer program for the computation of standard deviations was designed by Dr. Curt Meinert, with the assistance of Mr. Charles Tack. I am greatly indebted to all of these men for their kindness and cooperation.

Literature Cited

1. Alacron y Cañedo, J., and R. Pittini. n.d. (circa 1925). El Chaco paraguayo y sus tribus. Sociedad Editora Internacional, Turin.
2. Albani, F., C. Fletschner, and H. Ferreira. 1961. Paraguay clima. (Map.) USAID, Asunción.
3. Attenborough, D. 1959. Zoo quest in Paraguay. Lutterworth, London.
4. Belaieff, J. 1946. The present-day Indians of the Gran Chaco. *In* Steward, J. H. (Ed.). Handbook of South American Indians. Vol. 1. The marginal tribes. Smithsonian Institution, Washington, D.C.
5. Bradford, W. E., F. R. Fisher, J. W. Romita, and T. S. Darrow. 1955. El Chaco paraguayo. Misión de Operaciones de los Estados Unidos de América en el Paraguay, Asunción.
6. Dobrizhoffer, M. 1822. An account of the Abipones, an equestrian people of Paraguay. 3 vol. John Murray, London.
7. Domínguez, M. 1925. El Chaco boreal. Imprenta Nacional, Asunción.
8. Durrell, G. 1954. The new Noah. Viking, New York.
9. Durrell, G. 1961. The drunken forest. Rupert Hart-Davis, London.
10. Fiebrig-Gertz, C., and T. Rojas. 1933. Ensayo fitogeográfico sobre el Chaco boreal. Rev. Jard. Bot. Mus. Hist. Nat. Paraguay 3: 1–87.
11. Fontana, L. J. 1881. El Gran Chaco. Ostwald y Martínez, Buenos Aires.
12. Gibson, C. 1948. Enchanted trails. Museum Press, London.
13. Grubb, W. B. 1904. Among the Indians of the Paraguayan Chaco. Charles Murray, London.
14. Grubb, W. B. 1911. An unknown people in an unknown land. Lippincott, Philadelphia.
15. Grubb, W. B. 1914. A church in the wilds. Dutton, New York.
16. Kerr, J. G. 1950. A naturalist in the Gran Chaco. University Press, Cambridge.
17. Mendoza, J. 1937. El Chaco en los albores de la conquista. Imprenta Salesiana, Sucre, Bolivia.
18. Métraux, A. 1946. Ethnography of the Chaco. *In* (see Belaieff 1946).
19. Nordenskiöld, E. 1912. Indianerleben. El Gran Chaco (Südamerika). Bonnier, Leipzig.
20. Palmer, W. C. 1965. Meteorological drought. Research Paper No. 45. U.S. Weather Bureau, Washington, D.C.
21. Putzer, H. 1962. Geologie von Paraguay. Gebrüder Borntraeger, Berlin.
22. Ray, G. W. 1911. Through five republics on horseback. William Briggs, Toronto.
23. Thompson, R. W. 1936. Land of tomorrow. Duckworth, London.
24. Tolton, H. 1936. Enchanting wilderness. Selwyn and Blount, London.
25. Zerries, O. 1969. The South American Indians and their culture. *In* Fittkau, E. J., J. Illies, H. Klinge, G. H. Schwabe, and H. Sioli. (Eds.). Biogeography and ecology in South America. Vol. 1. Dr. W. Junk, The Hague.

Table 4.1. Rainfall Data from 29 Stations in the Paraguayan Chaco

Station Number	Station Name	Length of Record	Annual Mean mm	Summer Mean mm	Winter Mean mm	Highest Year on Record	Lowest Year on Record	Highest Month on Record	Lowest Month on Record	% of Zero Entries On Record	Months Having No Rainfall	Longest Period Without Rain	Longest Period With Rain
1	Bahía Negra	1933–62	1002	108	35	1417 mm 1958	605 mm 1944	335 mm FB 1947	0 mm	3	MR JN JL AG NV	2 months JL-AG 1937	95 months SP37-JL45
2	Puerto Sastre	1940–43 1955–62	1460	152	62	2852 mm 1956	840 mm 1958	652 mm JR 1956	0 mm	6	MY JN JL AG SP	2 months MY-JN 1958	42 months JR40-JN43
3	Puerto Casado	1927–62	1173	125	43	1659 mm 1935	763 mm 1932	461 mm NV 1943	0 mm	2	MR JN JL AG	1 month	132 months JL33-JN44
4	Puerto Pinasco	1958–62	1384	149	41	1574 mm 1961	1265 mm 1962	236 mm DC 1961	2 mm SP 1959	0	–	–	40 months SP59-DC62
5	Villa Hayes	1953–62	1411	141	68	2010 mm 1959	902 mm 1955	492 mm AP 1959	0 mm	0.9	JN	1 month JN 1962	103 months NV53-MY62
6	San Luís	1958–62	1620	171	69	1912 mm 1959	1452 mm 1960	545 mm AP 1959	0 mm	2	JN	1 month JN 1962	53 months JR58-MR62
7	Espinillo	1943–62	1142	116	54	1655 mm 1959	541 mm 1944	399 mm AP 1959	0 mm	4	MR MY JN JL AG	1 month	68 months SP54-MR60
8	Santa Rita	1942–56	1077	111	49	1545 mm 1943	591 mm 1948	442 mm MY 1953	0 mm	8	JL AG SP	1 month	35 months SP50-JL53
9	San José	1955–62	1163	122	41	1408 mm 1956	1048 mm 1960	339 mm AP 1956	0 mm	9	FB JN AG SP	1 month	21 months OC59-JN61
10	San Sebastián	1940–62	1002	106	37	1613 mm 1956	480 mm 1945	344 mm AP 1956	0 mm	9	all except MR OC NV	3 months JL-SP 1943	49 months AG55-AG59
11	Soledad	1947–49 1951–62	1126	114	54	1592 mm 1958	467 mm 1948	368 mm AP 1956	0 mm	10	MY JN JL AG NV	2 mo. MY-JN48; JL-AG49	66 months DC56-MY62
12	Misión Central	1940–62	1182	127	41	1763 mm 1957	805 mm 1944	354 mm NV 1941	0 mm	5	JN JL AG SP NV	2 months	67 months DC55-JN61
13	Campo Flores	1923–25 1933–45	802	79	28	1524 mm 1939	469 mm 1935	301 mm NV 1939	0 mm	14	all except FB MR	3 months SP-NV 1935	AG38-DC40 31 months
14	Hamaguera	1953–62	936	99	36	1279 mm 1958	461 mm 1955	296 mm AP 1961	0 mm	12	all except JN DC	2 months JL-AG 1953	23 months NV57-SP59

15	Los Patitos	1958–62	922	100	30	1053 mm 1959	639 mm 1962	0 mm	2	JN AG	1 month AG61; JN62	43 months JN58–JL61	
16	General Díaz	1941–62	536	61	12	816 mm 1947	281 mm 1954	0 mm	15	all except FR MR	4 months JN–SP 51, 62	21 months SP43–MY45	
17	Isla Poí	1942–59	596	67	15	1077 mm 1943	240 mm 1955	0 mm	15	JN MR–SP DC	4 months MY–AG 1948	21 months SP43–MY45	
18	Filadelfia	1941–62	798	88	24	1134 mm 1958	509 mm 1941	0 mm	8	MY JN JL AG SP	3 months JL–SP 1949	82 months SP53–MY60	
19	Kilometer 160	1942–62	676	74	20	1194 mm 1953	118 mm 1949	0 mm	18	FB–OC DC	8 months FB–SP 1949	33 months AG42–AP45	
20	Kilometer 180	1942–62	631	68	22	1091 mm 1943	187 mm 1949	0 mm	15	MR–OC DC	7 months MR–SP 1949	29 months AP57–AG59	
21	Kilometer 220	1942–62	658	74	16	1026 mm 1951	272 mm 1949	0 mm	18	MR–OC DC	7 months MR–SP 1949	26 months JL57–AG59	
22	Mariscal Estigarribia	1940–62	798	90	19	1171 mm 1940	526 mm 1955	0 mm	5	JN JL AG SP	3 months JN–AG 1951	59 months SP43–JL48	
23	Ingavi	1941–60 1962	457	50	12	844 mm 1943	71 mm 1956	0 mm	21	MR–DC	4 mos. MY–AG 51, 52; JN–SP62	AG42–JN44 23 months	
24	Garay	1941–62	387	46	4	777 mm 1943	125 mm 1956	0 mm	30	all months	6 months AP–SP 1948	18 months JN41–JR42	
25	Oruro	1942–61	344	42	3	606 mm 1945	113 mm 1959	0 mm	36	all months	9 months JR–SP 1948	24 months JL45–JN47	
26	Pozo Hondo	1944–49 1951	366	42	4	687 mm 1951	127 mm 1946	0 mm	21	AP–SP	6 months AP–SP 1951	18 months OC46–MR49	
27	Pedro P. Peña	1941–62	431	53	4	677 mm 1944	70 mm 1948	0 mm	24	JN–OC	8 months FB–SP 1948	24 months JL45–JN47	
28	Ballivián	1942–49	325	38	5	612 mm 1944	129 mm 1948	0 mm	28	FB–SP	7 months FB–AG 1948	12 mos. JN44–MY45; JL45–JN46	
29	Linares	1941–46	393	46	6	627 mm 1943	96 mm 1946	0 mm	26	MY–NV	6 months JN–NV 1946	12 months AG42–JL43	

Table 4.2. Monthly Rainfall Data from 14 Stations in the Paraguayan Chaco (Figures in Percentages)

$$\% = \frac{\text{number of observations in category } n \text{ for month } y}{\text{total number of observations for month } y} \times 100$$

Station	January				February				March				April				May				June			
	<20*	20-100*	100-200*	>200*	<20	20-100	100-200	>200	<20	20-100	100-200	>200	<20	20-100	100-200	>200	<20	20-100	100-200	>200	<20	20-100	100-200	>200
1	0	32	54	14	0	46	43	11	11	43	28	18	0	68	21	11	28	54	18	0	28	68	4	0
3	3	40	40	17	0	63	26	11	6	46	28	20	6	37	49	8	6	57	28	8	19	64	17	0
7	10	20	45	25	10	40	35	15	5	50	35	10	0	40	35	25	15	50	30	5	25	50	20	5
10	5	26	52	17	9	43	44	4	4	44	35	17	4	35	48	13	13	48	26	13	35	48	17	0
12	5	30	35	30	10	39	44	17	5	43	44	13	0	43	35	22	9	39	48	4	30	48	17	5
16	10	57	33	0	0	67	19	4	0	76	19	0	28	62	10	0	24	67	9	0	76	24	0	0
18	0	59	27	14	10	50	41	9	5	68	32	0	23	36	36	5	32	59	9	0	36	59	5	0
19	10	57	28	5	14	57	14	15	24	52	19	5	29	52	19	0	43	57	0	0	48	43	9	0
20	19	43	38	0	19	52	29	0	19	67	14	0	19	62	14	5	38	48	14	0	57	33	10	0
21	5	66	24	5	10	62	28	0	24	48	28	0	19	52	24	5	38	57	5	0	57	38	5	0
22	0	48	48	4	4	43	35	17	4	57	35	4	22	52	17	9	26	65	9	0	61	35	4	0
23	16	68	16	0	10	60	30	0	40	35	20	5	35	60	5	0	55	45	0	0	65	35	0	0
24	23	59	14	4	18	64	18	4	27	59	14	0	36	50	14	0	77	23	0	0	91	9	0	0
25	26	53	21	0	26	42	32	0	35	45	20	0	50	50	0	0	89	11	0	0	95	5	0	0
All	9	46	35	10	9	51	32	8	13	52	27	8	18	50	24	8	33	49	15	3	49	42	8	1

Station	July				August				September				October				November				December			
	<20	20-100	100-200	>200	<20	20-100	100-200	>200	<20	20-100	100-200	>200	<20	20-100	100-200	>200	<20	20-100	100-200	>200	<20	20-100	100-200	>200
1	50	36	14	0	61	39	0	0	17	69	14	0	3	50	44	3	3	44	40	13	3	40	44	3
3	42	47	11	0	53	44	3	0	25	61	14	0	0	33	53	14	0	36	39	22	0	36	47	17
7	20	70	10	0	50	50	0	0	10	70	20	0	5	35	40	20	5	35	45	15	10	55	30	5
10	44	52	4	0	56	44	0	0	26	70	0	4	0	65	35	0	17	31	39	13	9	69	13	9
12	48	52	0	0	44	56	0	0	35	48	17	0	0	35	56	9	9	26	39	26	0	44	56	0
16	76	24	0	0	95	5	0	0	68	32	0	0	23	59	18	0	24	57	10	9	23	54	18	5
18	68	27	5	0	95	5	0	0	50	45	5	0	5	54	41	0	9	59	27	5	4	41	50	5
19	90	5	5	0	81	19	0	0	57	38	5	0	9	62	24	5	14	59	10	14	24	38	24	14
20	76	24	0	0	76	24	0	0	43	52	5	0	5	71	19	5	14	66	9	9	9	62	29	0
21	86	14	0	0	81	19	0	0	57	38	5	0	5	67	28	0	5	62	33	0	10	52	38	0
22	74	26	0	0	91	9	0	0	43	56	0	0	4	61	30	5	4	56	35	5	0	52	43	5
23	80	20	0	0	95	5	0	0	48	52	0	0	43	43	14	0	14	67	10	9	29	52	19	0
24	95	5	0	0	100	0	0	0	86	14	0	0	41	54	5	0	27	59	14	0	0	57	14	0
25	100	0	0	0	95	5	0	0	100	0	0	0	37	53	10	0	32	58	10	0	16	68	11	5
All	66	30	4	0	75	25	<1	0	46	48	6	<1	12	52	31	5	12	50	25	11	11	50	33	6

Station	All Months			
	<20*	20-100*	100-200*	>200*
1	7	49	27	7
3	14	47	13	9
7	14	47	29	10
10	15	42	32	11
12	18	48	26	8
16	37	45	13	12
18	33	50	15	2
19	33	48	18	1
20	27	47	23	3
21	28	47	21	4
22	38	49	11	2
23	44	45	10	1
24	54	38	8	<1
25	58	32	9	<1
All	29	46	20	5

*millimeters

Table 4.3. Mean Monthly Rainfall (M) and Standard Deviation (SD) of the Mean for 22 Stations in the Paraguayan Chaco

(N = number of months on record)

Station	January			February			March			April			May			June			July			August			September			October			November			December		
	M	SD	N	M	SD	N	M	SD	N	M	SD	N	M	SD	N	M	SD	N	M	SD	N	M	SD	N	M	SD	N	M	SD	N	M	SD	N	M	SD	N
1	135	62	28	123	72	28	112	75	28	87	61	28	56	48	28	38	32	28	31	41	28	17	18	28	53	41	29	99	53	30	124	66	30	125	73	30
2	213	175	12	151	70	12	110	62	12	136	144	12	124	129	12	43	38	12	66	91	12	63	67	12	75	85	12	170	184	12	150	82	12	158	127	12
3	135	78	35	107	76	35	125	84	35	113	75	35	93	68	35	54	40	36	40	44	36	26	28	36	53	42	36	139	79	36	144	95	36	141	84	36
5	162	107	9	126	78	9	118	84	9	204	128	9	106	68	9	57	43	9	67	42	9	57	31	9	92	59	9	166	80	9	109	79	10	137	117	10
7	135	74	20	116	75	20	102	77	20	139	95	20	86	65	20	73	61	20	49	39	20	25	26	20	69	41	20	131	82	20	127	74	20	90	77	20
8	124	72	15	109	64	15	118	68	15	90	65	15	104	105	15	70	55	15	48	36	15	16	19	15	63	32	14	136	87	14	126	80	14	83	55	14
10	129	83	23	98	70	23	111	75	23	132	87	23	102	74	23	51	41	23	39	34	23	20	24	23	46	58	23	93	48	23	108	76	23	80	61	23
11	146	87	15	109	80	15	118	90	15	165	107	15	98	59	15	55	38	15	39	37	15	34	45	15	88	92	15	93	52	15	97	73	15	84	52	15
12	142	88	23	131	80	23	118	69	23	143	86	23	107	77	23	55	55	23	37	36	23	26	23	23	48	48	23	127	56	23	146	100	23	101	40	23
14	106	66	10	120	72	10	91	64	10	140	78	10	56	51	10	37	31	10	42	28	10	28	30	10	37	62	10	88	66	10	88	83	10	103	79	10
16	80	59	21	77	55	21	75	38	21	43	42	21	37	31	21	12	17	21	13	20	21	3	5	21	17	17	22	50	36	22	60	61	21	67	61	22
17	90	58	21	62	79	21	59	101	21	70	47	21	36	30	21	13	44	21	13	24	21	3	16	21	23	36	21	74	53	21	66	98	21	85	81	21
18	111	66	22	109	62	22	79	50	22	87	66	21	42	32	22	34	39	22	24	30	22	7	7	22	32	36	22	85	46	22	88	68	22	100	56	22
19	82	58	21	94	79	21	71	101	21	62	47	21	30	30	21	31	44	21	11	24	21	10	16	21	28	36	21	74	53	21	90	98	21	92	81	21
20	87	59	21	75	50	21	56	42	21	60	50	21	39	39	21	28	43	21	15	24	21	12	21	21	32	34	21	74	47	21	84	82	21	69	54	21
21	87	64	21	78	48	21	65	56	21	78	79	21	33	28	21	22	29	21	12	20	21	9	15	21	21	25	21	76	33	21	94	50	21	84	51	21
22	108	46	23	121	73	23	92	54	23	77	70	23	43	43	23	24	29	23	16	18	23	9	24	23	24	24	23	87	51	23	95	54	23	99	56	23
23	51	32	19	73	44	20	53	60	20	31	31	20	24	26	20	13	14	20	11	16	20	3	6	20	20	16	21	44	44	21	72	64	21	52	41	21
24	56	49	22	66	51	22	52	38	22	38	43	22	11	17	22	5	8	22	2	5	22	1	2	22	7	13	22	34	31	22	52	44	22	57	56	21
25	55	56	19	59	53	19	49	44	20	30	29	20	6	10	19	3	10	19	2	4	20	2	9	19	3	5	19	34	32	19	44	36	19	56	55	19
27	110	93	14	62	57	15	59	68	15	27	29	14	11	15	14	3	2	15	2	4	14	2	3	14	8	12	14	22	17	15	65	47	14	66	46	14
28	84	64	8	48	50	8	31	21	8	12	17	8	6	12	8	3	2	8	3	8	8	4	6	8	11	14	8	39	29	8	33	31	8	52	39	8
All	110	---	--	96	---	--	84	---	--	89	---	--	57	---	--	33	---	--	26	---	--	17	---	--	39	---	--	88	---	--	94	---	--	90	---	--

Table 4.4. Variability (Expressed as Standard Deviation of the Monthly Mean) of Rainfall Related to Month of Year and Average Monthly Rainfall, Based on 22 Stations in the Paraguayan Chaco, Each with 8 or More Years of Record

Month	Number of Stations with Standard Deviations of						Rainfall (All Stations)
	1–5	6–10	11–15	16–20	21–50	>50	
January					3	19	110
February					5	17	96
March					7	15	84
April				1	7	14	89
May		1	2	1	9	9	57
June	2	2	1	1	13	3	33
July	3	1		5	12	1	26
August	3	5	1	3	9	1	17
September	1		3	2	11	5	39
October				1	10	11	88
November					5	17	94
December					4	18	90

Table 4.5. Some Examples of the Variability of Rainfall in the Paraguayan Chaco

Station Number	Station Name		Same Month, Different Year	Same Year, Different Month	Different Years
1	Bahía Negra	Year	1957, 1958	1961	1958, 1959
		Month	March	April, May	–
		Difference (mm)	299	223	587
2	Puerto Sastre	Year	1961, 1962	1961	1957, 1958
		Month	October	September, October	–
		Difference (mm)	617	605	1673
7	Espinillo	Year	1955, 1956	1959	1949, 1950
		Month	October	March, April	–
		Difference (mm)	334	345	768
8	Santa Rita	Year	1952, 1953	1959	1946, 1947
		Month	May	May, June	–
		Difference (mm)	292	389	710
10	San Sebastián	Year	1955, 1956	1953	1955, 1956
		Month	April	November, December	–
		Difference (mm)	304	304	630
11	Soledad	Year	1955, 1956	1961	1960, 1961
		Month	April	April, May	–
		Difference (mm)	315	312	624
18	Filadelfia	Year	1942, 1943	1943	1943, 1944
		Month	November	October, November	–
		Difference (mm)	235	264	505
19	Kilometer 160	Year	1953, 1954	1954	1952, 1953
		Month	November	March, April	–
		Difference (mm)	370	451	886
27	Pedro P. Peña	Year	1943, 1944	1944	1947, 1948
		Month	January	January, February	–
		Difference (mm)	246	276	534
28	Ballivián	Year	1948, 1949	1949	1944, 1945
		Month	January	January, February	–
		Difference (mm)	166	158	443

Table 4.6. Some Examples of Variation in Rainfall at Several Paired Stations in the Paraguayan Chaco

Station Number	Station Name	Year	Month	Rainfall (mm)	Year	Month	Rainfall (mm)
1	Puerto Sastre	1959	August	0	1961	October	639
3	Puerto Casado			152			166
10	San Sebastián	1956	May	13	1956	May	15
11	Soledad			146			0
10	San Sebastián	1959	September	0	1961	August	0
11	Soledad			210			181
18	Filadelfia	1943	September	63	1949	March	48
21	Kilometer 220			0			0
18	Filadelfia	1954	December	50	1956	December	69
21	Kilometer 220			0			0
21	Kilometer 220	1954	December	0	1956	December	0
22	Estigarribia			42			24
24	Garay	1952	February	88	1953	December	31
25	Oruro			0			0
24	Garay	1956	May	45	1959	November	135
25	Oruro			0			10

Table 4.7. Total Annual (T) and Average Monthly (M) Rainfall at 14 Stations in the Paraguay Chaco, 1942–1962

(in mm)

Year	Bahía Negra 1 T/M	Puerto Casado 3 T/M	Espinillo 7 T/M	San Sebastián 10 T/M	Misión Central 12 T/M	General Díaz 16 T/M	Filadelfia 18 T/M	Kilometer 160 19 T/M	Kilometer 180 20 T/M	Kilometer 220 21 T/M	Mariscal Estigarribia 22 T/M	Ingavi 23 T/M	Garay 24 T/M	Oruro 25 T/M
1942	1025/ 85	1297/108	---/---	799/ 66	1069/ 89	726/61	734/61	494/ 41	747/62	751/62	719/60	572/48	528/44	299/25
1943	1114/ 93	1421/118	868/ 72	971/ 81	1150/ 96	787/66	1022/85	1005/ 85	1091/91	815/68	828/69	844/70	777/65	482/40
1944	605/ 50	951/ 79	541/ 45	540/ 45	805/ 67	592/49	518/43	764/ 64	627/52	532/44	550/46	536/45	323/27	496/41
1945	955/ 80	1286/107	736/ 61	480/ 40	909/ 76	469/39	716/60	797/ 66	648/54	603/50	768/64	651/54	677/56	606/51
1946	1342/112	1349/112	1231/102	952/ 79	1444/120	814/68	846/71	1132/ 94	1010/84	880/73	740/62	558/46	600/50	409/34
1947	1196/100	1387/115	1077/ 90	836/ 70	1164/ 97	816/68	928/77	677/ 56	723/60	707/59	749/62	411/34	338/28	527/44
1948	935/ 78	871/ 72	655/ 54	597/ 50	880/ 73	265/22	521/43	421/ 35	450/38	448/37	624/52	501/42	245/20	197/16
1949	958/ 80	998/ 82	777/ 65	626/ 52	1148/ 87	558/46	571/48	118/ 10	187/16	272/23	761/63	639/53	560/47	355/30
1950	928/ 77	1387/116	1545/129	1005/ 84	1089/ 91	642/54	1069/89	836/ 70	623/52	929/77	852/71	402/34	456/38	370/31
1951	917/ 76	1283/107	1010/ 84	881/ 73	1070/ 89	367/31	875/73	590/ 49	803/67	1026/86	1027/86	312/26	476/40	561/47
1952	1154/ 96	982/ 82	1302/108	877/ 73	1174/ 98	307/26	685/57	305/ 25	448/37	509/42	835/70	366/31	212/18	256/21
1953	1201/100	945/ 79	1258/105	1166/ 97	1566/131	400/33	983/82	1194/100	965/80	730/61	738/62	---/55	190/16	214/18
1954	771/ 64	---/---	1339/112	987/ 82	1198/100	281/23	757/63	1005/ 84	417/35	408/34	636/53	294/24	237/20	415/34
1955	---/---	946/ 79	910/ 76	983/ 82	842/ 70	316/26	622/52	418/ 35	294/24	436/36	526/44	279/23	431/36	182/15
1956	1262/105	1435/120	1538/128	1613/134	1530/128	327/27	845/70	431/ 36	612/51	600/50	712/59	71/ 6	125/10	317/26
1957	1287/107	1578/132	1441/120	1510/126	1763/147	552/46	980/82	593/ 49	818/68	643/54	938/78	405/34	192/16	184/15
1958	1417/118	1567/130	1096/ 91	1500/125	1305/109	499/42	1134/94	713/ 59	556/46	666/56	1123/94	572/48	333/28	243/28
1959	880/ 73	1090/ 91	1655/138	1322/110	1167/ 97	526/44	808/67	605/ 50	440/37	538/45	645/54	551/46	250/21	113/ 9
1960	619/ 68	1371/114	1219/102	969/ 81	1135/ 94	---/--	1069/89	1113/ 93	839/70	1011/84	1099/92	314/26	556/46	334/28
1961	1074/ 90	1400/117	1599/133	1396/116	1631/136	777/65	810/68	660/ 55	571/48	687/57	930/78	---/--	204/17	---/--
1962	655/ 54	958/ 80	1046/ 87	763/ 64	1023/ 85	451/38	553/46	317/ 26	388/32	613/51	766/64	---/--	---/--	---/--

Table 4.8. Drought in the Paraguayan Chaco

Station Number	Station Name	% Months with Zero Rainfall	No. of Droughts on Record (4 or More Months Zero Rainfall)	No. of Periods of 2 or More Months Without Rainfall	Longest Drought Period (Months)			
					Without Rainfall	Deficient Rainfall	Total	Year
16	General Díaz	15	2	10	4	1	5	1951. 1962
17	Isla Poí	15	1	6	4	1	5	1948
19	Kilometer 160	18	1	9	8	2	10	1949
20	Kilometer 180	15	1	5	7	1	8	1949
21	Kilometer 220	18	2	6	7	1	8	1949
23	Ingavi	21	3	11	4	3	7	1962
24	Garay	30	6	21	6	1	7	1948
25	Oruro	36	9	14	9	1	10	1948
27	Pedro P. Peña	24	5	8	8	2	10	1948

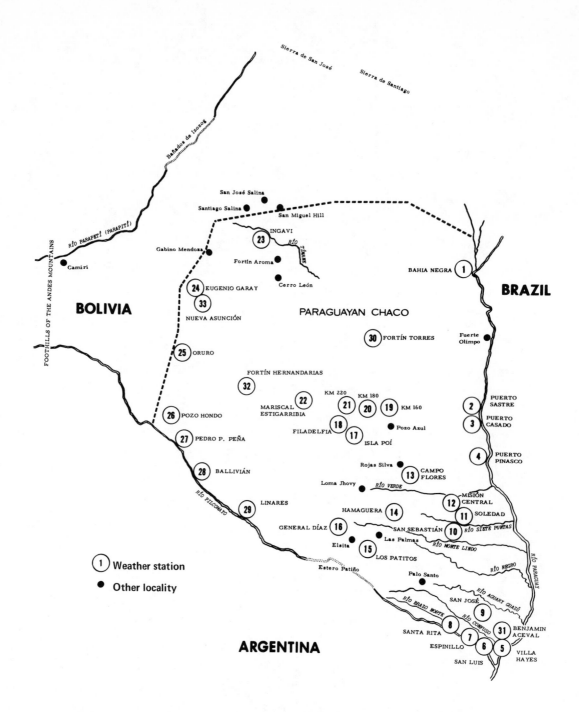

FIG. 4.1. WEATHER STATIONS, PARAGUAY

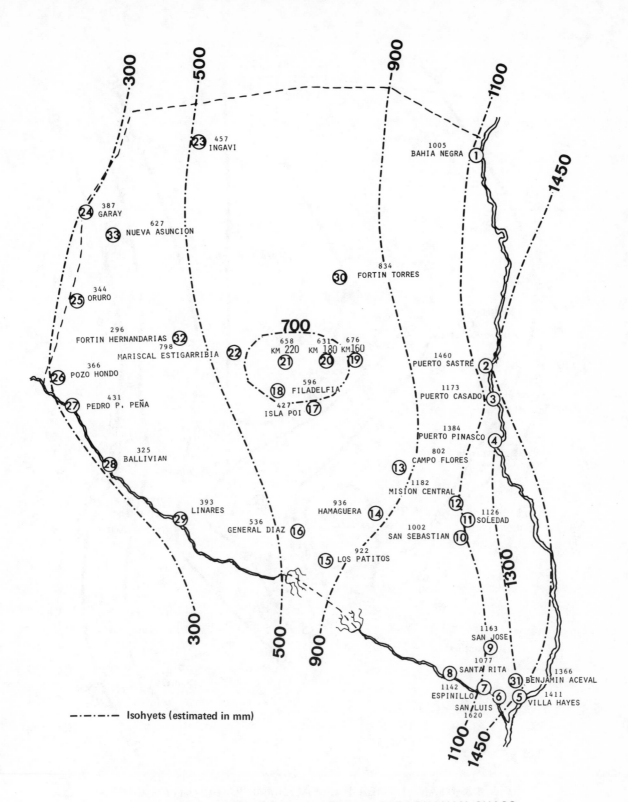

FIG. 4.2. ANNUAL MEAN RAINFALL, PARAGUAYAN CHACO
(Annual mean in mm given with each station)

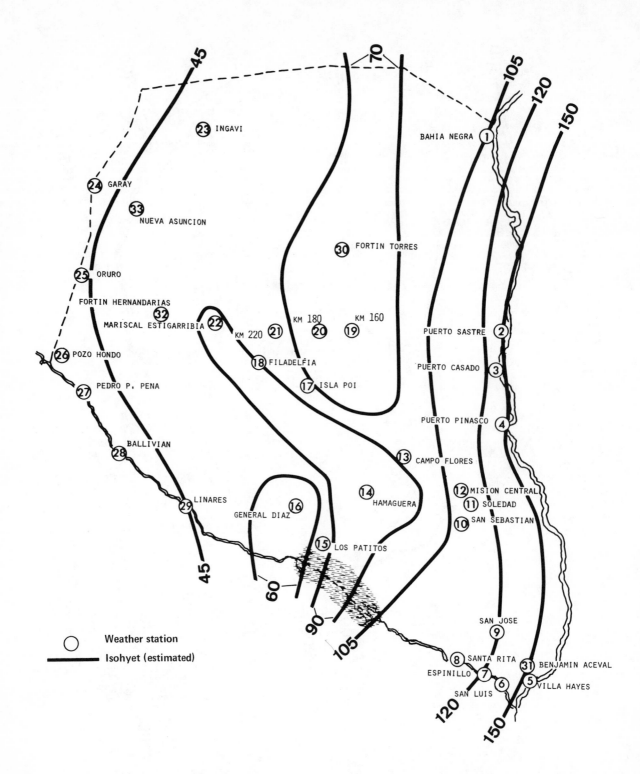

FIG. 4.3. MEAN SUMMER RAINFALL (MM), PARAGUAYAN CHACO

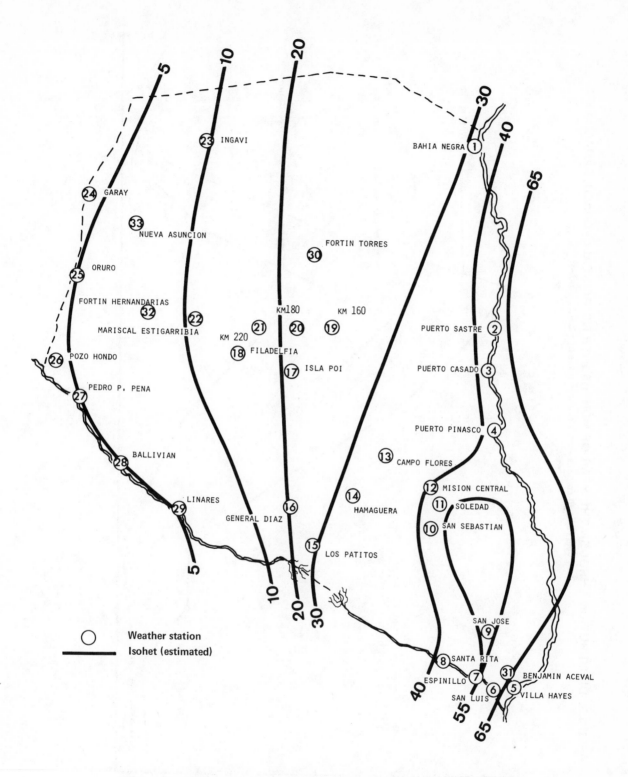

FIG. 4.4. MEAN WINTER RAINFALL (MM), PARAGUAYAN CHACO

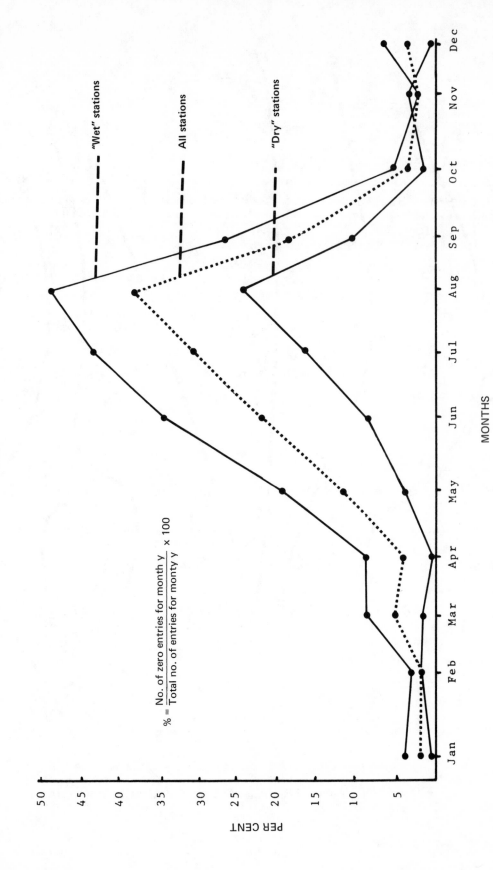

FIG. 4.5. DISTRIBUTION THROUGH THE YEAR OF MONTHS WITH NO RAINFALL. CHACO, PARAGUAY

(All years and all stations with 7 or more years of record included)

$$\% = \frac{\text{No. of zero entries for month y}}{\text{Total no. of entries for monty y}} \times 100$$

"Wet" stations

All stations

"Dry" stations

PER CENT

MONTHS

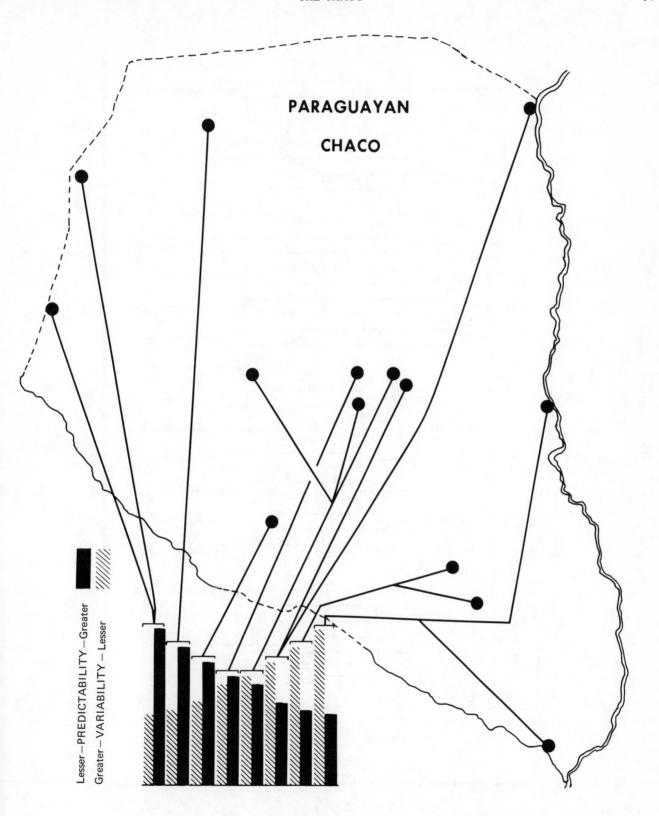

FIG. 4.6. GEOGRAPHIC GRADIENT OF PREDICTABILITY OF RAINFALL
(In terms of greater or lesser variability of rainfall records of 14 Chaco stations)

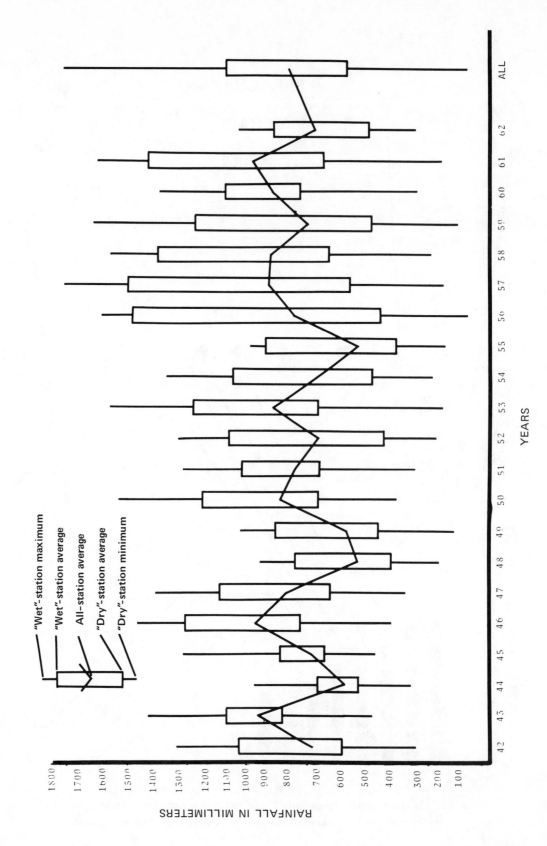

FIG. 4.7. RAINFALL IN THE PARAGUAYAN CHACO, 1942–1962
Based on 14 Stations

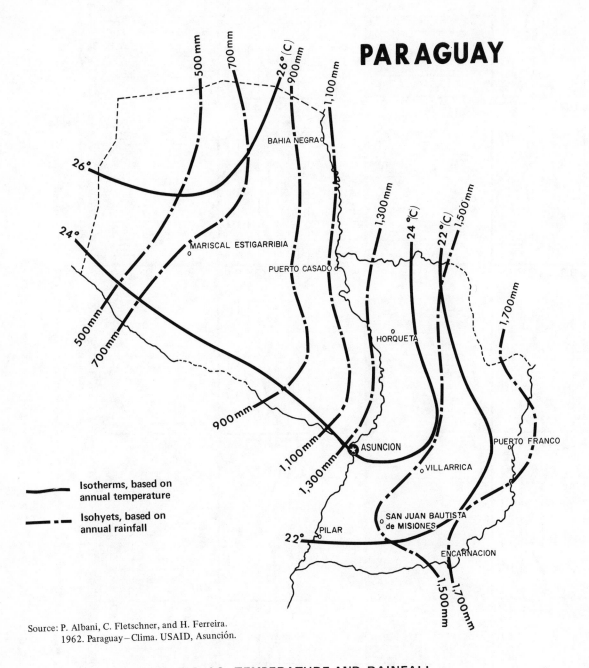

PARAGUAY

Isotherms, based on annual temperature

Isohyets, based on annual rainfall

Source: P. Albani, C. Fletschner, and H. Ferreira.
1962. Paraguay–Clima. USAID, Asunción.

FIG. 4.8. TEMPERATURE AND RAINFALL

FIG. 4.9. TEMPERATURE AND RAINFALL IN PARAGUAY

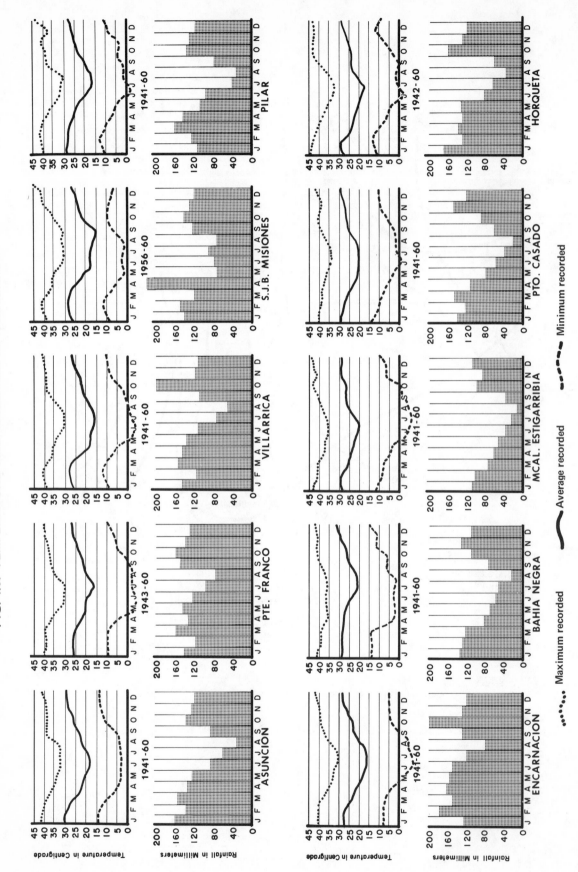

Modified from Albani, F., C. Fletschner, and H. Ferreira. 1962. Paraguay–Clima. USAID, Asunción

V. Reflections on the Geology of Paraguay

RICARDO BOETTNER

> *The Paraná-Paraguay depression is the central lowland zone in the southern part of the continent. The upper surface, consisting of immense, recent accumulations of rock lying over the deeply-submerged continental basal complex, does not exceed a height of 200 m above sea-level. . . . In addition to the main rivers, the Paraguay, the Paraná and the Uruguay, the lowland region is full of old tributaries, lakes and marshes. The Palaeozoic and Mesozoic mountain ridges . . . tower island-like between the rivers. . . . The Gran Chaco adjoins in the west . . . a region of low-lying ground on top of which the Quaternary upper strata of sands, clays and marls, with red and red-brown soils, rise up to the foot of the Andes.*
>
> Sick*

Historical Background

Soon after the Americas were discovered, the *conquistadores* dedicated themselves to the search for the legendary El Dorado. According to the stories, this was the site of enormous quanitites of gold and other mineral wealth. There was even talk about a Lake of Gold. With gold and wealth in the offing, the *conquistadores* risked, and often lost, their lives and suffered hunger and thirst as they searched through inhospitable and unknown lands. Some succeeded in reaching the *altiplano* of Bolivia and Peru, via the Paraguayan Chaco or "green hell." There on the high plateau of the Incas the explorers found gold, silver, tin, tungsten, and the other mineral riches of Peru and Bolivia. The intrepid conquerors had to be geologists of sorts, but they depended for much of their geoinformation on the Indians, who were already accomplished miners. The Spaniards took full advantage of this, and the sweat and blood of thousands of Indians contributed to the enrichment of La Madre Patria.

In spite of the tales of the great mineral wealth of Paraguay, the explorers were notably unsuccessful in finding it. Nevertheless, the belief in undiscovered mineral riches has persisted in some people's minds through the years and even to the present time.

JESUITS

Finally, long after the period of exploration, the first concrete evidence of the existence of mineral wealth in Paraguay came to light during the epoch of the Jesuit missions (1560–1767). The Jesuits knew how to make bronze. We know now that copper does exist in Paraguay, for example at Paso Pindo on the Río Tebicuary there are malachite deposits, and specimens of metallic copper

can be found near Encarnación, Itapua. But where did the Jesuits get the tin? The existence of tin has been claimed but the claim has never been confirmed. Dr. Rebaudi, Paraguay's first chemist, did find unworkable ores in the form of cassiterite, two percent in the clays of Tobatí, Cordillera, and four percent at Ybitimí, Paraguarí.

The Jesuits were proficient artists and artisans. They produced many beautiful works of art, examples of which can still be seen at some of the old mission sites or in many museums. The church altars were yellow with real gold and the Jesuits shipped no mean quantity of gold to Spain. Pfotenhauer,[14] a German Jesuit, states in his basic work on the Jesuit missions of Paraguay, that ". . . because of their monopoly on salt from the *salinas* of San José and Santiago, they gained prodigious sums of money (gold?) selling salt to Santa Cruz, Moxos, Mato Grosso and Paraguay; prodigious amounts of gold came from the placers of San Javier and Santo Corazón, and silver from the mines at San Juan."

Understand that the old Jesuit missions of Paraguay were scattered over a territory much larger than present-day Paraguay. Ahlfeld and Braniša[1] located the San José *salina* some 40 miles south of San José, Bolivia, west of San Miguel Hill. The Santiago *salinas* are located east of the San José salt beds. The gold placers are in the same region.

In 1767, Charles III ordered the expulsion of the Jesuits from Paraguay. The missions fell into ruins then and many of the incidents of that day and age reach us only in the form of legends.

FRANCIA

Little is known about the history of geology during the dictatorship (1814–1840) of José Gaspar Rodríguez de Francia, who purposely isolated Paraguay from the rest of the world. Possibly first utilized during that time were

---

*Sick, W. 1969. Geographical substance. *In* Fittkau, E. J., *et al.* (eds.). Biogeography and ecology in South America. Vol. 2. Dr. W. Junk, The Hague. Quoted by permission of the publisher.

the immense limestone and marble deposits in northern Paraguay, near the confluence of the Río Apa and the Río Paraguay. The first lime burner was probably located at Puerto Francia.

C. A. LÓPEZ

The next dictator (1844–1862), Carlos Antonio López, reversed the isolationism of Francia. Don Carlos had faith in the idea of undiscovered mineral wealth in Paraguay. He imported several European geologists and mineralogists to discover and develop these resources. As a result, several important industries related to geology or mineralogy were initiated.

IRON

The iron foundry at Ybicuí, Paraguarí. The existence of good iron ore near San Miguel and Caapucú, Paraguarí, was demonstrated by the mineralogists. Therefore, in 1854 the foundry was set up. Wood charcoal was used as fuel and reducer. Two tons of charcoal were required to produce one ton of iron. The foundry was situated at Ybicuí, about 15 miles from the ore beds. Here there were extensive forests, the raw material for charcoal. A creek was dammed to provide water and power to operate the bellows. Nearby stream beds contained a fine white clay used to line the furnaces. The country around the ore beds lacked both adequate water and forests. The lime, used as scorifier and flux, was brought in from Paraguarí, 30 miles away.

At first, the Caapucú oligist, about 50 percent iron, was utilized. But these mines flooded, so the mining operation was moved to the deposits at San Miguel (Misiones) and Quyquyó (Paraguarí). The ore was transported in oxcarts over very crude roads. This system proved to be too slow and inefficient. A plan was projected to dredge out Mburicasy (Mbuyapey) Creek and bring down the ore by barge. But the outbreak of the Triple Alliance War (1864–1870) terminated the plan. Some 3000 tons of ore were ready to be transported to the foundry when the war broke out (Schuster[16]). The foundry was destroyed during the war. To the present date this important industry has not been reinstated in Paraguay.

GUNPOWDER

Black gunpowder, a mixture of charcoal, sulphur, and saltpeter, was the *frappe de force* in those days. Of the three ingredients, only charcoal was locally available. The sulphur came from Italy and the saltpeter was shipped in from Chile via the Straits of Magellan. However, thanks to the ingenuity of the European technicians imported by don Carlos, black gunpowder soon became a purely local product. A deposite of marcasite, FeS_2, a dimorph of pyrite, was located at Minas-cué in the State of Cordillera. On heating, marcasite gives up half its sulphur. A sulphur factory was set up at Minas-cué and at one time at least one thousand persons were employed there. All of the hardware for the factory came from the iron foundry at Ybicuí. Some of these tools are preserved in various museums.

The saltpeter was derived from the urea present in human urine by a certain fermentation process carried out in specially constructed shallow holes in the ground. Chile saltpeter promptly became unavailable to the Paraguayans at the outset of the War of the Triple Alliance. So the local production of saltpeter was stepped up in order to meet the demands for gunpowder during the war. This explains why there are so many places in Paraguay named Salitre-cué ("a place where saltpeter used to be produced").

WAR

But the terrible Triple Alliance War destroyed all of this, and many years passed during which geology was scarcely even thought about. Eventually, Paraguay began to recover and to awaken little by little from the lethargy produced by the devastations and deprivations of the War.

RECONSTRUCTION

One of the postwar administrations contracted a foreign mineralogist to conduct a country-wide mineralogical survey. By the time of the Exposition at Buenos Aires in 1910, Paraguay was able to show high-grade ores of 50 minerals, "thanks to the good work of the contracted mineralogist." Somehow, however, the locality records of the mineral specimens got "lost." Dr. Rebaudi was charged with the task of finding out the origin of these wonderful specimens, but unfortunately he never did find out, even though he directly questioned the mineralogist who supposedly gathered the specimens. Most of the minerals presented as coming from Paraguay in the Buenos Aires Exposition have never subsequently been found in Paraguay.

The myth of mineral riches in Paraguay has been propagated by such stories as the one above, by the exaggerated report of the geologist imported by Carlos Antonio López, and by other publications, both foreign and local, which freely name minerals like gold, silver, mercury, lead, manganese, arsenic, zinc, tin and many others.

It is true, of course, that most of these minerals do exist in Paraguay but only in minute quantities. Perhaps somewhere in Paraguay there are significant mineral deposits, but this is a matter requiring serious investigation. The existence of a mineral and its exploitability are two quite different things. For example, I have found gold in Paraguay, but only two specimens, one in quartz from Misiones, the other a tiny nugget from the shore of the Río Paraguay near Bahía Negra.

Contemporary Geological Work

The scientific treatment of the geography of Paraguay began in 1911 with a publication on the morphology of Paraguay by the German geographer Carnier.[5]

In 1918 a notable advance in the study of the soils of Paraguay was made with the publication of an agronomic-petrographic map of Paraguay by the great Swiss-Paraguayan naturalist, Moisés Bertoni.[4]

Expeditions

There have been many geological expeditions into the interior of Paraguay, and some of these resulted in notable discoveries. Beder and Windhausen[3] described Devonian rocks in central Paraguay (Putzer[15] strongly contests this classification). Beder[2] reported the finding of a Permian fossil (Mesosaurus) near Villarrica, Guairá. This discovery, confirmed by Harrington,[10] should be of considerable stratigraphic importance. Conradi[6] described a fossil beach (Devonian) at Cariy-Loma, Cordilleras.

Four foreign geologists have produced important and basic works on the geology of Paraguay. Harrington[10] was the first to publish a proper geologic map of eastern Paraguay, along with excellent descriptions of the paleontology and stratigraphy of that region. Eckel[9] presented an ample classification of rocks and a geologic map of all of Paraguay. Silurian and Devonian fossils and stratigraphy were investigated by Wolfart[18] in 1957. Putzer[15] also worked in Paraguay in 1957. His book contains a very useful map and the most complete and best integrated description of the geology of Paraguay.

Each of the three countries adjacent to Paraguay has also been the object of geologic investigations: Argentina (Windhausen[17]), Bolivia (Ahlfeld and Branisă[1]), and Brazil (de Oliveira and Leonardos[13]).

Historical Geology

If we look at the various geologic maps of Paraguay, we note certain similarities in stratigraphic distribution; but there is a tendency of the more recent authors to consider the strata to be considerably older than earlier observers had thought them to be. There are reasons for this change of opinion. During the Age of Exploration it was thought that because Paraguay and the rest of South America were new, the geological formations should be recent as well. Besides this, during the Conquest very few rock outcrops were observed in Paraguay because the land was covered by profuse and impenetrable forests, and these were traversed by only a few trails and no roads.

STRATIGRAPHY

With the passage of time, however, several interesting outcrops were found, and among these were the beds of granites, which probably pertain to the Brazilian Shield and consequently link the stratigraphy of Paraguay with that of Brazil. There are also stratigraphic correlations between Paraguay and Argentina.

CAMBRIAN–ORDOVIDIAN

A limestone deposit, the Itapucumí Series, covers an extensive region of Paraguay in the State of Concepción. Since fossils were previously unknown from this limestone, geologists could only estimate its age. Windhausen,[17] for example, classed it tentatively as Silurian. Harrington[10] considered this limestone to be Ordovician, and Eckel[9] tentatively places it between Ordovician and Cambrian. Putzer[15] correlates this limestone with the Bodoquena Series in the Mato Grosso of Brazil and estimates that it is of late Algonkian or early Cambrian age. The writer has recently obtained a well-preserved fossil from a limestone outcrop near Vallemí, Concepción, which when properly classified, should help date the Itapucumí Series.

SILURIAN–DEVONIAN

Several geologists have reported their ideas about Silurian deposits (the Caacupé Series) in central Paraguay (Harrington,[10] Eckel,[9] Wolfart,[18] Putzer[15]). Sandstones and clays, often fossil-bearing, are most characteristic of this region. Differing opinions on the stratigraphy seem to be as numerous as the geologists who have studied the area. Beder and Windhausen[3] considered the rock to be of Devonian age, and they probably came to this conclusion via comparisons with Devonian deposits in Argentina. Harrington originally classed the Caacupé Series as Devonian, but later called it Silurian.[11] But at the same time he, along with Conradi,[7] considered the Cariy-Loma sandstone to be Devonian, especially after seeing the fossils found there by Conradi.

Wolfart,[18] however, contends that of all the fossils described by Harrington from Cariy-Loma, there is only one from the Devonian, namely *Chonetes falklandicus* Harrington. Wolfart notes that *C. falklandicus* is not represented in my fossil collection at the Facultad de Química y Farmacia. But Wolfart did not see the Conradi Collection in the Facultad de Ingeniería, neither did he personally visit Cariy-Loma. On the other hand, Harrington did study the Conradi Collection, and I accompanied Harrington on his visit to Cariy-Loma. Thus, the significance of *C. falklandicus* and the Cariy-Loma sandstone is still an open question.

Although Putzer and Wolfart deny the existence of Devonian rocks in eastern Paraguay, they do class as Devonian an outcrop near Fortín Aroma, Boquerón, known as Cerro León. This fact had already been observed by Mr. Moran (personal communications, 1947–1950), geologist with the Union Oil Company, who gave the writer rock specimens from Cerro León (see Moran[12]).

PERMIAN

Harrington[10] has placed the Independencia Series and the Tubarao Series in the Permian. Putzer[15] terms the latter series Upper Carboniferous, and de Oliveira and Leonardos call it Permocarboniferous. The Mesosaurus cited by Beder[2] and Harrington[10] is apparently Permian. Thus, it seems logical that the region around Villarrica, Guairá, should relate to the Permian as well.

GLACIATION

There are differences of opinion, and quite naturally so, about the time of glacial activity in Paraguay. Both Conradi[7] and Harrington[10] believe that it occurred during the Permian; Windhausen[17] and de Oliveira and Leonardos[13] tentatively suggest Permocarboniferous glaciation; and Putzer[15] speaks of glaciation during the Upper Carboniferous. We might note in passing that Conradi was born and educated in Russia where the Permian is best known and characterized.

TRIASSIC-JURASSIC

The various geologic maps of Paraguay that are currently available show considerable agreement concerning the Mesozoic Era, the watershed of the Río Alto Paraná and the Cordillera de Amambay being roughly designated as such. But there is disagreement about whether such areas as the Serra Geral formation (melaphyre effusion) are Triassic (my opinion) or Jurassic (Putzer[15]). Unfortunately, no dinosaur fossils, so abundant in Argentina (Darwin[8]), have thus far been found in Paraguay.

A Paraguayan Geology

The beginning of a "Paraguayan geology" has now been realized. But the major share of this beginning work has been done by foreign geologists, who have both literally and figuratively just "scratched the surface" of the subject. I believe that the government of Paraguay should grant far greater importance to the geology of the country, somewhat in the tradition of Carlos Antonio López in the 1850s. I propose the formation of a national geological commission composed of Paraguayan geologists, with technical assistance from foreign consultants.

Literature Cited

1. Ahlfeld, Federico, and Leonardo Braniša. 1960. Geología de Bolivia. Editorial Don Bosco. La Paz.
2. Beder, R. 1923. Sobre un hallazgo de fósiles pérmicos en Villarrica. Bol. Acad. Cienc. Córdoba 27.
3. Beder, R., and A. Windhausen. 1918. Sobre la presencia del Devónico en la parte media de la república del Paraguay. Bol. Acad. Cienc. Córdoba 23.
4. Bertoni, Moisés S. 1918. Mapa agrológico, fisiográfico y climatológico. Imprenta y Edición "Ex Sylvis," Puerto Bertoni, Paraguay.
5. Carnier, Karl. 1911. Paraguay. Versuch zu einer morphologischen Betrachtung seiner Landschaftsformen. Mitt. Geogr. Ges. Thüringen 29.
6. Conradi, Sergio. 1935. Informe sobre los trabajos geológicos realizados en el viaje a Pedro Juan Caballero en calidad de geólogo de la Expedición Científica del Jardín Botánico, agregada a la Comisión Paraguaya demarcadora de límites con el Brasil. Rev. Jar. Bot. Mus. Hist. Nat. Paraguay 4:63-71.
7. Conradi, Sergio. 1942. Una playa marina fósil en Itacurubí de la Cordillera. Rev. Min. Agricult. Com. e Industria (Asunción) 5.
8. Darwin, Charles. 1871. Journal of researches into the natural history and geology of the countries visited during the voyage of H.M.S. Beagle round the world, under the command of Capt. Fitz Roy, R.N. Appleton, New York.
9. Eckel, Edwin B. 1959. Geology and mineral resources of Paraguay, a reconnaissance. Geol. Surv. Prof. Paper 327.
10. Harrington, Horacio J. 1950. Geología del Paraguay Oriental. Fac. Cienc. Exact. Fís. y Nat. Serie E. Geología (Buenos Aires) 1.
11. Harrington, Horacio J. 1956. Paraguay. In Jenks. Handbook of South American Geology. U.S. Memoir 65.
12. Moran, W. R. 1956. Geology of Cerro León, Chaco Boreal, Paraguay. Resumen Trab. Pres. XX Congr. Geol. Intern. México, S. 228.
13. Oliveira, Avelino de, and Othon H. Leonardos. 1943. Geologia do Brasil. Ministerio da Agricultura, Rio de Janeiro.
14. Pfotenhauer, J. 1892-93. Die Missionen der Jesuiten in Paraguay. C. Bertelsmann, Gütersloh.
15. Putzer, Hannfrit. 1962. Geologie von Paraguay. Gebrüder Borntraeger, Berlin.
16. Schuster, Adolf N. 1929. Paraguay. Land, Volk, Geschichte, Wirtschaftsleben, und Kolonisation. Strecker and Schröder, Stuttgart.
17. Windhausen, Anselmo. 1929-31. Geología argentina. Jacobo Peuser, Buenos Aires.
18. Wolfart, Reinhard. 1961. Stratigraphie und Fauna des älteren Paläozoikums (Silur u. Devon) in Paraguay. Jahrb. Bundesanst. für Bodenforschung (Hanover) 78.

Author's address: Prof. Ricardo Boettner
Colegio Goethe
Asunción, Paraguay

VI. The Conditions of Animal Life in Paraguay*

MOISÉS SANTIAGO BERTONI

The animal world of South America is exceedingly rich and diverse. It is true that on this continent the spectacular large mammals of the Afro-asiatic region are absent, but we find here, overwhelmingly and unexcelled, an abundance of many other animal groups, e.g., the molluscs, insects, fishes and birds. There is no lack of superlatives.

Fittkau**

The Forest

The conditions of animal life have, up to a point, already been stated in the foregoing chapters. In effect, they are the circumstances of climate and vegetation that primarily regulate the life and distribution of the fauna in general and the various species in particular.

TRAVELERS' IMPRESSIONS

In this respect, Paraguay Oriental has a special importance. With its abundant flora, rainfall and good soils, it could not help but have abundant animal life as well. Nevertheless, the majority of people who have made brief visits to Paraguay have not found this to be the case. Some clarification is appropriate here, and doubly so, since visitors to the adjacent portions of Brazil and the Misiones of Argentina have come to the same conclusion.

Of course, most of the travelers that visit these areas are attracted by exaggerated claims as to the natural richness of the country, and they are understandably disillusioned when they do not observe the large numbers of animals which they presumed would exist in an area so luxuriantly forested.

Actually though, the false impressions of the visitor can be properly blamed on the brevity of his visit, on the peculiarities of these forests, and on exaggerated and preconceived ideas about what he expected to see here.

CONCEALMENT

The Alto Paraná forest is so dense and tangled that a person unaccustomed to it can only with great difficulty enter it and move about in it. A hunter in the plains or the open forests of the Temperate Zone can easily make three miles an hour on foot, but in our forests he could scarcely cover 500 yards in equal time. It follows, of course, that the number of animals encountered in the second case would be proportionately fewer. Furthermore, the extraordinary denseness of the forest greatly facilitates the animals in their efforts to find cover. While in open forests animals are sometimes observed some hundreds of yards away, in the exceedingly dense virgin forest of Alto Paraná the hunter continually passes by without seeing the animals that are observing him from only a few yards away. Apparently the animals feel very secure in the dense cover and consequently remain completely motionless in the face of danger.

The foregoing then sufficiently explains why a brief visit to these parts prompts a false impression of the abundance of animal life in the forest. To these reasons may be added another, perhaps the most important of all. In places like Africa or even in the Chaco of Paraguay, there are great plains with few succulent plants and fruits, scanty rainfall, and seasonal droughts. The rivers are widely separated and ponds and other collections of surface water are scarce. The animals of the plains and forests congregate in those areas where sufficient food and water can be found. When these become depleted the animals must necessarily concentrate around the few remaining water holes and food supplies. At certain hours of the day the animals congregate at the river or waterhole, forming the large herds that so greatly impress the observer or the person who reads about it.

*Translation of the chapter *"Las condiciones de la vida animal"* of a book by M. S. Bertoni, *Condiciones generales de la vida orgánica*, 1918, Ex Sylvis, Puerto Bertoni, Paraguay.

**Fittkau, E. J. 1969. The fauna of South America. *In* Fittkau, E. J., *et al.* (eds.). Biogeography and ecology in South America. Vol. 2. Dr. W. Junk, The Hague. Quoted by permission of the publisher.

DISPERSION

A completely opposite situation exists in our great forest. Here the animals find grass, fruits and water everywhere. Thirst never forces the animals to migrate long distances. Similarly, they are never obliged by lack of food to concentrate in certain areas, leaving the rest unpopulated. The natural advantages of this forest permit the animals to remain well distributed over the area. It is paradoxical that the very richness of the forest, in terms of food, water, and especially shelter, has led some people to believe that it is poorly populated with wild animals.

AGGREGATIONS

Actually, the skilled hunter or the persistent tourist or naturalist, desirous of seeing everything, will not be deprived of the pleasure of seeing aggregations of animals in our forests. Herds of peccaries frequent the salt licks, which are located at mud holes or, more usually, at certain points along a stream. The animals lick the salt-bearing mud, or even eat it. Many animal species and individuals gather at the salt lick, including the most assiduous of all, the tapir. After a night of visitation by mammals, certain beaches along the great rivers look like the floor of a corral. The social species of birds also form great flocks; for example, the toucans, swallows, pigeons, and the large and small parrots, whose swarms plague the farmer.

DIVERSITY

From another point of view, it is possible for a country to have large numbers of animals but few species. A region may thus appear to be richer in animal life than it really is. But this is not the case in Paraguay, especially not for eastern Paraguay. In the latter region just the opposite condition occurs, at least with respect to certain classes and orders of animals. In general, a highly varied flora cannot but help contribute to a highly varied fauna. With regard to certain large groups, such as the insects, a highly varied flora is the principal requisite of a rich and varied fauna.

We have seen now how large is the number of species that live in a small amount of space in the forest. Where the number of species is very large, the number of individuals of each species is in general relatively small.

SNAKES

The snakes are a good example of this. Surely there are no less than 60 species of snakes in the Alto Paraná region. This figure could easily give the impression that this is one of the "snake countries" and give credence to the legends fabricated by certain celebrated cicerones of Misiones (Argentina). But even without considering that poisonous snakes form only a very small fraction of the total number of species, the fact remains that most of the species are so uncommon that the natives of the country are completely unfamiliar with them. Some species are so rare as to have been taken only once during many years of exploration. I must note, however, that the number of snakes is smaller here than in other parts of Paraguay, definitely less, for example, than in Trinidad near Asunción.

During 33 years of observations, I have noted only four cases of snakebite (three survived with treatment, one fatal without treatment) in my holdings and those of my neighbors on the Río Alto Paraná (namely, Yavevihríh, Misiones, Argentina; Yaguarasapá and Puerto Bertoni, Alto Paraná, Paraguay). I must add to these cases two more which I observed in Bajas Misiones, Argentina, during a stay there of three and one-half years. This region is quite distinct from the Alto Paraná forest. Summing up then, during a third of a century there have been just five snakebite cases in a population that varied from 50 to 500 persons. This is something very rare for a tropical country.

THE SEASONS

All things considered, the seasons here do not exercise a very great influence on the populations of animals. This will be understood by taking into consideration the latitude and, more important, the special climatic conditions already mentioned. With regard to the higher vertebrates, the conclusion that changes of residence are very limited, as compared to the sort of thing that is observed in temperate regions, was arrived at after many years of observations. This is explained in large part by the fact that conditions vary only slightly from season to season.

The changes from season to season are notably less pronounced than the meteorologic charts indicate. This fact, which will be demonstrated in detail in another section, became clear and evident to me as the result of phenologic and bioclimatic observations which I made from 1884 to 1896, and even more extensively from 1907 to the present (1918). This generalization does not apply to the Chaco, and is not especially applicable to the states of Concepción, Ñeembucú, and Itapua. But it does apply in general to eastern Paraguay, especially the valley of the middle Río Alto Paraná, limited on one side by the great Mato Grosso plateau and on the northeast by the alternatively arid and lush botanic province of Kaatinga.*

BIOTHERMOMETER

The difference between the synthetic data based on observations made with the usual instruments and the conclusions based on direct observations of nature is due to factors so diverse that they cannot be fully elaborated within the scope of this work. But I must point out that this difference would disappear almost completely if my phytothermometer were used in making meteorological observations. This apparatus, which is not limited to simply registering the temperature or temperature and

---

*Author's note: Even though I do not want to attack the error of a prince of botany like Engler, I cannot admit as simply a province what present-day botanists call the "South Brazilian Province" because, besides being enormous in size, it presents in its various regions such profound differences of flora and climate that I am sure that the botanists will not delay in dividing it into several new provinces, at least the Kaatinga, the uniqueness of which is so evident that the Guaraní Indians long ago noticed it and gave it its graphic name, which appropriately indicates the appearance of this "province" during the long annual drought which blights the region.

evaporation, but registers the combined result of the temperature, relative humidity, evaporation, and insolation, all of which factors have their effect on the flora and fauna.* It can be said that the instrument in question only indicates that portion of the ambient conditions which is of importance to living things.

INCIDENT ENERGY

An example. In Paraguay Oriental, and more specifically in Alto Paraná, the plants utilize more of the incident energy than is the case in almost any other part of the continent. This is associated with a minimal amount of diurnal evaporation. Even though the sun shines brightly as usual and a light breeze blows most of the time, the rate of evaporation is very low due to the absorption of most of the heat by the leaves and the soil. Under such conditions, the phytothermometer will register a maximum of 30 degrees in full winter. The temperature seldom gets that high even during a dry summer month. This example demonstrates that the differences between the seasons can be much less than the usual instruments indicate them to be. The latter have the recognized but unremedied defect of reflecting only the state of the weather and the inorganic portion of nature.**

CLIMATIC FACTORS

The climatic factors affecting animal life in Alto Paraná can be ascertained from the following chart, in which are gathered the accurate data, rounded off, which I have recorded since 1884.

Although the data refer specifically to the northern part of the littoral zone, they can with slight variations be considered representative of the whole Alto Paraná and Caaguazú regions, as well as the adjacent portions of Argentina and Brazil. The data may also apply to northern and east central Paraguay with the qualification that in these regions the quantity of rainfall and the level of relative humidity decreases significantly as compared to Alto Paraná. These meteorologic observations, made in the virgin forest, are of great biological importance and

will give the reader a fairly exact idea of the conditions of living things in these regions.

Climatic Data from Alto Paraná, Paraguay, 1884–1918

Month	Average Temperature	Average Relative Humidity	Rainfall in mm	Average Relative Humidity in the Forest
January	27 C	90%	205	93%
February	26	90	175	93
March	25	88	125	92
April	22	92	200	95
May	19	93	150	96
June	17	93	150	96
July	17	90	120	95
August	18	87	100	92
September	20	89	150	93
October	23	91	225	94
November	24	89	180	92
December	26	88	180	92
All Months	22	90%	2000	94%

It would be very instructive to compare the results of these biothermometric observations made by me in this country with, at least, the averages of wet-bulb thermometer data obtained in other countries in the same latitudes. On making this comparison it would be seen that the difference between averaged wet-bulb readings obtained in two widely separated points in the same latitudes is much greater than that which results from the averages obtained by means of the dry-bulb thermometer. For example, while the dry-bulb thermometer at Puerto Bertoni (Alto Paraná) might have only one degree higher temperature (22 compared to 21) than Corrientes (Argentina), the wet-bulb thermometer registers about four degrees higher (21 at Puerto Bertoni and 17.3 at Corrientes). Another interesting comparison: The dry-bulb temperature at Bahía Negra (Olimpo) might be two degrees higher than that of Puerto Bertoni, but the wet-bulb reading would be one degree less, and this seems to be nearer reality since Bahía Negra is of a somewhat less tropical nature than Puerto Bertoni.

What I have just stated does not in itself explain completely, but it does explain at least in part, the fact that the intensity of animal life continues throughout the year with very little seasonal variation. Of course, this statement must not be construed as an absolute rule. It is only natural that certain groups of animals do show notable seasonal variations in population. But such variations, and even greater ones, exist in all of the hot countries.

To understand this well, it must not be forgotten that the climate of almost all the tropical countries is composed of two seasons in terms of that most important factor of moisture. But this situation does not exist in Paraguay Oriental, especially not in Alto Paraná. In most tropical countries the rainy season is followed by a long dry season, and this sequence of events produces changes as great or greater than those which we note here, notwithstanding a change of temperature which is apparently, indeed, actually smaller, smaller in fact than data from

---

*Author's note: I referred for the first time to this apparatus in my paper *"Influence des Basses Températures sur les Végétaux,"* Buenos Aires, 1886, 50 pages, in the "Boletín de la Academia Nacional de Ciencias de Córdoba," vol. 9, which was a summary of studies done in Switzerland from 1874 to 1883. Later, I described the instrument in a long chapter of my "Agricultural Meteorology Course," offered from 1897 to 1900 at the Escuela Nacional de Agricultura in Asunción, and in several articles in the "Revista de Agronomía." Finally, I described the phytothermometer before the Scientific Congress at Rio de Janeiro in 1905. I have data from 40 years of phytothermometric observations. See my "Boletín de Meteorología Agrícola." Now it seems to me that the name biothermometer is more appropriate because it indicates the temperature to which both animals and plants are exposed, although of course, only approximately.

**Author's note: one of the best known botanists told me on the occasion of his much too short visit in 1914, that, in reference to the usual meteorologic observations, "these are no good; it will be necessary to initiate special observations for botany." By means of this bio- or phytothermometer, the drosometer for calculating dewfall, and my method for calculating "vegetative potential," I believe that I have satisfied that necessity. I say "unremedied" because the nature of the publications in which I published was such that few people have become aware of my methods and up to the moment only a few meteorologic stations have adopted them.

the usual type of meteorological thermometer would lead us to believe.

SEASONAL PROGRESSION

On the other hand, there is an additional reason for the relative lack of seasonal variation in the intensity of animal life, namely, that the seasons do not progress from year to year in a rigorously set pattern, that is, the progress of the seasons in a given year may vary considerably from the year preceding and the one following. This will be better comprehended if, instead of considering that the year is composed of two seasons, as is usually done in Paraguay, let us suppose that the year is composed of six or seven seasons or natural meteorologic periods. Comparing several years then, it may be seen that one of these natural periods is lacking altogether or that the periods may be transposed, producing an abnormal sequence.

Thus in some years September has been the coldest month, while in other years it was May, instead of June or July, one of which is normally the coldest month. January is normally the hottest month, but March has been the hottest several times and November was the hottest month one year. The same sort of thing can be observed as well with regard to rainfall.

MIGRATIONS

Among the animals, the higher vertebrates seem to be least influenced by normal or abnormal weather factors. The effects of these factors here is nothing compared to what is seen in cold regions of the world. This is not to say, of course, that our small variations of weather simply have no influence on the mammals. The study of just what these effects are will be most interesting. Now the birds are evidently more sensitive to these factors. Their migrations are not so general nor so periodic as those of temperate regions, but here they are more complicated because the migrants that follow the meridians get mixed up with the birds that migrate along the parallels. In other words, the birds that migrate north and south cross paths with those flying east towards the Río Alto Paraná or west towards the hills. These complicated migration patterns are, of course, difficult to study, the main problem being to define with sufficient confidence the migratory behavior of a given species. My son, Winkelried,* and I have made many observations, however, on this subject and we hope soon to publish the results.

SEASONAL INFLUENCES

The reptiles are even more susceptible to seasonal influences. I collected reptiles for ten years (1884–1893) and recorded the number collected per month. The monthly data were averaged and are presented below as percentages of the total:

July	1	October	21	January	4	April	9
August	9	November	18	February	5	May	7
September	9	December	9	March	4	June	5

---

*A. de Winkelried Bertoni.

These data apply to the zone of subtropical climate below 27° or 27°31′ latitude near the Río Alto Paraná. Probably less seasonal variation would be observed in regions farther north and farther inland. It appears evident that sensibility to seasonal influences becomes greater at progressively lower evolutionary levels. At least some of the insect groups are very sensitive to seasonal changes of meteorologic factors.

INTERRELATIONS

Insects follow in their development the same seasonal succession as do the plants. But it is interesting to note that this parallelism occurs also in groups that at first glance would seem to be devoid of direct ecologic ties with plants. This is the case with the snakes. From the data above it may be seen that the snakes take on renewed activity in April. This coincides perfectly with renewed plant growth, especially of herbaceous plants. The plants begin to grow and flower after the hot summer has passed and just before the cold season begins. The renewed activity on the part of the plants is readily understood, but that of the snakes, except the insectivorous ones, is much more difficult to explain. But this is another admirable example of the supreme law that all things in nature are somehow interrelated.

Of those insects which are economically important and are least sensitive to the influences of the cold season, we may list the ants, coccids, termites, curculionids, butterflies, moths, and in some years the cicadellids and simuliids *(mbariqwí)*. These last mentioned, the simuliids or black flies, may occur any year or any season of the year so long as the other requisites for their multiplication are satisfied.

What I have just explained applies best to the Alto Paraná-Caaguazú-Amambay region, but to a certain extent it applies to all of Paraguay Oriental.

Rivers

One important part of the fauna, namely the fishes, lives under conditions completely different from the rest of Paraguay Oriental. The river bed of the middle section of the Río Alto Paraná in its entire course from Saltos del Guairá (Alto Paraná) to Encarnación (Itapua) is completely different from that of the rest of the rivers of Paraguay. This section of the Río Alto Paraná is characterized by a rocky bottom and shores, very considerable depth, fast-moving current, and the absence of malaria in its littoral. Its waters are generally clean, carrying practically nothing but sand and pure minerals. It lacks organic matter and microscopic plants.

These characters are as rare as they are appreciated, from the human point of view. Before the great war (1864–1870), and probably even long before, the ships that came up from Buenos Aires or Corrientes had the custom—someone said it was an obligation—to enter the Río Alto Paraná to take on drinking water for the trip on up the Río Paraguay to Asunción. Perhaps this river is unique among all the great rivers of the world.

FISH

The fish fauna of the middle Río Alto Paraná is less varied than that of the other Paraguayan rivers, notably less varied than that of the Río Paraguay. Many species cannot maintain themselves in face of the current, the rocky bottom, and the enormous changes of water level. This last must be added to the list of special characteristics of this most interesting river.

The river is boxed in by a continuous series of hills which rise up steeply from the water's edge without leaving a lateral escape route for the rising water. With each rainfall of any importance, the water level rises rapidly, then drops in the same way. Normally, the water level increases by one or two meters each day. But great storms in Brazil can cause the Río Alto Paraná to rise seven meters (1905) or even 7.5 meters (1915) in 24 hours. At Puerto Bertoni the distance between the minimum low-water mark and the maximum high-water is 41.96 meters.

Actually the fish population is quite satisfactory in the middle and southern sections of this great river, that is, from Candelaria (Misiones, Argentina), 27°30' latitude, to the mouth of the Río Ihkan-guazú or Kambaíh (25° latitude). This latter river was the northern limit of the fishing excursions of the Guayana and Ikvihtihrokaí Indians. Certain species reach considerable size, and due to the exceptional purity of the water of the Río Alto Paraná, the flesh completely lacks the taste of mud or swamp which, unfortunately, can be noted in the fish from the Río Paraguay and Río Paraná.

The northern section of the Río Alto Paraná, between 25° latitude and the Saltos del Guairá, has a very poor fish population. The number of fishes diminishes rapidly above the mouth of the Río Kambaíh and continues very much reduced to the mouth of the Río Ingarihih (Karapá). From this point to the falls of Guairá fish are practically absent, especially when the water is low. The rapid current and the tumbling of the water over the rocks simply makes life too difficult for fish. Of course, this section is unnavigable as well. Now in order that a contrast, as complete as it is pleasing, should not be lacking, there is located about six miles below the falls a small and beautiful island close to the Paraguayan side. An arm of quiet water lies protected between this island and the shore, and this tranquil pool is simply full of many species of fish.

TRIBUTARIES

The tributary streams of the middle Río Alto Paraná are quite different from those that empty into the Río Paraguay or the lower Río Alto Paraná (between Candelaria and Corrientes). The tributaries of those last two mentioned produce the same fish species as are found in the big rivers. The affluents of the middle Río Alto Paraná have a fish fauna quite distinct from that of the main river.

Most of these streams, and all of them between parallels 24° and 26° (these constitute the most numerous and most important tributary streams of the region), are separated from the main river by a falls, which is always found very near to or right on the bank of the Río Alto Paraná. Thus a more or less impassable barrier is located between the fish of the tributary and those of the main river. Consequently, the fish fauna of the tributary rivers has two characteristics: It is poor and it is different from that of the Río Alto Paraná. Of course these are not absolute characteristics, but the first comes close to it. There are streams, even rivers, which contain no more than three or four common species of fish.

ABOVE THE FALLS

North of the Saltos del Guairá conditions change almost completely, and it may be inferred that the aquatic fauna changes as well. The upper Río Alto Paraná is a great, wide river, shallow, slowly moving, with low banks, often inundated. There are many islands. I believe that the great falls completely inhibits the passage of fish in either direction. Those that are caught in the current could scarcely survive the torrent of the falls. It is true that the greatest increases in the water level of the river—this is 60 meters above the low-water mark—almost covers the great falls. Nevertheless, there remains at that time the most violent sort of rapids about three miles in length, and this constitutes an impassable barrier. Ichthyological data from the upper Río Alto Paraná are notably insufficient.

The upper Río Alto Paraná looks a lot like the lower section of this river, that is between Candelaria and Corrientes. Of course, there is no obstacle between the lower section of this river and the Río Paraguay or the Río Paraná, and the same conditions of life prevail in all three. The fish fauna is probably very similar as well (see A. de Winkelried Bertoni, 1939, Catálogos sistemáticos de los vertebrados del Paraguay, Rev. Soc. Cien. Paraguay 4(4): 1–59, for a list of the fishes of Paraguay).

VII. The Snails and Mussels of the State of Guairá, Paraguay

FRANCISCO H. SCHADE

What, then, is this thing we call a shell?
*Bartsch**

Introduction

Paraguayans include all kinds of snails in one Guaraní word: *Yatytá*. It is not, however, just the common folk who recognize only a few kinds of snails. Some explorer-scientists have also found only a few kinds.

ACTIVITY

There are several reasons why the snails of Paraguay have attracted little attention. The land snails, for example, are mainly nocturnal, and their time of greatest activity is during rainy weather. Also, many kinds of snails have an extremely limited geographic range, which sometimes involves only a few acres of prairie, or just one pond (as in *Taphius tenagophilus*). Only a few kinds of snails grow to more than one centimeter in greatest dimension; most are less than two millimeters.

It is no wonder then that the explorers readily overlooked the snails. I have encountered these same difficulties, and others too, during many years of systematic searching for new species of mollusks in the State of Guairá. My objective during those years was to collect all of the species of mollusks that inhabit Guairá. But apparently my work is not yet finished, for just recently I collected a new species in a place that I had previously searched very carefully.

The foregoing applies to snails that live on the surface of the ground. Looking for subterranean species is quite a different matter, and when such a snail is found it is likely to be just a matter of chance. I should also refer to certain rarely occurring species, e.g. *Taphius peregrinus* and *Bulimulus bonariensis sporadicus*. These appear all of a sudden by the thousands, and then after a few days disappear for years from a given locality.

My experience indicates that a rainy summer night is the best time to collect snails in Paraguay. Even species that would be practically impossible to find on a sunny day can be readily observed actively feeding on a warm rainy night.

RANGE

The distribution of the aquatic species is even more severely limited than that of the terrestrial ones, apparently because the former are less tolerant of even slight variations from their optimal environment. For example, of the various species in a pond, perhaps one inhabits only a small area of just a few square meters near the shore line, while another is confined to only a few square meters of muddy bottom. Such species remain unknown until someone happens on to them in their respective and geographically limited habitats. Factors such as shade, influent streams, currents, the nature of the substrate, and the chemical composition of the water apparently have profound limiting influence on the range of many aquatic species.

ECONOMIC IMPORTANCE

Actually, like many other small animals, snails are much more important than they would appear to be at first glance. There is no doubt that snails cause considerable damage to crops, but often other pests get blamed for the damage. On one occasion I observed a case in which semi-aquatic snails, or "water slugs" *(Omalonyx unguis),* defoliated a 200 m² patch of watercress *(Nasturtium)* during just one night. Only the submerged portions of the plants escaped damage. During the day the snails stayed hidden along the edge of the pond, but when night came they sallied forth *en masse.*

I have also observed that the large terrestrial species,

*Bartsch, P. 1968. Mollusks. Dover, New York. Quoted by permission of the publisher.

especially *Strophocheilus* spp., are capable of causing considerable harm to gardens and truck farms. Many other pests have been blamed for damage done by these snails. This is because the snails feed only at night, especially rainy nights. During the day they bury themselves in the soil and are therefore out of sight when the damage is discovered.

It would be unfair and untrue to cast all the snails in the role of pests. Many species are definitely beneficial to mankind. Thus it is essential to know the habits and the correct identity of each snail species. At the top of the list of beneficial snails are the carnivorous ones whose voracity allies them with man against the larvae of harmful insects. These snails readily become cannibalistic when they are placed in the same cage. Some snails, especially the large terrestrial *Strophocheilus* spp., have some importance as items of human food, and are prepared according to traditional European recipes. Apparently, such snails are not thus utilized in the State of Guairá. Snails are eaten in Asunción but not commonly, probably due to the scarcity of snails.

The scarcity of snails also probably accounts for the fact that snail shells are not used as a source of calcium in poultry food supplements and agricultural fertilizers. Generally speaking, a soil that does not support snails is calcium deficient, unless the calcium is supplied from some other source. When such other sources are absent, the fertility of the soil, in terms of calcium, is directly proportional to the quantity of snail shells in the soil.

Snails and mussels have their esthetic values too, mostly as ornaments for beautifying the home and garden. Mother-of-pearl is of considerable importance, particularly for buttons and jewelry. But the fact of the matter is that in the State of Guairá practically no commercial or dietary use is made of snails or mussels, again probably due to their scarcity.

SYMBIOSIS

Snails harbor a variety of guests in and on their bodies, either as parasites or commensals. I have observed in the rectum of *Strophocheilus oblongus* small coprophagic nematodes, occurring singly and *in copula*. Also, I have seen about five species of water mites (Parasitengona) on naiads of the genera *Anodontites* and *Diplodon*.

Thus far I have been unable to learn whether or not the sheep liver fluke *(Fasciola hepatica)* or *saguaypé* occurs in Guairá. Species of the genus *Lymnaea (L. viator* in Argentina*)* usually serve as the intermediate host of this parasite, but there are no representatives of *Lymnaea* in Guairá. Liebermann[2] says that because caimans, the principal predators of aquatic snails, have been so severely reduced in numbers by hide-hunters, the sheep liver fluke has multiplied to such an extent that sheep raising has become unprofitable in parts of the "mesopotamian" region of Argentina.

In our local bivalves, usually *Anodontites* and rarely *Diplodon,* I have found pearls of moderate size, but in every case they were marred by imperfections. Pearls from freshwater mussels have no commercial value.

Annotated List of the Mollusks of Guairá, Paraguay[a]

GASTROPODA

STREPTAXIDAE

Streptaxis (Artemon) apertus. This is a carnivorous and cannibalistic species, as are many streptaxids, eating mostly earthworms in addition to its own kind. It is found throughout the wooded portions of Guairá, but always in small numbers. The body of the snail is yellow and the shell is a calcareous white, almost translucent in some instances. The shell of the largest specimen in my collection measures 7 mm in height and 15 mm in width.

SCOLODONTIDAE

Drepanostomella banghuasi. A four-whorled white shell 1.5 mm high and 4.5 mm wide. This species is very similar to *D. ammoniformis.*

Scolodonta beskei. A five-whorled yellow shell, 2 mm high and 3 mm in diameter.

LIMACIDAE

Several types of slugs have been found in Guairá. None has been specifically determined; some may even belong to other families. One of these does a great deal of damage to gardens around Asunción, but is apparently of no great economic importance in Guairá. The other two types do cause a certain amount of damage on truck farms in Guairá.

ZONITIDAE

†† *Habroconus (Pseudoguppya) semenlini.* The six-whorled shell of this snail is nearly spherical (2 mm in diameter) and is in its shape and color very similar to a flax seed. It is common in areas with fertile soils.

ENDODONTIDAE

Endodonta discoidea.

Endodonta (Stephanoda) pleurophora. These two minute species are locally abundant in the prairie-forest ecotone, gradually decreasing in numbers in the deeper forest. Both have five-whorled shells, 0.5 mm high and 2 mm in diameter.

Endodonta sp. The single specimen of this undetermined species looks like a tiny ammonite. The shell is similar in size to that of *E. discoidea,* but the color is a dirty white. The shell has large transverse warts.

CAMAENIDAE

†† *Solaropsis (Solaropsis) brasiliana.* The Guairá race of this species is about half the size of the Brazilian form. The juveniles have the lip of the aperture markedly raised toward the outside, and thus are easily distinguished from the adults. This species is widely distributed, being especially common under old logs, where the white, bird-shot sized eggs are laid, or among the roots of Paraguayan sisal *(caraguatá)* on cleared hillsides.

---

[a]Symbols (*, **, †, ††) in this section mean: species illustrated in Jaeckel 1969 (*) and in van der Schalie 1948 (**); genus illustrated in Jaeckel 1969 (†) and in van der Schalie 1948 (††). See index entry of each taxon for complete scientific name.

STROPHOCHEILIDAE

†† *Strophocheilus (Megalobulimus) oblongus.* This large terrestrial species is the best known snail in Guairá. The shell (80 mm high and 46 mm in diameter) is a calcareous white with red lips. These snails are found in hilly sections, especially where the land has been cleared for truck farms and field crops. During the day only the empty shells are seen above ground. The snails forage only at night. By sunup they bury themselves in the soil, with only the apex of the shell protruding slightly through the surface. The snow-white eggs, about the size of dove eggs, are laid in soft soil. The embryos are pink. The newly-hatched snails bear shells with an olive-green periostracum. This later peels off, leaving the shell a calcareous white. Occasionally, this periostracum persists to the adult stage, in which case the shell tends to be much thinner than that of the white-shelled forms. *S. oblongus* is much more common around Asunción than in Guairá. People frequently use the shell for house and garden decorations.

Strophocheilus (M.) oblongus (atypical form). I have found only one specimen of this double-lipped form in Guairá, but in Asunción this interesting form is much more common. I have not found in Guairá the common variety, *S. oblongus albus* which abounds in the Paraguayan Chaco.

Strophocheilus (M.) sp., similar to *oblongus musculus*. This is one of the many snails having a localized distribution. I have found it only in a grassland area, about twelve acres in size, near Villarrica. This snail is much smaller than *S. oblongus,* but its morphological features are otherwise similar.

Strophocheilus (M.) proclivis. This species is common in Rio Grande do Sul, Brazil, but it is extremely rare in Paraguay. I have collected only two live specimens, one near Colonia Independencia, the other from the forest near Río Monday.

BULIMULIDAE

††* *Bulimulus (Bulimulus) bonariensis sporadicus.* This is one of the more common snails in all of South America. In some places in Guairá, this snail appears by the thousands after a rain. But after three or four days they disappear completely, leaving as testimony of their visit only the damaged plants which served as their food. I have never been able to find out where they go or where they hide. The size of the shell is from 1.5 cm to 2.5 cm in height (some giant-sized specimens reach 3.5 cm) and 1 cm in width.

Bulimulus (Bulimulus) bonariensis form *schadei.* This form is limited in range to Cerro Pelado near Villarrica. The characters of *schadei* are similar to those of *sporadicus,* but the two are easily separated since the last whorl of the shell of *schadei* is much more inflated than that of the subspecies *sporadicus.*

Bulimulus sp. The beige-colored shell has 5.5 whorls, and is 11 mm high by 6.5 mm wide. It is rare in Guairá. I have found it only in the virgin forests of Santa Bárbara. This snail has a most unusual talent. It is the only snail that I know of, at least, that can jump. If you hold the snail in the palm of your hand, it will suddenly and forcefully extend its body, causing it to jump a few centimeters into the air and land on the ground.

† *Peronaeus (Lissoacme) turritellatus.* This variety was found in several places (Cerro Naville near Capiitindy, Campo Legal at Colonia Independencia, and Colonia Carlos Pfanell). These snails have been collected only in the winter, at which time they were observed crawling through the crystals of frost. This variety is a little smaller than *sporadicus* and has a pink, six-whorled shell about 18 mm high and 19 mm in diameter.

†† *Drymaeus fourmiersi.* This species is found in all the hilly regions of the state, but is nowhere common. The shell has 3.5 whorls, and is 13 mm high and 8 mm wide. The shell is glassy and transparent. The black outlines of the body of the snail can easily be seen through the shell.

Drymaeus interpunctus. This is one of the most common snails in Guairá. The shell colors vary widely. Usually the background color of the shell is yellow, with dots of blue and red. The shell measures 30 mm in height and 14 mm in width and has seven whorls. I have never seen any plant damage directly attributable to *D. interpunctus,* but I have collected it many times from citrus trees and other cultivated plants.

Drymaeus papyraceus. Although similar in its mode of existence to *D. interpunctus,* the shell of this species is a clear gray with black transverse markings. The six-whorled shell is 28 mm high and 15 mm wide. This species is very common in all parts of the State.

Drymaeus papyraceus "form" *latior* (= *papyrifactus?*). This form is about twice as big (more globose) as the typical *papyraceus.* Only two specimens have been found.

Drymaeus poecilus. The shell is practically transparent except for the longitudinal brown stripes. The shell has 4.5 whorls and measures 12 mm high and 8 mm wide. I have found specimens only on one side of Arroyo Mbobo near Villarrica. The other side of this stream has not yielded this species.

Drymaeus sp. [possibly *D. poecilus ictericus*]. This undetermined specimen came from San Blas. It has a shell with seven whorls and transverse stripes. The shell is 22 mm high and 9 mm wide.

ODONTOSTOMIDAE

Cyclodontina (Spixia) sp. Five undeterminable juvenile specimens were found in Villarrica. I do not believe that they are native to Guairá, rather they were probably brought in on logs from Caaguazú. They look very much like *C. (Spixia) spixii minor,* which occurs in the State of Caaguazú.

SUBULINIDAE

** *Lamellaxis (Allopeas) gracilis.* This species may be found, always in small numbers, wherever there are banana patches. The shell is pure white and tends to be translucent. The nine-whorled shell is 12 mm high and 3 mm wide.

Lamellaxis (Allopeas) gracilis "form" *martensi.* I have found this form only in the nests of the Paraguayan leaf-cutting ant *(ysaú), Atta sexdens rubropilosa.* I do not know just what relationship exists between the ants and the snails. They may be lestobionts, symbionts, or simply commensals, using the galleries of the nest as a hiding place. I have frequently seen the ants carrying snails out of the nest, as if they were granules of soil. The white, seven-whorled shell (12 mm high and 4 mm wide) is easily distinguished from the typical *gracilis.*

**Lamellaxis micra.* This species is smaller, but otherwise very similar to *L. gracilis.* It is apparently very rare in Guairá.

FERUSSACIIDAE

***Cecilioides (Cecilioides) consobrinus pygmaeus.* This is the smallest species in our snail fauna, being 1.5 mm high and 0.25 mm wide. My collection contains only eight specimens. Its minuteness and transparent shell make it very difficult to locate. It lives in humus on the floor of virgin forests.

PUPILLIDAE

***Gastrocopta servilis oblonga.* This small snail (2 mm high and 1 mm in diameter) is dark brown and has a shell with 5.5 whorls. These snails are found in great numbers under flat rocks and boards on the truck farms of Colonia Independencia, and under dry branches on the forest floor. Certainly these snails, even though small, must by virtue of their great numbers do some damage to crops. But direct evidence of such damage is lacking.

CYCLOPHORIDAE

† *Adelopoma paraguayana.*[3] This tiny snail is found under fallen leaves in the dense forests of Guairá. The sinistral shell is a translucent or calcareous white, 2 mm high and 0.5 to 1 mm wide, with six whorls. Five of the whorls are strongly inflated.

HELICINIDAE

†† *Helicina densestriata.* In general, this snail prefers swampy woods to thickets, but its distribution is very localized, and often it can be found only on the bark of trees or on small weeds. During drought and cold weather, the snails may be found under fallen leaves in the forest. The beautiful shell is pinkish yellow and has a thick white lip. The shell is 4 mm high and 6 mm in diameter.

SUCCINEIDAE

†† *Succinea meridionalis.* This is one of the species having a very limited range. I have found it only on the wet, algae-covered bank of Arroyo Itá at Colonia Independencia, and then only a few specimens were found. The pitch-colored shell measures 8 mm high by 5 mm wide.

**Omalonyx unguis.* The shell of this interesting snail consists of just one whorl and is very similar in appearance to a fingernail, as its specific name suggests. It is not especially common in Guairá, but it is very common

around Asunción where it causes considerable damage to watercress and rice plantations. It is found along the shores of ponds and streams, under logs, under leaves, or in any other wet situation. The body of the snail is bluish and transparent, and is about three times bigger than its shell, which is 0.5 mm high and 5 to 9 mm in width, depending on the direction of measurement.

ANCYLIDAE

†† *Ancylus (Hebetancylus) moricandi.*
Ancylus (Gundlachia) nordenskioldi.

The members of this family are sometimes called water coccids because the shell is in the form of shield, somewhat like *Chrysomphalus.* The relationship of the limpets to aquatic plants is roughly similar to that of coccids to their host plants. The snails are found on aquatic plants and on pieces of wood, and are so flat and well-covered with algae that one can scarcely recognize them. They are found throughout the region wherever there is sufficient water to support life. The largest of these species measures scarcely 0.5 mm high. The diameter of a given specimen varies from 7 to 12 mm, depending on the direction of measurement.

PLANORBIIDAE

Taphius (=Australorbis††*) tenagophilus.*
Taphius (=Australorbis) bahiensis.
Taphius (=Tropicorbis††*) heloicus.*
Taphius (=Planorbis††*) puchella.*
Taphius (=Planorbis) halophilus.
Tahpius (=Planorbis) peregrinus.
†† *Drepanotrema (D.) castaneonitens.*
Drepanotrema (Fossulorbis) kermatoides.

The genus *Taphius* is known to parasitologists as *Biomphalaria.* All of these orb snails have discoidal shells. Their distribution is rather localized and limited to certain areas of habitats. For example, *T. bahiensis* is found only in a certain well in the center of the village of Villarrica; *T. puchella* is found only in a certain backwater of Arroyo Tacuara; and *T. tenagophilus* is limited to a particular pond at Carovení near Villarrica. Most of these species are very small. *T. tenagophilus* is the largest, measuring 6 x 15 mm. The most unusual is *T. peregrinus,* a migratory species, which appears all of a sudden in large numbers in a stream or pond during three or four days, and then disappears completely, only to appear again in another place, perhaps quite far removed from the first.

PHYSIDAE

***Physa sowerbyana (=Physa cubensis).*[9] This is the only aquatic snail in Guairá which has a sinistral shell. These snails are very common, and I believe that they do cause some damage to watercress plantings. The amber-colored shell is 15 mm high and 8 mm wide.

HYDROBIIDAE

Littoridina sp.? or *Lyrodes* sp.? I found this tiny snail stuck to rocks in a rapids of Arroyo Tacuara at Colonia

Independencia. It is difficult to recognize because it looks a lot like a grain of sand. Only a few specimens were collected; their precise determination remains unsettled.

AMPULLARIIDAE

†*Ampullarius insularum.* This is the most common and best known of the snails of Guairá. It is found wherever there is water, even in temporary pools. These snails may live for months buried in the mud during a drought. The raspberry-shaped eggs are laid in pink bunches on aquatic plants, sticks, fence posts, etc., always about 20 or 30 cm above the surface of the water. The country people mistakenly think that these eggs are frog eggs. The shell of the snail is olive-green and has longitudinal stripes of dark brown or black. The inner surface of the aperture is lilac-colored. The average size of the shells is 50 mm high by 50 mm wide. The body of the animal itself is black. I found in Arroyo Tacuara at Colonia Independencia a variety in which the shell is translucent white with lilac-colored stripes inside the orifice and the body of the snail a clear silver-gray. I have not found here the melanistic form that occurs in Brazil. Many of the country people think that this snail is harmful to crops, but that allegation is unfounded since these animals do not leave the water. However, the snails may compete with cattle and horses for available forage in marshy pastures, especially in the province of Ñeembucú.[10]

Ampullarius australis. This species is restricted in its range to a pond in the prairie between Villarrica and Hiaty. In size, color and habits it is very similar to *A. insularum* but it has a flat shoulder around the suture.

PELECYPODA[8]
MYCETOPODIDAE

*Anodontites tenebricosus (= Bartlettia stefanensis). This very interesting mussel is found only in torrential rapids of Río Tebicuary and Arroyo Guazú. It is a sessile species, attached by its shell to the rocks throughout its adult life. The morphology of the valves varies greatly, this being determined by the shape of the substrate to which it is attached. Actually, no two specimens are alike. Some are practically round, and others are long, curved and slender. In every case though, the valves are very rough and rugose. Naturally, the length of the valves varies as well, but it is on the order of 80 mm. The valve exposed to the water is the color of Paris green, while the one next to the rock is a calcareous white. Individuals aggregate in closely spaced groups on the rocks. The collection of specimens requires the use of a hammer and chisel to break off chunks of rock to which the mussels are attached.

*Anodontites trapezialis. Probably all the rivers and streams of Guairá yield this species, the largest in the State. The shells are commonly employed as ash trays and household decorations. The mother-of-pearl is of the quality necessary for button making. Some of the storekeepers use the valve as a scoop for handling flour, salt, etc. The bright olive-brown shells may reach 240 mm in length, but the average size is about 90 x 170 mm.

Anodontites mortonianus.
Anodontites sp., similar to *patagonicus.*
Anodontites elongatus.
These three species are common in ponds with aquatic vegetation.

*Anodontites soleniformis. Arroyo Tacuara at Colonia Independencia is the only place where this sedentary species has been found. It lives firmly fixed in sand under the rocks in rapids. The greenish-gray valves are very elongate.

Anodontites trigonus georginus. Two types of habitats—ponds with grass growing in them, and sandy stream beds with no vegetation—yield this beautiful mussel.

Anodontites schadei. I found four specimens of this mussel in a backwater of the Río Tebicuary. It is very similar to *A. mortonianus.* The shell is a bright reddish brown. It is no doubt a very rare species with a very localized distribution.

†*Monocondylaea corrientesensis.* The velvety greenish-gray shell has the shape of a large lentil. This rather uncommon species has been collected from the Río Tebicuary, Arroyo Tacuara, and Arroyo Guazú.

†*Monocondylaea minuana.* This species is very similar to *M. corrientesensis,* except that the valves are much smoother and much smaller. I have collected only two specimens from Guairá, but the species is common in some other parts of Paraguay.

†*Mycetopoda soleniformis.* As the generic name suggests, the foot of this delicate little mussel is mushroom-shaped. The animal holds itself very firmly in the sand by means of its foot. The specimen cannot be pulled directly out of the sand without doing damage to the long, fragile shell. Rather, it must be exposed by gently clearing away the surrounding sand. I have found this species only in Arroyo Doña Juana, near Villarrica.

HYRIIDAE, HYRIINAE

Difficulties of identification of members of the Hyriinae, especially in the genus *Diplodon,* arise because of hybridization of closely related species, with the production of enigmatic offspring of uncertain identity.[7]

*Castalia ambigua. During thirty years of collecting, I have found only five very small specimens of this naiad. These were located in the sand of the streams and rivers of Guairá. Much larger specimens occur in Lake Ypacaraí and the Río Paraguay.

†*Diplodon burroughianus.*
Diplodon sp., similar to *charruanus.*
Diplodon sp., similar to *funebralis.*
These three species are found in practically every pond and stream in Guairá. *D. burroughianus* is very similar in appearance to *D. parodizi.* I have found four specimens of a rare variety of *D. burroughianus*—three from Asunción Bay and one from a backwater of the Río Tebicuary-mí, near the town of Tebicuary. The olive-green shell of this rare variety is rather small, measuring scarcely 20 to 30 mm in length. The umbo is rugose.

Diplodon parallelipipedon. This species is difficult to collect because its habitat is on the bottom of deep ponds. It has the thickest nacre layer of any of the Guairá species.

SPHAERIIDAE

Musculium argentinum. The fragile white valves of the transparent shell measure about 7 or 8 mm in length. I have taken this species only from floating debris in a backwater of Arroyo Guazú near Colonia Independencia.

††*Pisidium (Eupera) platensis.* This species lives among the roots of floating plants *(camalotes)* to which the mussel is attached by means of a byssus. This is the only mussel of Guairá which produces a byssus, the form of which is very much like that of the sea mussel *(Mytilus edulis).* Only ponds which have a particular type of floating plant yield this species. Specimens are about 4 x 6 mm in size.

    Pisidium (Neopisidium) sterkianum.
    Pisidium (Neopisidium) globulus.
    Pisidium (Neopisidium) dorbignyi.
    Pisidium (Neopisidium) vile.

Populations of these species of *Pisidium* have very localized distributions, often limited to clones of a few square meters, on the bottom of ponds and in the sand of streams. They are very difficult to collect because they are so small (1 to 2.5 mm in diameter, spherical) and closely resemble fine gravel.

The following list of molluscan species known to occur in Paraguay but not mentioned on the preceding pages was supplied by Dr. J. J. Parodiz.

Scolodontidae
    Drepanostomella ammoniformis
Zonitidae
    **Zonitoides arboreus* (introduced)
Strophocheilidae
    Strophocheilus sanctipauli
    Gonyostomus turnix albolabiatus
Bulimulidae
    Bulimulus prosopidis
    Bulimulus (Scansicochlea) jorgenseni
    Bulimulus (Lissoacme) apodemetes
    † *Peronaeus (Obstrussus) chacoensis*
    † *Protoglyptus montivagus*
Odontostomidae
    † *Odontostomus odontostomus jorgensenianus*
    Cyclodontina (Bahiensis) guarani
    Cyclodontina (Spixia) spixii major
Achatinidae
    † *Leptinaria bacterinoides*
Helicinidae
    †† *Helicina carinata*
Hydrobiidae
    Lyrodes guaranitica[5]
Pleurodontidae
    † *Solaropsis heliaca minor* (also placed in Camaenidae)

Veronicellidae
    Veronicella soleiformis
Helminthoglyptidae
    † *Epiphragmophora trigrammephora*
    Epiphragmophora dormeri
Succineidae
    † *Omalonyx patera*[6]
Hyriidae
    † *Diplodon guaranianus*
Mycetopodidae
    * *Leila blainvilleana*
    * *Monocondylaea paraguayana.*

Two other species that occur in adjacent Brazil and Argentina probably also occur in Paraguay: *Streptaxis regius* (Streptaxidae), and *Bulimulus flossdorfi* (Bulimulidae).[4]

Acknowledgements

Dr. Juan J. Parodiz (Carnegie Museum, Pittsburgh) and Dr. David Stansbery (Ohio State Museum, Columbus) reviewed the manuscript and offered many useful suggestions for improving it. Their assistance is gratefully acknowledged.

Literature Cited

1. Jaeckel, S. G. A., Jr. 1969. Die Mollusken Südamerikas. *In* Fittkau, E. J., J. Illies, H. Klinge, G. H. Schwabe, and H. Sioli. (Eds.). Biogeography and ecology in South America. Vol. 2. Dr. W. Junk, The Hague.
2. Liebermann, J. 1959. Curso de zoología. Editorial Kapelusz, Buenos Aires.
3. Parodiz, J. J. 1944. Contribuciones al conocimiento de los moluscos terrestres sudamericanos, I. 1. Una nueva especie de *Adelopoma* del Paraguay. Com. Zool. Mus. Hist. Nat. Montevideo 1 (8): 1-9.
4. Parodiz, J. J. 1957. Catalogue of the land Mollusca of Argentina. Nautilus 70 (4): 127-135; 71 (1): 22-30; and 71 (2): 63-66.
5. Parodiz, J. J. 1960. Neotype for *Lyrodes guaranitica* Doering and description of a new species. Nautilus 74 (1): 24-26, 1 pl.
6. Parodiz, J. J. 1963. Observaciones anatómicas sobre *Omalonyx patera* Doer., con una nota biográfica acerca de Adolfo Doering (1848-1926). Sterkiana 12 (Dec): 1-7, 2 pl.
7. Parodiz, J. J. 1968. Annotated catalogue of the genus *Diplodon* (Unionacea—Hyriidae). Sterkiana 30 (Jun): 1-22.
8. Parodiz, J. J., and A. A. Bonetto. 1963. Taxonomy and zoogeographic relationships of the South American Naiades (Pelecypoda: Unionacea and Mutelacea). Malacologia 1 (2): 179-213.
9. van der Schalie, H. 1948. The land and fresh-water mollusks of Puerto Rico. University of Michigan Press, Ann Arbor.
10. White, S. W. 1972. Too many snails, an ecological problem. War on Hunger 6 (10): 9-12.

Author's address: Prof. Francisco H. Schade
    Museo Zoológico, Facultad de Agronomía y Medicina Veterinaria
    Universidad Nacional de Asunción, San Lorenzo, Paraguay

VIII. The Ecology and Control of the Leaf-Cutting Ants of Paraguay

FRANCISCO H. SCHADE

The Portuguese have an old saying, that the ants are queens of Brazil. Certainly we have found them the sovereigns of Paraguay. There may be said to be more trouble in conquering these insects, than all the savages put together; for every contrivance hitherto devised serves only to put them to flight, not to banish them effectually.

Dobrizhoffer, 1754.

Introduction

The number-one enemy of agriculture in Paraguay is the leaf-cutting ant or *ysaú,* as it is called in Guaraní, the native language of Paraguayans. This paper deals primarily with the form most common and most widely distributed in Paraguay, *Atta sexdens rubropilosa* Forel, and incidentally with two variants, the *ysaú vidrio, Atta sexdens vollenweideri* Forel, and a form of unknown identity. It occurs to me that the attine ants merit a good deal more attention from taxonomists than they are getting now. Simple observations of the formicaries and habits of the ants lead one quickly to the conclusion that probably several other species of attines, still undescribed, occur in Paraguay.

Summary of Life History

Colonies of the leaf-cutting ants of Paraguay are typically both highly populous and highly polymorphic. There are several worker forms: gardeners (2 mm in length, seldom leave nest); leaf-cutters and leaf-carriers (3–8 mm long); and soldiers (9–12 mm long, with head and mandibles highly developed). The males are about 15 mm long and the reproductive females, 23–25 mm. The abdomen of the queen is, of course, greatly enlarged. The *ysaú* are generally of a reddish-brown color. So far as their above-ground activities are concerned, these ants are primarily nocturnal.

The life of the colony centers around the subterranean cultivation of a fungus, *Rozites gonglyophora* Moeller, which the ants eat. The fungus gardens are located in chambers *(hongueras)* down to a depth of about 2 m. The various chambers are joined by communication galleries. The fungus is cultivated on a medium of cut-up plant leaves. The fungal mass is roughly spherical and looks something like a bath sponge.

The excavated soil from the nest is piled in a mound, which sometimes reaches two meters in height. The mound *(túmulo* or *mina)* is perforated by aeration holes. The nest entrances may be located right at the periphery of the mound or at varying distances from the mound. From the nest entrances radiate the trails to the places where the leaf-cutting is done. The trails are cleared of vegetation.

Nuptial flights occur in October and November, usually after a good rain the preceding day. By early morning of the flight day the mound is covered by thousands of workers. The sexual forms surface around two or three o'clock in the afternoon. Sometimes there are so many ants flying around they form a veritable cloud above the nest. During the flight the potential queens are fertilized. The supply of spermatozoa received at that time lasts throughout the life of the queen. The males die after copulation. After the impregnated female loses her wings, she digs into the soil and establishes a small *honguera,* using spores carried in her mouth from the parental nest. She fertilizes the fungus with her feces.

The description just given of the life history of the *ysaú* is based mainly on statements made in various publications. Some of these observations are incomplete or even erroneous. Because of the subterranean and noctural habits of the leaf-cutting ants, direct observation of certain aspects of their life history is difficult if not impossible. Consequently, a good deal of theorizing has to be done. In the following account there is presented a precise description, based on my own observations, of the various aspects of the life history and social organization of the common *ysaú.* Some questions are raised and left unanswered. Others are answered. I hope that this account will stimulate other more exact studies of this interesting and prejudicial species, to the end that suitable control measures will eventually be devised.

Observations and Experiments

THE MOUND

The most apparent part of the nest is the mound, and because of its conspicuousness, people commonly think of it as "the nest." The mound (Figs. 8.1, 8.2) varies considerably in appearance and form. It is composed of loose soil particles. Sometimes there is just one cone, 0.5 to 0.75 m in height, with a diameter of 10 to 12 m at the base, or there may be several overlapping cones. In dry weather the mound increases markedly in height, reaching in rare instances 2 m. A heavy rain always causes the height of a mound to decrease considerably or even to practically disappear. The mounds of old nests often cover an area of 25 to 50 m² or even, in rare instances, one or two hectares, the mound being composed of thousands of cones.

Each cone surrounds the mouth of a gallery. The cone is made up of particles of soil excavated from the galleries and the chambers of the nest. Much can be learned just by observing the cone. The soil and subsoils are composed of various strata, each having a distinct color. If a well is located near the nest, it is easy to determine the depth of the nest by comparing the color of the soil particles of the cone with the color of the various strata as seen in the well. Usually at least two soil types (colors) are represented in the cone, but frequently as many as five types are present.

I have often seen the interesting sight of two cones, scarcely 15 centimeters apart, composed of different types of earth. This tells us that although the two galleries emerged at about the same place on the surface, the galleries themselves go to different depths of the earth. This is an important observation with regard to ant control with insecticides. One must avoid placing the insecticide only on galleries that lead to the upper parts of the nests.

The size and shape of the mound depend a great deal on the specific location of the nest. The nests are usually located in shady places, close to the roots of a big tree or hidden among aggregations of the Paraguayan sisal *(caraguatá),* a bromeliad. If the surrounding vegetation is very dense, the loose earth of the mound is little affected by rainfall and, on the other hand, is firmed-up by the humidity of the air. The mound may therefore acquire considerable size and height even though the colony itself is relatively small. The opposite situation exists on the open plains where wind and rain rapidly reduce the size of the mound, leaving only a small residual of soil particles on the surface.

A simple calculation can give us an idea about the size of the nest. Suppose we say that the rain carries off nine parts of the loose excavated soil and leaves only one part as a residual. Now if that residual is about 10 m³, then the mound must have contained 100 m³ and would have reached a height of 8 to 10 m if it had not been reduced by wind and rain. This estimate is admittedly very rough, but it is also probably too conservative, since the age of the nest has something to do with the size of the mound. I will take up this question again later.

The loose earth brought up from the interior of the nest is placed around the nest opening in such a way as to form a sort of crater. The ants always construct a circular crater, but they place more particles on one side of the crater than on the other. Thus the lip is higher on one side than on the other. That is the situation if the crater is formed on level ground, that is, one side of the crater is higher than the other side. If the cone is located on sloping ground, the ants put most of the soil particles on the down side of the slope, thus making a crater with a horizontal opening. If the slope is considerable, the ants may place all of the soil particles on the down-side of the slope and none on the up-side.

In those cases where one lip of the crater is higher than the other, the slope involved generally amounts to about 45 degrees. But in another type of nest opening, called filter holes, which are small openings without radiating trails, the inclination of the crater is seldom greater than 10 degrees and the lip of the crater is perfectly formed all the way around.

The slopes of craters do not follow any particular pattern of orientation when they are on level ground. The slope bears no relation to the points of the compass, to the sun, to the direction of prevailing winds. Craters are sometimes built practically on top of one another. If a nest entrance happens to open out onto an overall slope of about 80 degrees, then no craters are formed. The earth particles are simply dumped over the edge and accumulate below, forming a small pile.

Old ant nests do not show any evidence of cones or craters. The mound is covered by plants, which makes it difficult to see. It looks dead, but there is, nevertheless, considerable activity inside the nest.

The mound of the *ysaú vidrio,* which is quite different from that of the common *ysaú,* has the form of a hemisphere, something like half an egg or the shape of a Paraguayan oven. These mounds get to be at most 1.5 to 2 m high and about 3 to 4 m wide at the base. There are no cones or craters. Those gallery openings used for carrying leaves into the nest open out about 10–15 cm up on the side of the mound. Such openings are never found outside the periphery of the base of the mound. The openings of the aeration tubes are located at the top of chimneys about 10–30 cm tall. These chimneys bulge out at the apex, forming a sort of platform. The mound is composed of clay and it is quite solid, easily supporting the weight of five or six men. This species is quite uncommon. I have found it only on low wet ground near ponds and streams.

This mound which I have just described also differs from that of another variety of *ysaú vidrio,* which occurs in great numbers in eastern Paraguay. The mounds of this latter variety are quite similar to those of the common *ysaú.* But they differ in that the openings through which leaves are carried are located on the mound itself rather than around the mound as is the case with the common *ysaú.*

I have found only one nest of the small black *ysaú.* I do not know the scientific name of this species. These ants do not construct a mound. Rather they make a smooth area as level as a playing field, which contains myriads of gallery openings.

NEST OPENINGS

The mound (tumulus) always has a certain number of openings that serve for bringing up particles of soil from the nest. Such openings are quite small and they are always surrounded by a crater. They are often moved from one place to another. This is not the case with the nest openings that are found at the base of the mound or around the base of the mound. These openings are often quite large but they are almost always surrounded by a cone or crater. They are not the openings through which leaves are carried. The latter are almost always located somewhat farther from the mound, usually about 5 or 10 m away from it, but often a long distance from the mound itself, on the order of 100 m, or even up to 500 m. The entrances through which the cut leaves are brought into the nest have several characteristics. Trails radiate from these entrances. The leaves are brought into the nest over these trails. There is usually little or no loose earth around the leaf entrances, and these openings are usually oval in shape. I have found such entrances large enough so that I could easily stick my arm into them.

The last type of nest opening is called a filter hole. These are characterized by cones or craters. Craters are quite large, but the opening itself is very small and round and usually there is quite a lot of vegetation around it, so that it looks like a small nest or the small mound over a nest. The filter holes are located 200 m or more from the nest and there are usually three or four such holes very close together in one spot.

GALLERIES

The nest itself is made up of galleries and chambers. The fungus is cultivated in the chamber and the many chambers are connected with one another by the galleries. The galleries vary considerably in both form and use. They comprise a system of communication, a means of regulating temperature and humidity, a ventilation system, and a drainage system. The galleries form such a complex labyrinth that it is difficult for us to discover their organizational plan.

One type of gallery is oval in cross section and usually runs in a horizontal direction. This type serves as a route of communication and also receives the cut leaves that are brought into the nest. The ants walk only on the floor of this type of gallery, not on the ceiling. Another type of gallery is round, about 12 to 15 cm in diameter. Its orientation is vertical and the ants use all surfaces of this type for walking up and down in the nest. The round vertical galleries no doubt serve for ventilation. These galleries often turn a few centimeters below the surface and go in all directions horizontally; they are often curved in the shape of a siphon, which prevents the entrance of loose earth or water into the depths of the nest.

The nature of the soil has a great deal to do with the size and shape of the gallery. In one place where the surface layer of sand measured 3 to 4 m in thickness, I found that all of the galleries passed vertically through this cap or layer of sand. Then upon reaching the firmer soil beneath the sand, the galleries turned horizontally or became inclined downward. Sandy soil does not permit horizontal galleries, which easily cave in; but vertical galleries are much more resistant to cave-ins.

I want to emphasize that we are not yet certain that galleries for ventilation and drainage actually exist. But one may observe a stream of rainwater, comprising thousands of liters, disappear into an ant nest without filling it up, even though the rain may last several days. Although there are cases where such treatment has actually killed a colony of ants, the majority of nests are quite unaffected by this treatment. We may at least suspect then that the ant nest has a well-perfected system of drainage down to the ground-water level. The entrance of a certain amount of water may even be required in order to maintain the necessary humidity in the nest.

Now it may be that what we have thus far called galleries of ventilation are just that and have no other function. Or they may be the same as the galleries for drainage. One thing we do know is that the galleries in the deeper parts of the nest, that is from 5 to 18 m, are much larger in diameter than those at the surface. The movement of air in the depths of the nest is no doubt caused by the differences in the temperature between the surface air and the subterranean air. A small sample of some of my observations in this regard will serve to illustrate this phenomenon (Table 8.1).

There exists a considerable difference in the temperature at various levels in the nest and these undoubtedly cause a movement of air that is sufficient to ventilate the nest. But changing the air in the nest is not the only function of this phenomenon. It also serves to equilibrate the humidity. One liter of air at zero degrees centigrade can hold only 0.0049 grams of water vapor. At 25 degrees centigrade one liter of air can hold 0.0228 grams of water vapor. In both cases the air is saturated with water. Now if this air is cooled off or warmed up it must, respectively, give off or gain water. We may suppose that the ysaú take advantage of this phenomenon, and regulate the humidity of the air in the fungus gardens. Regulation is carried out by means of opening or closing the galleries leading to various parts of the nest, thus exposing the fungi to warmer, more humid air or colder, drier air, the end result being continuously optimal conditions for fungal growth. Later on I will detail some observations made in this regard with an experimental nest.

I feel sure that the galleries always go down to the water table, and that this is necessary in order for the ants to obtain water which is indispensable for the life of the colony. In periods of severe drought, when the water table lowers and wells go dry, one may observe that the mounds grow tremendously as the ysaú bring up soil from great depths. This indicates that the ants are following the descent of the water table, thus maintaining contact with the indispensable humidity which the ground water provides.

The galleries sometimes extend some 500 to 800 m

from the mound. Obstacles such as streams or paved roads or buildings with deep foundations do not deter the ants. The galleries go under streams, protected from seepage by the impermeable layer of soil which forms the stream bed. In mountainous regions, the galleries are often quite superficial, running along side the rocks in the superficial layers of the soil. The rocks block the ants from digging more deeply in the soil.

FUNGUS GARDENS

The most important parts of the nest of the *ysaú* are the fungus gardens. The caves in which the fungus gardens are located vary in size and shape, but they always have one character in common. That is a low vaulted roof with a flat or nearly flat floor. Their size may best be indicated by the amount of air which they will hold, this being anywhere from 0.5 liters up to 15 or 20 liters. The shape is always like that of half an egg cut lengthwise through the center.

The fungus cave of the *ysaú vidrio* is somewhat different. The floor is level, but the roof has the form of a "gothic arch" that is very pointed at the top. This type of architecture is no doubt related to the sandy soil in which these ants live, the high arched roof of the cave providing the greatest resistance to cave-ins.

In these caves the ants grow the fungus which they eat. In new nests the fungus gardens are found very close to the surface, the maximum depth being 0.5 to 1 m. But in old nests the fungus gardens are distributed at various levels all the way down to the water table.

In those places where there are several superficial soil strata, each colored differently, it is easy to determine how deep the galleries go into the soil. This procedure has already been described. However, where the superficial stratum is 30 or 40 m thick and composed of uniformly colored earth, the question can be resolved only by direct excavation of the nest. This has been done accidentally many times during the process of digging a well. A few of these incidents, which I have personally verified, are given in Table 8.2.

In each of the three cases mentioned in Table 8.2, the fungus gardens were found quite far from the mound itself. In other words, the well was located some 20 to 80 m from what was recognized as being a nest on the surface. This serves to point up the fact that the "nest" is not found only under the mound of earth, but is distributed through the subsoil on all sides of the mound.

Why do the ants place some of the fungus gardens so near the surface and others so deep? This is just one of the many questions which I can answer at this time only on hypothetical grounds. We may suppose that the factors of humidity, temperature, and chemical composition of the soil play important roles in this matter. As we saw in the temperature data (Table 8.1), the deeper parts of the nest undergo very little change in temperature. It happens that temperatures between 23 and 25 C are optimal for the cultivation of the fungi. The ants are apparently able to take advantage of the fact that temperatures fluctuate very little in the deeper levels of the nest. It

could be, also, that a certain culture might require greater humidity or less fluctuation of humidity in order to form a certain type of alimentary requirement of those larvae destined to become soldiers or reproductive individuals. Tests and observations along this line are still very incomplete.

Going back to the idea that the fungus gardens may be located at considerable distances from the mound, this has been observed in places where the superficial strata of soil are oblique. I have seen a mound composed of two different types of soil particles, red and white. Inspection of a nearby well revealed the presence of only the red stratum, corresponding to the red soil particles on the mound. Soil corresponding to the white soil particles was found in a gulch about 200 m from the mound, indicating that the ants had intercepted this white stratum a considerable distance from the mound. Also, from these observations, we may conclude that the ants carry practically all of the excavated earth to the main mound.

My own investigations in the field lead me to believe that a single ant colony may have more than one mound. These two or three mounds, all belonging to the same colony, may be well-separated from each other. In one series of experiments I colored about 100 ants that were carrying leaves. I wanted to learn whether or not the same individual ants always carried leaves or if they also did other kinds of work in the nest. During three consecutive nights of observations none of the ants appeared at the nest opening that they were using when I first marked them. But I did find them coming out of another nest located 83 m away. The two mounds appeared to be about the same size and age, but they obviously belonged to a single colony of ants.

It is well-known that individuals of neighboring ant colonies fight and even kill each other if they happen to get mixed together. By carrying an individual of one nest to another nest, one can prove very easily any confamiliarity between the two nests. If the individual ant belongs to the same colony, it joins forces with its hosts and enters the galleries as if it were in its own home. If the ant does not belong to the same family, the ants immediately start fighting with the intruder and cut it up into pieces. I took advantage of this phenomenon to determine which and how many mounds belonged to a single colony of ants. I found that a single colony usually had three or more mounds. A colony with just one mound was quite rare.

Why do the ants construct two or more mounds with myriads of fungus gardens beneath? All of the nests that we have so far excavated have had very similar architecture. Each nest is composed of 500 to 2,000 fungus gardens. Thus, we may calculate that an ant colony with three mounds might have 6,000 fungus gardens. We may suppose then that a colony of ants increases to millions and millions of individuals, but it cannot increase the number of fungus gardens beneath the parental mound without dangerously weakening the earth. It is therefore necessary to extend the nest. Or it may be that the location of the nest is inadequate in certain seasons of the year, that is, a part of the nest is in dry soil with little or no shade, well-located for the winter months. The other part may be in a location well-shaded and cool, therefore, appropriate for the summer months. Exact observations on temperature, humidity, effect of sunlight, etc., and of ant activity at fraternal mounds during different seasons of the year are lacking at this time.

I have often observed that in those nests which were broken open in order to apply insecticides, after two or three days, even without having placed insecticide on the nest, the ants vacated the nest. We suppose that the entire population of ants moved to one of the other nests just after having been disturbed.

We have failed to give proper attention to the filters; these are miniature mounds, sometimes scarcely perceptible, in the vicinity of the main mound. The filters are frequently located 5 to 10 m away from the main mound, but they may also be found 100 or more meters from the mound. They are characterized by the lack of trails and by the fact that the three or four openings are very small. Excavation of these small filter mounds often reveals fungus gardens scarcely 20 cm beneath the surface. Very often the narrow gallery, at a minimal depth, suddenly becomes greatly widened, up to 20 or 25 cm in diameter, and drops straight down to great depths. Sometimes it is inclined or curved in such a way that it deviates away from the filter mound. I believe that these fungus gardens, which are located a long way from the main mound and are occasionally encountered at considerable depths by well-diggers, are ventilated by these filter holes. These filter holes play an important role in the control of leaf-cutting ants, and I will deal with them in some detail below.

TRAILS

Leading from some of the nest openings are trails or roads (Fig. 8.3). Only those openings through which the cut leaves are carried are associated with trails. These trails vary a great deal in their length, width and shape. Often there is a single more or less straight road, but usually there is a wide trail (20–25 cm wide) that breaks up into smaller branches leading to the various sources of leaves. The ants keep the trails clean. Vegetation and any other small objects are cleared from the path. The trails detour around objects—rocks, fallen trees, etc.—that are too big for the ants to carry away. Sometimes the trail is so wide and clean that it looks like a path made by people or by cattle.

Now with regard to the direction of the trails, we may note that they are not located radially around the mound. Sometimes, when the leaf entrance is located 100 or more meters from the mound, the trail will curve back toward the mound. Five or six trails, leading out in various directions, may radiate from a large leaf entrance. The length of these trails is quite variable. Generally speaking, they do not exceed more than 20 to 50 m, but sometimes they are 100 to 200 or even 500 m long.

It is interesting to note in passing how the ants cross cart tracks in sandy areas. It is practically impossible for the ants to climb up the steep slopes of the cart tracks on account of the loose sand. A large number of ants grab each other by their legs and mandibles, forming a living bridge over which the leaf-carriers pass without any difficulty. They cross small streams and narrow inlets of marshes in a similar manner. The ants place twigs, leaves, or dry grass on the water surface, forming a bridge. I have personally seen the ants construct a bridge only once. Normally they use natural accumulations of flotsam for this purpose. But I have seen the ants making living bridges over sand traps several times in various parts of Paraguay.

PLANTS

The leaf-cutting ants employ leaves, flowers, seeds, etc., as the culture medium for the fungi which they eat. The idea that the ants eat the leaves is erroneous. The damage which they cause by cutting off the leaves of cultivated plants is sometimes catastrophic. I have seen large orange trees, full of semi-ripened fruit, completely denuded in one night. The fruit, which the ants did not touch, soon fell to the ground after having been sunburned for lack of shade. The ants seem to prefer some cultivated plants more than others: citrus trees, roses, violets, medlar trees, onions, carrots, strawberries, alfalfa, and peanuts. Somewhat less popular are avocado trees, mandioca *(Manihot utilissima),* peach trees, guava trees, mulberry leaves and fruits, privet leaves, flamboyant trees *(Delonix regia),* and many other trees, shrubs and plants of agricultural or ornamental value. Corn and beans are sampled somewhat less frequently. Members of the Compositae, Solanaceae, and Euphorbiaceae, especially the tallowtree *(Sapium* spp.), are frequently attacked. The castor-oil plant, *Ricinus communis,* a euphorb, is not touched.

A complete list of all the plants used by the *ysaú* would be very long indeed, because, according to my observations, there is no set rule about which plants the ants will use and which they will not use. The entire country, district by district, would have to be covered in order to do this. In other words, in one district the ants preferentially use certain plants and leave others strictly alone. For example, in the District of Acahay (Paraguarí) the farmers are virtually prohibited from planting cotton and watermelons because the ants immediately strip these plants of their leaves. But in the District of Itacurubí (de la Cordillera) the farmers believe that cotton and watermelons are the only plants which the ants do not touch. In the latter district the ants utilize mandioca and *curupicay (Sapium* sp.), plants which are seldom bothered by the leaf-cutting ants of Acahay District. The same sort of thing happens with respect to corn—in one region the ants utilize corn more frequently than any other plant; in another region they scarcely touch corn.

So we ask ourselves the question: Why do the ants use the leaves of one type of plant and not of another? Or why do the ants select certain species of plants instead of sampling from all the available species of green plants? Moreover, why do the ants select from a grove of orange trees, all originating from the same nursery and planted at the same time, only a certain few trees, while in another orange grove the ants make no distinction between trees? I believe that the answers to the questions could be partially resolved by chemical analysis of the plants, analysis which would no doubt reveal differences in their chemical composition. If such differences do exist, are they reflected in the composition of the fungal mass, and if so, does this in turn have some influence on the development of the larvae? We have no answers at the present to any of these questions.

There are times when the ants use only green living leaves and other times when the ants use only dry dead leaves. By careful observation, I have established that in dry weather the ants use the green (moist) leaves and in wet weather the ants use dead (dry) leaves. Tests which I have carried out in an experimental nest have gone a long way toward confirming these observations. When the air of the fungus garden is made very humid, the ants immediately bring dry leaves into the chamber and press them against the floor and walls of the chamber, achieving a blotting effect. As the leaves become saturated with water, the ants carry them out of the nest. The opposite effect is observed when the humidity of the fungus garden is lowered drastically. The ants bring quantities of fresh green leaves which they pile up around the fungal mass. These leaves are not used as culture medium for the fungus. If at this very dry moment some water is placed in the garden chamber, the ants immediately react by throwing out the leaves. It must be pointed out that an experimental nest is deprived of any connection with ground water and lacks the ventilation system of a natural nest.

But there are times when even in a natural nest the ants use the above-described methods to equilibrate the humidity in the fungus gardens. We have now an explanation for frequently observed phenomenon of a tree completely stripped of its leaves and these are lying undisturbed on the ground. In other words, the ants cut the leaves during the night but do not carry them into the nest. The country folk see the leaves lying there in abundance on the ground in the morning and get the impression that the ants "bit off more than they could chew," and have thus been even more destructive than was necessary. But the leaf-cutting ants never work in vain and anything which they are observed to do must have its logical and biological explanation. In this case, when the cut leaves have dried thoroughly under the sun, the ants carry them into the nest and presumably use them just as they did in the abnormally wet experimental nest.

The leaves used by the ants must contain some particular factor required by the fungus. My impression is that this important factor is starch. For one thing, the ants use not only leaves, but also seeds, mandioca tubers, corn, and even starchy paper and starched cloth. But this brings us to another question: Why do the ants sometimes preferentially utilize leaves containing very little starch and leave untouched readily available leaves that are well-supplied with starch. For example, orange tree leaves, which are very low in starch, are very often used by the ants, but begonia leaves, which are loaded with starch, are never used by the ants. Obviously, there must be some other important requirement.

PREPARATION OF LEAVES

The leaf-cutting ants use the leaves of trees, shrubs and herbaceous plants. Ants working up in the host plants cut off the leaves almost whole or in large pieces and let them drop to the ground. There other ants cut up the leaves into smaller pieces and carry them off to the nest. I found one medium-sized worker (weight 22 mg) carrying a leaf weighing 100 mg. On the average the weight of the pieces of leaf is about 20–30 mg. If we remember that often the ants must carry the load 400 or 500 meters, the amount of energy expended in supporting a load four times body weight is truly remarkable.

The leaf pieces are carried into the nest and dropped in a special place. At this point other smaller ants cut up the leaves into even smaller pieces and then sort out the usable pieces from the unusable and carry the latter out of the nest by way of the filter holes. The ground around the filter openings is littered with these discarded pieces. The usable pieces are carried to still another depository where they are worked over by the gardeners (minima caste) in preparation for their use as culture medium for the fungus. For hours on end the gardeners lick and rub the leaf fragments, no doubt cleaning off all the dirt and breaking open the cell walls. I have not been able to observe precisely what happens at this stage of the operation.

After the leaf fragment has been properly prepared, it is carried to the fungus garden. There one, two or more of the minimas hold the leaf fragment against the fungi mass for as many hours as it takes for the hyphae to become securely attached to the leaf. During this entire lengthy operation the ants remain absolutely immobile, only slightly quiverings of their antennae giving evidence that the ants are alive. These observations were made in an experimental nest. In this same nest I was able to see that while the ants were providing fresh leaves for one fungal mass, they were cropping another. Each few days the procedure was changed. The fungal mass that had been cropped for food became the recipient of fresh leaves, while the ants began to crop the other garden. I gave the ants some rose petals. These the ants placed on one of the gardens, which was about the size of a tennis ball. This fungal mass turned pink but the other garden retained its usual greenish-gray color. Four days later the pinkish-gray color disappeared from the first garden. The second garden then turned pink. I will point out later how important these observations are in the control of the *ysaú*.

LARVAE AND PUPAE

The legless larvae are found in the fungus gardens where they are cared for by the tiny nurse ants *(niñeras)*. The nurse ants crop the fungus and feed the larvae. These ants also carry the larvae from one place to another in the nest. The larvae are fed as follows: the nurse ant bites off bits of fungus and forms the strands into a tiny ball which she shoves into the mouth of the larva. Does nutrition have anything to do with caste production? Is caste strictly inherited or is it influenced by the nature of the fungus or the quality of the food? Why do the ants carry the larvae from one fungus garden to another and bring other larvae to feed on a garden recently vacated? It is difficult to observe the growth of the larvae because the ants are continually moving them from place to place. All of the shifting from one place to another must make sense, but just now we do not understand it.

The pupae are moved around, too. I have never found larvae and pupae together in the same chamber, although they are often quite close together but in separate chambers. I have often observed that the ants bring in pupae to a chamber which has just been vacated by very small larvae, but I do not know if this is significant. Unfortunately, I have not been able to observe the larvae and pupae of the reproductive caste.

The newly-emerged adults (callows) are yellowish white in color but soon the color changes to a clear brown which lasts several days. The exoskeleton is quite soft at this early stage, having never been exposed to the sun, and the hardening process is very slow. These young ants are still cared for and fed by the nurse ants. After five or six days the young ants begin to feed themselves. This observation is very important in the control operations described later.

CASTES

The *ysaú* have a well-developed polymorphism. Individual lengths vary from 2 mm to 25 mm, several castes being represented in this range. The gardeners, which are scarcely 2 mm long, leave the confines of the underground nest only on one occasion, that is, when the reproductives emerge from the nest before the nuptial flight. The larvae are cared for exclusively by the nurse ants, which are slightly larger (2–3 mm) than the gardeners. Other ants are referred to as leaf-cutters, carriers, cleaners, soldiers, and explorers.

It may be perfectly proper to assign these various roles to the several castes. For my own part though, after many observations, I have never been able to prove that a given task is assigned to any particular group or caste. I have seen all sizes of ants, from the small nurse ants to the big-headed soldiers cutting leaves, carrying leaves, cleaning trails and exploring. I have painted thousands of leaf-carriers and soldiers but I have discovered no differences in their work. One day they cut, the next they carry, etc.

The most difficult work of the colony and the job that is most probably done by specialists is exploration. The explorers go out singly in all directions looking for suitable plants, often traveling 100 m from the nearest nest opening. If an explorer happens to find a suitable plant, it carries a leaf fragment as a sample back to the nest. Soon quantities of ants sally forth from the nest, following the chemical trail of the explorer.

The ants do not always use the same gallery opening for bringing leaves into the nest, even when the source of the leaves remains the same. One gallery opening will fall into disuse as the ants change over to another opening. Later the ants may switch back to the first gallery opening and begin using it for bringing leaves into the nest. They may use the old trail or make a completely new trail. One may also see entrances that are apparently in continuous use. The trails leading away from such openings are cleaner than the trails serving entrances of intermittent use.

Often on the trails one may see soldiers walking back and forth among the throngs of smaller ants. Since these big-headed ants are engaged in no apparent work, such as leaf-carrying, leaf-cutting or cleaning, the idea has arisen that they are protecting the other ants on the trail. But if the ants on the trail are molested, it is precisely the soldiers that run away and the smaller ants that rally to the defense. Just the opposite occurs if the nest mound is attacked. When this happens the big-headed soldiers take over the defense of the nest. We may say then that the soldier caste defends the principal fungus gardens. All of the working castes carry leaf fragments. As it happens, the smallest ants carry the biggest loads.

NUPTIAL FLIGHT

The nuptial flights occur during the months of October and November. Just after a heavy rain, the ants begin a period of intense activity. They clean the galleries, widen the nest openings, and carry the soil particles out of the nest. During the night and the first hours of morning, thousands of ants, heads raised and mandibles open, nervously run about on the surface, ready to defend the nest against an invisible enemy. The entire mound and the adjacent surface 10 m out from the edge of the mound swarm with ants. The ants immediately crawl on and bite anyone who gets too close. The ants bite vigorously and almost always cut the flesh. The wound bleeds freely. The ants can cut rope and the leather of shoes with their mandibles.

About 10 o'clock in the morning, the first sexual forms make their appearance at the main gallery openings. They cautiously approach the opening, then scurry back into the nest. Between 1 and 2 o'clock in the afternoon the first reproductives begin to fly. A little later they leave in enormous masses, like clouds of migratory grasshoppers. Sometimes, though, the flight is composed of only a very few individuals. I have calculated that a large nest may produce a nuptial flight of 15,000 to 20,000 reproductives. A given nest may produce up to three flights each year. I have seen flights composed of only males, only females, and both males and females. It is not a matter of males leaving one nest and females leaving a separate nest on the same day. On one occasion I observed a flight of males only from eight neighboring nests. They flew to a great height and disappeared. Later, I found not a single dead reproductive nor any of the typical small holes made by females establishing new nests.

It is said that the females are inseminated during the nuptial flight. But I have caught females as they emerged from the parental nest and found them to be already fertilized. One of these placed in an experimental nest, laid eggs, cultured a fungus garden, and raised a brood of larvae. Now it could be that the males which leave the nest and fly off at a great height are looking for other nests. They fertilize the females in these other nests, thus avoiding consanguinity. But the *ysaú* follow the same law of family that other ants and other social insects follow, namely, that a stranger attempting to enter a nest is promptly killed, even though the stranger is of the same species. I have watched females leave the nest, fly a short distance, then dig into the ground after the manner of a female forming a nest, without having had any contact with a male outside the nest.

It is abundantly clear then that there is much we do not know about the nuptial flight. The queens might be parthenogenetic, fertilized in the nest, or fertilized during the nuptial flight. How is consanguinity avoided if both males and females from the same nest fly at the same time? Only by many years of careful observations in the field and with experimental nests can the answers to these questions be obtained.

There does seem to be little doubt that the aggregation of thousands of worker ants on the mound just before the nuptial flight does represent a form of defense for the reproductives. I have observed around a nest in this stage of activity quantities of small birds, chickens, partridges, hawks and other birds of prey, lizards, snakes, and toads. All of these animals were gorging themselves with ants so that thousands must have been killed. By mid-day, though, the predators were so full of ants that they did not bother the reproductives when they emerged for the nuptial flight. Certainly the danger of the reproductives becoming objects of predation was very greatly decreased by the time they made their appearance.

ESTABLISHMENT OF NEW COLONY

After the nuptial flight the female drops to the ground and begins nervously looking for an appropriate place to dig in. A preferred place seems to be in slightly sandy soil in a shady place, such as at the base of a tree or among bromeliads. There she digs with her mandibles in the soil, which is still damp and workable from the rain of the preceding day (there seems to be a definite correlation between rain and the nuptial flight). The new queen shapes the excavated earth into tiny balls which she deposits in a circle or semicircle around the deepening tunnel. As the gallery increases in length she disappears into it and must turn around inside it in order to bring the soil to the surface. During this operation her wings rub against the sides of the tunnel and eventually break off. She does not actively break off her own wings, as is often reported in the literature. When she reaches a depth of 20–25 cm, the new queen excavates a small chamber and uses the resulting soil to tightly seal off the gallery opening. Having been very active and "nervous" until this moment, she now becomes lethargic. She establishes the fungus garden and begins to lay eggs.

The first offspring, the gardeners, emerge, on the average, 40 days later. These gardeners excavate a very narrow gallery alongside the one made by the queen and begin to cut and bring in leaves. The leaf fragments are so small and so few in number that the ants cause no noticeable damage. In the third month of colony life the workers begin to excavate new chambers and establish new and larger fungus gardens. A one-year-old colony is not noticeable on the surface of the ground, neither does it cause any apparent damage to plants. A mound is formed over the nest in the third year of colony life. Throughout this entire time the queen scarcely moves. She stays in front of the fungal mass with her head almost touching it. Only when she is molested will she grab a few larvae or pupae in her mandibles and try to escape.

Most of the preceding observations on colony founding were made in an experimental nest. What happens in nature is a great deal more difficult to observe. Queens dug up three days after the nuptial flight had not yet established a fungus garden. But when these queens were put into an experimental nest they did not form a fungus garden and had apparently lost the power to do so. They remained completely immobile until they died two or three weeks or months later. I examined several of these and found them parasitized by nematodes. We may suppose that only a very small fraction of fertilized queens ever succeed in establishing a new colony. Most of the new queens die during the first few days after burying themselves. I marked hundreds of excavations made by new queens just after the nuptial flight. I watched these for five years and not one developed into a colony.

DIMENSIONS OF NEST

This is the most interesting and most important part of our discussion because if we do not know where the nest is we will not be able to control the ants. As I have already mentioned, each nest goes down to the water table. We do not know if all nests have fungus gardens near the level of the water table, but we do know that there are large chambers at that depth as is evidenced by the proportion of the various types of soil brought up from the several different-colored strata of soil. It is easy to determine the depth of a nest if there is a well nearby which shows us the colors of the various strata and the level of the water table.

The depth of the water table varies considerably depending on the location. We have functional wells only two meters deep, but the majority are 15–20 m deep, and a few go to 30–40 m or more. My own observations, still incomplete, indicate that most nests of the *ysaú* are found where the water table is 10–20 m below the surface. Very few nests are found where the water table is deeper. Nests located in areas where the water table is close to the surface are spread out horizontally over a very large area and have a very low tumulus. We may generalize then by saying that where the water table is far from the surface, the entire nest is concentrated beneath a few square meters around the tumulus. And where the water table is superficial the nest may extend horizontally beneath a hectare or more of surface area. There could well be exceptions to this and I have already admitted that my observations on this point are incomplete.

In any case, statements about the horizontal extension are quite hypothetical since all of our nest excavations have been limited to the area beneath the tumulus. The principal fungus gardens are no doubt found beneath the mound and consequently the principal part of the nest is there too. But there are fungus gardens well removed from the cover of the mound. I have already mentioned finding live fungus gardens at a variety of depths during the process of digging wells far from the tumulus. Since these wells are always located far from the mound (no one in his right mind would try to dig a well through an ant nest) and since galleries containing the ants are so often uncovered, we may guess that a mound of 30–50 m² might correspond to an entire nest of 2,500 m². Of course, this whole area is not honeycombed with fungus gardens. The fungus gardens are scattered about, singly or in groups, each one well separated from the next. Just as we have scattered towns connected by roads, the *ysaú* have fungus gardens connected by galleries.

Now if the ants of a given colony find a place particularly appropriate for the cultivation of fungi, they will establish a subdivision of the main nest and build a new mound above it. This subdivision looks to us like a new colony, but we can easily prove its family ties by moving individual ants from one mound to another and noting their acceptance by the other ants. I personally found a colony with three mounds, arranged at the apices of a triangle, each separated from the other by a distance of 80 m. These three mounds definitely belonged to the same family. The entire nest then surely had a horizontal diameter of at least 200 m.

Often I find mounds that are covered with plants and are apparently inactive. Upon excavating such a mound it is found to be very active. Such mounds no doubt represent the old principal mound of a colony. This nest beneath this mound probably for some reason could not be deepened or otherwise enlarged so the ants built a neighboring mound, a sort of "branch office" which serves as the new center of activity for the colony. Thus the question of how big a nest really is becomes quite difficult to answer without a complete excavation of the nest, something which is rarely achieved.

EXCAVATION OF NEST OF *YSAÚ*
(ATTA SEXDENS RUBROPILOSA FOREL)

In order to learn more about the organization of a colony of the *ysaú*, I decided to completely excavate a nest. I chose a young, small nest with a mound of loose earth covering about 6 m². This nest was located close to the College of Agronomy and Veterinary Medicine in San Lorenzo, a suburb of Asunción. To make the operation more convenient and comfortable for the laborers, I treated the nest with 150 g of Mirex ant bait about two months before the digging was started.

The operation was carried out under the combined supervision of the author and Dr. George York of the Servicio Técnico Interamericano de Cooperación Agrícola.

The manual labor was done by Plant Inspectors Hernan Jiménez, Mauricio Gómez, and Mario Jara, whose assistance is gratefully acknowledged. Using shovels and wheelbarrow, the diggers removed about 100 m³ of earth over a period of 16 eight-hour days in June, 1964.

The excavation was carried out systematically. A rectangle, 8 x 5 m, was marked off around the mound. A trench 1 m wide and 1.3 m deep was dug on this boundary line. Successive layers, each 20 cm thick, were then removed from the central portion of the rectangle. The water table was reached at 2.3 m and digging was stopped slightly below this level. Before the digging was started, I set up a plane table, equipped with a compass, to serve as a fixed point of reference a short distance from the dig. Using this reference point, we fixed and recorded the exact location of each fungus garden and chamber.

Details concerning the 136 fungus gardens or cavities are given in Table 8.3. Their spatial arrangement is shown in Figures 8.4 and 8.5. In summary, their distribution was as follows: From the surface to 0.5 m—42; 0.5 to 1 m—42; 1 to 1.5 m—27; 1.5 to 2 m—24; 2+ m—1. A few cavities were located below the water table. These were filled with water, of course, and perhaps served as "cisterns." The fungus garden cavities near the surface were quite small. The size of the chambers increased with depth. At the 1.5 to 2 m level a chamber was found that measured 1 m in length, 0.75 m in width, and 0.35 m in height.

The walls of the chambers were covered with a sort of "pitch." Presumably this pitch prevents the seepage of water into the cell and reinforces the ceiling against cave-ins. The layer of pitch was only a few millimeters thick. It was much darker in color than the earth it covered.

Most of the chambers had been filled with fungi under active cultivation before the ants were killed. Although at this time the fungal masses were dry and blackened, one could still see the hyphae and the small pieces of leaves used as the culture medium. A few of the chambers contained a very fine powdery sand. In one of the cavities there appeared to be a sort of midden heap containing fragments of dead ants. In only a very few cases were ants found in the fungus garden chambers. No more than five ants were found in any one fungus chamber.

Thousands upon thousands of dead ants were packed into the deeper galleries. The dead ants formed "hawsers" 50 cm long and 8–10 cm in diameter, in some cases. No living ants were found. Many specimens, both alive and dead, of the tiny snail *Lamellaxis gracilis martensi* (see Chapter 7) were found in the fungus gardens down to a level of 1.5 meters. The ecologic role of this snail is uncertain. Some small millipedes and many isopods were present and had probably been feeding on the dead fungi. A juvenile snake, *Sibynomorphus* sp., was found in a fungus chamber 50 cm beneath the surface.

Most of the galleries associated with the mound descended vertically from the surface straight to the water table. These galleries, which were 8–10 cm in diameter, did not lead directly to the fungus gardens. Branching off horizontally from these vertical galleries were a few long galleries that led to fungus gardens. The horizontal galleries curved upward near the fungus garden chamber and entered the chamber from beneath. There was, in fact, no direct connection from the surface to a fungus chamber. The galleries almost always descended deep into the nest and then curved upward to the fungus chambers.

Some large horizontal galleries were found at the 1.5 to 2 m level. It appeared that the ants had fashioned "bottlenecks" in these horizontal galleries. A gallery 5–8 cm wide would suddenly narrow down to scarcely 1–1.5 cm, and this narrowed section would continue for 30 to 40 cm. Perhaps the ants use these bottlenecks as doors which they can quickly close with soil or with their own bodies, preventing or regulating the passage of air or water or enemies.

The principal galleries used for bringing leaves into the nest were located at 1 m or more in depth. These spacious galleries lead in a straight line directly to the leaf-cutters' entrances about 25 or 30 meters from the mound.

COLONY: ITS AGE AND POPULATION

In response to the question "How long does an *ysaú* colony live?" Paraguayan farmers usually say 30 or 40 years. But often they say that a given nest is only two or three years old, but it is already causing them trouble. We know though that a three-year-old colony is scarcely noticeable on the surface, that the soldier caste first appears about that time, and that the reproductives do not appear until about the fifth year of colony life. A 92-year-old man showed me a nest beside the house where he was born. This nest was just as active as it had been in his childhood. A conservative estimate of the age of this colony would be 130–140 years. Probably it is much older. Certainly all nests do not reach such an advanced age, but at least it is possible. One cannot tell simply by looking whether a new mound belongs to a new colony or is the "branch office" (*sucursal*) of an old colony. These branch colonies are formed in response to an increasing population.

The queen, of course, establishes the new colony. After the first brood of workers emerges, she dedicates herself to eating and egg-laying. The population increases very slowly. By the end of one year there may be several thousand workers. An average-sized nest, already several years old, may have five million or so workers. I think this latter estimate is much too low. An old nest probably has 15–20 million workers. But an old nest is probably just a "branch office" of a colony, the entire colonial family then being composed of 60–80 million workers.

We do not know how long a queen can live. Her longevity is generally supposed to be greater than 15 years. We do not know how the colony acquires a new queen when the old one dies. I am not suggesting that the *ysaú* queen can live and lay eggs for 150 years. There must be at some time in the life of a colony an equilibrium between natality and mortality. A large colony, with several branches, might have three or four or more queens, each one serving a different branch, but all belonging to the same family. Is it unreasonable to think that there might be more than one queen to a nest? This question requires clarification.

DAMAGE

It is difficult to calculate how much damage the leaf-cutting ants are responsible for. Much depends on the geographical region and on the type of crops planted. But as a generalization we may say that some 40–45% of the crops are lost through the activities of the *ysaú*. In some areas the farmers must limit their crops to those plants which the *ysaú* do not use, even though the climate and soil might be better suited to other crops.

It has been estimated that a large fungus garden requires 1.5 kg of leaves per day. My own observations lead me to think that this estimate is too large. But taking 1.5 kg as a base, and a nest of 500 fungus gardens, the ants would have to carry in 750 kg of leaves each night (or 22,500 kg per month). As was mentioned in an earlier section, the ants do not supply each fungus garden with fresh leaves each day. I believe that an estimated requirement of 1,000 kg of leaves per month for a nest of 500 fungus gardens would not be too far wrong. But taking just half that amount as a base, in a small area having 3,000 mounds (which is not out of the ordinary), the yearly requirement of fresh leaves would be 18,000,000 kg. It is not hard to imagine that the satisfaction of this requirement would have a distinctly deleterious effect on the agricultural production of the region.

ENEMIES AND PARASITES

I have found no natural enemy of the *ysaú* that particularly specializes in the destruction of the ants. The most voracious eaters of ants must be the various species of armadillos (*Dasypus sexcinctus, D. novemcinctus,* etc.). I have often seen the tunnels of armadillos in the mounds of the *ysaú,* but I have never known a colony to be completely destroyed in this fashion, as happens sometimes in the case of termites. The armadillos do not dig deeply enough to reach all of the fungus gardens.

The remains of leaf-cutting ants have been found several times in the crops of nocturnal birds. Only occasionally do wild and domestic fowl have opportunity to feed on the ants, because the latter are seldom active during the day. The ants are most vulnerable during the season of nuptial flights, as previously pointed out. Toads (*Bufo paracnemis* A. Lutz) have the greatest effect on the nocturnal streams of ants along the trails. Often these extremely useful animals will sit at a nest opening eating practically every ant that tries to leave the nest.

There is another type of ant, known as the army ant (*Eciton),* or *guaykurú* in the Guaraní language, which is a fierce enemy of the *ysaú*. The army ants are quite uncommon in Paraguay. Millions of individuals making up the migratory column of the army ants enter a nest opening of the *ysaú* and kill off the colony in a short time. I have personally seen this remarkable phenomenon only once, but reliable persons have reported having seen this happen on several occasions, especially in the region of Bellavista in the Province of Amambay.

There is a snail, *Lamellaxis gracilis martensi,* that lives either in the galleries or the fungus gardens, I am not sure which, of the *ysaú*. Sometimes the ants carry it about like a pebble and deposit it on the crater around the nest opening.

I cannot say with certainty that there are pathogens or parasites that significantly affect the *ysaú*. One time I happened on to a mound that was covered with workers, as happens at the time of the nuptial flight. However, this was not the season for nuptial flights. I visited this nest again a few weeks later and found the colony inactive and the mound covered with dead moldy ants. This mound was a long way from any cultivated crops. Unfortunately, I lost the specimens collected there before any determination of the cause of death was made. It is only in the new queens that I have found nematodes and fungi that have apparently caused or contributed to the death of the queens.

Control

People have been trying to control the leaf-cutting ants ever since colonial days. The older methods of control consisted of placing malodorous and repellent substances (creosote, tar, froth from sugar-making, urine, motor oil, etc.) around the nest openings with the idea of preventing the exit of the ants and thus starving them to death. The ants, of course, simply made new nest openings.

Later various poisons were employed, especially the arsenates of copper and lead. These poisons were placed on the trails and on the workers and were much more effective than the repellents, even achieving the liquidation of a few colonies. Gases of sulfur and arsenic were pumped into nests with fairly good results, but with no noticeable effect on the total problem of ant damage to crops.

The era of modern insecticides has arrived more recently. We have the chlorinated hydrocarbons and organic phosphates applied with special equipment. The result is that the ants abandon the main nest and move into the filter holes; eventually they build supplementary nests. DDT, dieldrin, aldrin, gammexane, methyl bromide, folidol and hostatox applied as liquids or dusts gave good results and caused a noticeable decrease in damage to crops, but after a few months or a year the ants were back at work again in the treated areas.

With the techniques at our disposal it is impossible to treat all of the fungus gardens. A blower can place dusts a few meters inside the nest, but the dusts have no effect on fungus gardens 100 m from the mound. Then excavation of the mound was tried in order to more effectively place the insecticides. But when the mound is molested, the ants move the queen and the brood away from it to a safer place, this being especially simple when the colony is composed of more than one mound. The insecticides kill only a few individuals but no great damage is done to the colony in general.

Fast-acting contact poisons were tried but these produced insecticide avoidance by the ants. The *ysaú* are very susceptible to all the modern insecticides. Treatments with these insecticides have given good results where they have been tried. But, since we do not know where the nest extends beyond the limits of the mound,

the treatment is necessarily incomplete and must be repeated later when the ants again become active.

The belief that only potent, fast-acting insecticides can give satisfactory results in ant control is in my opinion erroneous. These ants are quite intelligent in their own way. They immediately abandon a poisoned area when they perceive many of their fellows dying, even when the insecticide has no repellent effect. If the insecticide is volatile, the ants modify their aeration system, stopping up some of the ventilation galleries, thus avoiding the gases. Fumigation with methyl bromide, a heavier-than-air gas, has been successful in some cases, but has failed completely in others. By closing off certain galleries, the ants deviate the gas into the drainage system leading to the water table, with the result that the upper parts of the nest are unaffected.

Why does an incomplete application of Paris green (copper arsenate) sometimes give fairly good results while a thorough application of a potent, fast-acting insecticide often fails? Paris green has no repellent effect for the ants and is slow acting. I have seen ants that were still alive after having been dusted with Paris green four or five days earlier. These dusted ants walk all through the nest, including no doubt the fungus gardens. It is precisely the fungus gardens that we cannot reach.

A slow-acting insecticide, the effects of which are practically imperceptible to the ants, would be ideal for *ysaú* control. Introduced as a dust into the most frequently used galleries, the insecticide would be picked up on the feet of the ants. The ants then, in walking over the fungi, would poison it and this would happen in those places which we could not otherwise reach. Unfortunately we do not have an insecticide that meets these ideal requirements.

Even such an ideal insecticide might also fail to give good control. Understand that only an extremely small fraction of the nest population leaves the nest at night. Therefore only these would pick up the poisonous dust. These relatively few individuals may not carry the poison long enough or to enough fungus gardens to cause profound damage to the colony before the rest of the workers perceive that something is wrong. Another good method would be to apply potent insecticides to all the nest openings within a radius of 100 meters from the mound. This would theoretically keep the ants prisoners in their own nest and any that did leave would be poisoned. This fails because it is impossible to find all the nest openings. In any case, if all the openings were poisoned, the ants would promptly make new ones.

In summary, then, it may be said that all the insecticides, applied with modern apparatus as liquids, dusts or gases, are effective against the *ysaú*. The trouble is that we cannot reach all parts of the nest. An application of powerful insecticide may kill thousands, even millions, of ants and the colony appears dead. If the queen or queens are killed, then the colony does in fact die. But if a remnant of even a few hundred or thousand workers with their queen survives in one of the remote fungus gardens, the colony will eventually revive. This revived colony will be similar to a one, two or three-year-old colony in that its activity will be scarcely noticeable on the surface. It will be one or two more years before the colony becomes visibly active in the treated area.

My observations on this next question are definitely incomplete, but it may be possible for the workers to produce a new queen, possibly by special nutrition of larvae in the manner of the honeybees, if the old queen is killed. This queen would, of course, be parthenogenetic.

BAITS

In recent years a new system for applying insecticides has been tried. This system uses baits and I believe that it is the best method so far. These baits are prepared with bran and some insecticide which the ants themselves carry to the fungus gardens. The baits Tatuzinho and Iscatox contain aldrin, again a potent fast-acting insecticide. The ants readily accept these baits. I have seen the ants drop their legitimate leaf burdens in order to pick up the bait. They carried the bait into the nest during two hours, in one field trial which I conducted. Then they began to carry the bait out of the nest, dropping it far from the nest opening.

All of this can be explained quite logically. In the first place the bait is impregnated with a powerful, fast-acting insecticide. Secondly, the ants have prolonged contact with the insecticide, considering the time required to carry the bait into the nest, transport it to the fungus gardens, and then hold it firmly against the fungus until the mycelial strands attach to it. The result is that the exposed ants die quickly. The ants are sufficiently intelligent to perceive the dangerous quality of the bait. They promptly throw it out of the nest and will not accept it again.

We have also seen that the ants do not supply with nutrient medium every culture every day. In one application of the type just mentioned, the ants carry in no more than 50 grams of bait. They bring about half of that back to the surface. If the bait contains 5% aldrin, then we have about 1.25 grams of active ingredient to treat roughly 1,000 fungus gardens. This is obviously a very small amount.

MIREX IN THE CONTROL OF THE *YSAÚ*

We have seen then that many insecticides have already been tried in the control of the *ysaú*. The results achieved have been quite as varied as the agents tested. But rarely has the complete extinction of an *ysaú* nest been obtained. Why has failure so often been the result of control attempts when the most effective insecticides and the most efficient modern machines have been employed? I believe that the root of the problem lies in a complete lack of understanding of the construction of the nest of the *ysaú*.

The mound of earth built up by the ants is for us the only indication of the presence of the *ysaú*. We refer to the mound as the "nest" and suppose that the galleries, the fungus gardens and the brood are found only under this mound. But in wells located 50 m or more from the mound living fungus gardens have been found at various depths. It was formerly believed that the nest descended only one or two meters from the surface. But it is easy to prove that galleries may go down to about 25 m. The subsoils of Paraguay in many places are composed of horizontal strata of different-colored earth: red, black, gray, and white. Soil particles of all these colors may be found on the mound of the *ysaú*. If a well is close by, the depth of the galleries may be determined by comparing the color of the soil particles on the mound with the various strata seen in the well.

The size of a nest was commonly thought to be the number of square meters covered by the mound. A tumulus 4 x 5 feet in diameter covered a nest of 20 m² and therefore required some recommended quantity of insecticide per square meter. This would be fine if the nest were confined to the area beneath the mound and if the galleries descended no more than one meter. But what happens if the galleries go down 15 meters and some fungus gardens are located 50 meters from the mound? But the size of the mound is the only basis we have for estimating the size of the nest.

We have to face the fact that none of the methods previously at our disposal can reach the depths and distances required to affect vital parts of the nest, even though the most potent insecticides are used. The queen is the vulnerable point of the colony. She is seldom located under the mound. If the queen survives, the colony survives. If the queen dies, the extinction of the colony is assured. Insecticides, applied as gases, liquids or dusts, on or in the tumulus, cannot reach all the galleries and fungus gardens. Three or four months later the surviving ants will reactivate the life of the nest.

The *ysaú* are intelligent animals. They quickly perceive any dangerous or poisonous substances. They close off the part of the nest that is poisoned and move into galleries and gardens far removed from the poisoned section. For all practical purposes they establish a new nest. They plug up the poisoned galleries with the soil extracted from the new nest. A new mound is not constructed, so the only superficial evidence of their activity is the nightly leaf-cutting.

The only reason why a few of the insecticide treatments worked was that the queen was by chance killed. It was not because the insecticide reached all parts of the nest. The only things that do reach all parts of the nest are the ants themselves. On this principle then baits were utilized, with the idea that the ants themselves would carry the poisons to parts of the nest that the usual applications of insecticide do not reach. This method at first failed because fast-acting insecticides were used. If it normally takes an ant two or three hours to carry the bait to the depths of the nest, and if the normal lethal exposure time is 15 minutes, the ant obviously does not reach its destination. The ants promptly perceive the danger and carry the bait out of the nest. Some manufacturers interpreted the failure to achieve control to be some fault of the insecticide. So they prepared baits containing even more potent and more rapidly acting insecticides. Even though these insecticides were not in the least repellent to the ants, the ants did not carry them into the nest. They died even before reaching the nest entrance. Thus baits were discredited in the control of leaf-cutting ants, but some good results were achieved in the control of *Acromyrmex* species, called *akeké* in Guaraní, because these ants have only one fungus garden in a very shallow nest.

It was my idea then to cover the bait with an innocuous and temporarily impermeable capsule in order to prevent the ants from coming into contact with the insecticide. I coated the bait balls with a paste of mandioca flour. Results were remarkable. The ants accepted the bait immediately. During 10 nights the ants carried 1,750 g of bait into the nest. None was left on the trail and none was returned to the surface. This nest is still inactive. The coating of starch paste held up during the period of transport by the ants and during the process of holding the bait granules against the fungi. The coating prevented action of the insecticide during the period of several days required to supply all of the fungus gardens, even the most remote ones. After all this had taken place, the fungi finally broke through the starch coating, releasing the insecticide. It is quite easy to imagine that 1 kg of insecticide applied directly and only to the fungus gardens would be considerably more effective than the same quantity blown into a nest in the form of dust or gas. But this system had one great fault. Only freshly coated bait satisfied the requirements of good acceptance and good kill. After a week the insecticide began diffusing through the layer of paste and again started to directly and rapidly affect the ants. This type of preparation was therefore unsuitable for commercial use.

I was still convinced that the idea of a bait for the control of the *ysaú* was feasible, but the various techniques for application had failed because our knowledge of the ecology of the *ysaú* was insufficient. The requirements of the ideal bait were again reviewed: no action by contact, no evolution of gasses, slow-acting. Another attribute was considered—fungicidal action—but any material whose fungicidal action could be perceived by the ants would be immediately rejected by them. The usual stomach poisons would, of course, be useless because the ants do not eat the bait. What we needed was some toxin that would, along with the innocuous coating, support fungal growth, that would be absorbed by the fungus, and that would be inadvertently ingested by the ants, at which time its toxic qualities would have their effect. The various pesticide manufacturing companies sent me numerous materials for testing. Most of these turned out either to be repellent or to have a direct toxic effect by contact.

General Chemical Division of Allied Chemical, Morristown, New Jersay, sent me a new bait called Mirex (also known as GC-1283 or dodecachlorooctahydro-1, 3, 4,-metheno-2H-cyclobutal(*cd*) pentalene). This chlorinated hydrocarbon insecticide is insoluble in water and moderately soluble in certain organic solvents. In preliminary toxicological studies done by the manufacturer it showed an LD_{50} (acute oral) value for white rats above 4000 mg/kg. It does not harm plants.

Field tests of the Mirex bait were done in cooperation with two consultants, Mr. Guy Howe and Dr. George York, of the Servicio Técnico Interamericano de Cooperación Agrícola.

The first form of bait that we tried was crushed wheat. The ants readily accepted the crushed wheat, but they picked up only the largest pieces. Thus much of the material was lost. We then tried to determine how much weight an ant can carry. From the columns of leaf-carrying ants we selected an ant carrying a comparatively large piece of leaf. This ant weighed 20 mg and could easily carry 200 mg, or 10 times its own weight. The chemical company made up for us a bait something like broken-up spaghetti, each piece weighing about 50 mg. The shape and weight were both very suitable for the ants. Even the smallest leaf-carriers could handle the bait. But the acceptance was not satisfactory. The ants always left some of the bait particles on the trail or just carried them off to one side and dropped them.

We therefore tried baits of crushed barley and corn, but the results were similar. Whole grains of barley were not accepted. Why were some baits accepted and others rejected? Why do ants of one nest accept a given bait but ants of another colony reject the same material? This problem was studied in considerable detail and observations were made on temperature, humidity, atmospheric pressure, time of leaf-carrying, types of leaves utilized and regional variations in this. The results of these labors were interesting and shed much light on the ecology of the ants, but the problem of bait acceptance was not solved.

One day I picked up an ant in order to study more closely the load it was carrying. I held it in my sweaty hands for several minutes and then released it on the trail. Its cohorts immediately fell upon it and cut it to pieces. This observation was the key to the problem of variable and unpredictable bait acceptance. We had been handling the bait with our sweaty hands. Any particles thus contaminated with sweat were rejected by the ants. Moldy baits were similarly rejected.

The bait arrived from the factory completely clean and uncontaminated, provided the shipping containers had remained intact. Subsequent tests, during which we rigorously avoided contaminating the bait, were completely successful. The ants accepted the bait any hour of the day in any region of Paraguay. Before the field trials, the bait was packaged in polyethylene bags of convenient size. The bait was emptied directly from the bag onto the ground, thus avoiding any contact between the hands and the bait. The bags were kept tightly sealed.

Mirex was tested as a mixture with several different baits—wheat, barley, orange seeds—at concentrations of 15 to 45 percent of the active ingredient. The various preparations were numbered and then placed in small piles on the trails in order to observe which bait was accepted first. The best manner of application was also investigated. In some cases the bait was scattered on the trail, placed along side the trail, placed far from the mound and placed near the mound. All this was tried at different times during the day and night. Incidentally, it was noted that the ants were negatively thermotaxic at a fairly low threshold with respect to the Coleman-type lanterns used in the nighttime experiments.

Briefly, the results showed that the ants without exception immediately accepted the orange seed bait at all concentrations of insecticide in all the methods of application tested. When bait was applied at noon, under a clear sky, at an inactive nest opening, the ants promptly sallied forth and carried off all the bait. Good results were subsequently obtained with other attractant materials mixed with Mirex.

In all of the preliminary tests just described, only small amounts of bait were used. We were interested only in determining acceptability of baits. Having obtained a suitable bait, we then set out to determine how much bait must be used to eradicate a nest of leaf-cutting ants. We started with one kilogram per nest, and then tried successively smaller amounts—0.75 kg, 0.50 kg, 0.25 kg, and 0.1 kg. We tested a series of colonies that varied in size, age, and location (grasslands, forests, towns). Tests were conducted during both rainy and dry weather and the temperature varied between 7 C and 28 C. Each of the ant colonies to which the bait was applied was successfully eradicated.

During the first four or five hours after bait application, the ants would carry off one kilogram of the bait. This time period was subject to some variation because some colonies were more active than others at the time the bait was applied. Three or four days after bait application, we noted a change in the behavior of the ants. They stopped cutting and carrying leaves. A few workers, moving about in an abnormal, uncoordinated fashion, wandered outside of the nest. Then all surface activity stopped. From 8 to 14 days after bait application, callows began to wander about aimlessly on the surface These callows had been non-feeding pupae at the time the adults and larvae were eating the poisoned fungus. The callows would of course starve to death, but their emergence unharmed from the pupal stage at this time demonstrates that Mirex is only a stomach poison and has no fast-acting contact toxicity for the ants. The fungal gardens, too, die either from lack of care (the gardeners are probably the first to die) and the resultant invasions of parasites or saprophytes (the gardeners normally suppress these opportunists). One month after bait application the colony is dead.

The amount of bait preparation needed to eradicate an ant colony is 0.75 kg for a large nest and 0.10 or 0.15 kg for a small nest. Just exactly what happens inside the nest as a result of bait action is unclear. This subject requires further study in experimental nests where ant behavior can be continuously observed. Since the bait supports such luxurious fungal growth, I believe that the queen feasts first on the delectable but deleterious hyphae, and promptly dies. The rest of the colony follows

suit. This hypothesis is supported by my observations of ant behavior in experimental nests, namely, that when the queen dies, the rest of the ants immediately become inactive.

A few tests of bait acceptability by domestic animals were done. We scattered some Mirex directly in front of some chickens. The chickens picked up the bait particles, then immediately tossed them aside. We mixed 10 grams of Mirex with a handful of cracked corn and scattered this in front of the chickens. They ate all of the corn but none of the Mirex. Pigs would not eat Mirex. We scattered known quantities of Mirex in the forest to see if wild birds would eat it (they did not).

In summary, we can now say that Mirex is completely effective in the control of the *ysaú*. Mirex is easy to apply. It is not necessary to know the location of the nest; simply placing the bait on a trail is all that is required. The ants themselves carry the toxin to the nest, wherever it may be. On the average, 0.24 kg is sufficient to eradicate the largest nest. The bait may be applied during the daylight hours. There is no danger to domestic animals. Where chickens are present, the bait should be placed in a protective shelter over the ant trail, otherwise the chickens will scatter the bait with their feet. Do not disturb the ants at the time of application. The ants will carry off the bait much more quickly if they are undisturbed. Apply the bait only once to a given nest. A few days after application, the ants will accept no more bait. Therefore any subsequent applications would be wasted.

These precautions should be observed. Do not touch Mirex with the bare hands (use rubber gloves). Always keep the polyethylene storage bags tightly sealed. Do not store Mirex with drugs, foods, other insecticides, petroleum products, or any strongly odorous materials (odors absorbed by Mirex during storage make the bait repellent to the ants). Like all pesticides, Mirex should be carefully handled and stored in a place inaccessible to children.

Further Studies

We have thus seen that the social organization of the *ysaú* has received comparatively little study. We cannot say with any certainty how many queens there are in a nest. We know very little about the deepest fungus gardens in the nest. There appear to be morphological differences between the fungi near the surface and those deep in the nest. We do not know what utility such differences might have in the maintenance of the colony. We do not know why the ants form colonial subdivisions far from the parental nest or why the ants utilize only certain plants. Is it possible by special nutrition to convert a worker larva into a reproductive larva? Where is the queen fertilized? Can the queen reproduce parthenogenetically? All of these problems must eventually be solved in order to achieve the most effective control of these ants. The ecology of the *ysaú* must be worked out little by little, the result of careful observations and experiments, until we have a thorough understanding of this most interesting and prejudicial species.

Author's address: see p. 76.

Table 8.1. Temperatures at Various Levels in an Ant Nest

		Date			
Temperature (Centigrade)		11 Jun 62	25 Jul 62	14 Nov 62	12 Dec 62
Air	Maximum	19	15	33	36
	Minimum	6	3	14	21
Soil surface (1400 hours)		16	14	33	37
5 cm subsurface		15	12	29	34
10 cm subsurface		15	12	29	34
20 cm subsurface		15	13	28	33
50 cm subsurface		17	15	27	31
12 m subsurface (ground water)		22	22	23	23

Table 8.2. Depth of Fungus Gardens in Paraguay

Location of Well	Depth in Meters
Villa Morra (Asunción)	12
Villa Morris (Asunción)	18
Lambaré (Asunción)	25

Table 8.3. List and Description of Fungus Garden Chambers in a Nest of *Atta sexdens rubropilosa* Forel in Paraguay, June 1964
(See Figs. 8.4 and 8.5 for Spatial Distribution of Chambers)

Number	Depth in cm	Size in cm	Observations	Number	Depth in cm	Size in cm	Observations
1	25	12 x 12 x 12	Fungus	29	135	13 x 13 x 13	Fungus
2	95	20 x 20 x 20	Fungus	30	220	Small	Full of water
3	25	20 x 20 x 12	Fungus	31	170	Small	Fungus
4	65	15 x 15 x 12	Fungus	32	165	Small	Fungus
5	40	35 x 35 x 15	Fungus	33	140	Small	Fungus
6	40	25 x 25 x 20	Fungus	34	170	Small	Fungus
7	90	22 x 25 x 12	Fungus	35	140	Small	Fungus
8	60	15 x 15 x 10	Empty	36	110	Small	Fungus
9	85	40 x 35 x 20	Fungus	37	70	Small	Fungus
10	100	30 x 20 x 17	Sand	38	100	Small	Fungus
11	120	Small	Dead ants	39	110	Small	Fungus
12	144	Small	Dead ants	40	105	30 x 25 x 10	Fungus
13	145	Small	Fungus	41	50	30 x 25 x 15	Fungus
14	140	Small	Fungus	42	35	15 x 20 x 10	Fungus
15	115	Small	Fungus	43	35	20 x 13 x 12	Fungus
16	150	Small	Fungus	44	35	15 x 15 x 15	Fungus
17	145	Small	Sand	45	30	12 x 13 x 10	Fungus
18	170	Small	Fungus	46	30	15 x 19 x 13	Fungus
19	130	Small	Fungus	47	170	—	—
20	150	Small	Fungus	48	190	—	—
21	180	Small	Fungus	49	60	20 x 15 x 12	Fungus
22	180	Small	Fungus	50	100	30 x 35 x 30	Fungus
23	180	Small	Fungus	51	30	25 x 20 x 15	Fungus
24	180	Small	Fungus	52	60	11 x 12 x 10	Fungus
25	180	Small	Empty	53	60	50 x 25 x 15	Fungus
26	165	Small	Full of water	54	90	10 x 10 x 6	Fungus
27	160	Small	Midden heap	55	120	Small	Fungus
28	190	Small	Sand	56	80	Small	Fungus

Table 8.3 continued

Number	Depth in cm	Size in cm	Observations	Number	Depth in cm	Size in cm	Observations
57	55	Small	Fungus	97	70	20 x 20 x 15	Fungus
58	200	Small	Fungus	98	30	20 x 25 x 15	Fungus
59	190	Small	Fungus	99	105	30 x 30 x 20	Fungus
60	30	20 x 20 x 15	Fungus	100	130	30 x 30 x 20	Fungus
61	200	Small	Fungus	101	50	20 x 18 x 10	Fungus
62	185	Small	Fungus	102	169	15 x 25 x 10	Fungus
63	170	Small	Fungus	103	170	Small	Fungus
64	40	20 x 20 x 16	Fungus	104	185	Small	Fungus
65	100	15 x 15 x 12	Fungus	105	30	Small	Fungus
66	30	15 x 15 x 8	Fungus	106	30	Small	Fungus
67	30	25 x 22 x 12	Fungus	107	45	Small	Fungus
68	90	30 x 30 x 20	Fungus	108	60	Small	Fungus
69	35	30 x 25 x 15	Fungus	109	70	Small	Fungus
70	35	30 x 25 x 20	Fungus	110	15	Small	Fungus
71	35	Small	Fungus	111	50	Small	Fungus
72	75	Small	Fungus	112	200	Small	Fungus
73	75	10 x 30 x 8	Sand	113	200	Small	Fungus
74	80	20 x 20 x 18	Fungus	114	70	Small	Fungus
75	50	Small	Fungus	115	30	Small	Fungus
76	50	18 x 20 x 12	Fungus	116	90	40 x 65 x 20	Fungus
77	60	15 x 15 x 12	Fungus	117	50	Small	Fungus
78	40	20 x 15 x 12	Fungus	118	50	Small	Fungus
79	70	55 x 40 x 30	Fungus	119	30	Small	Fungus
80	40	Small	Fungus	120	50	Small	Fungus
81	40	30 x 23 x 20	Fungus	121	80	Small	Fungus
82	25	Small	Fungus	122	65	22 x 25 x 30	Fungus
83	95	45 x 70 x 40	Fungus	123	115	30 x 40 x 20	Fungus
84	145	Small	Fungus	124	60	20 x 20 x 15	Fungus
85	50	Small	Fungus	125	35	20 x 20 x 15	Fungus
86	50	23 x 25 x 15	Fungus	126	120	40 x 25 x 20	Fungus
87	70	15 x 20 x 15	Fungus	127	70	Small	Fungus
88	120	100 x 55 x 30	Fungus	128	100	30 x 40 x 30	Fungus
89	110	40 x 32 x 20	Fungus	129	60	Small	Fungus
90	105	30 x 25 x 10	Fungus	130	130	25 x 25 x 20	Fungus
91	95	20 x 35 x 15	Fungus	131	30	30 x 30 x 15	Fungus
92	35	20 x 35 x 10	Fungus	132	20	Small	Fungus
93	100	20 x 15 x 15	Fungus	133	130	15 x 15 x 20	Fungus
94	40	45 x 45 x 30	Fungus	134	135	15 x 15 x 10	Fungus
95	80	30 x 25 x 20	Fungus	135	100	Small	Fungus
96	60	35 x 35 x 25	Fungus	136	60	Small	Fungus

Figure 8.1. Mound of *Atta sexdens vollenweideri* Forel near Asunción, Paraguay. Photo by Schade.

Figure 8.2. Mound of *Atta sexdens vollenweideri* Forel near Toro Blanco, Caaguazú, Paraguay. Photo by Schade.

Figure 8.3. Trail of *Atta sexdens rubropilosa* Forel; mound in left background.
Paraguay. Photo by Schade.

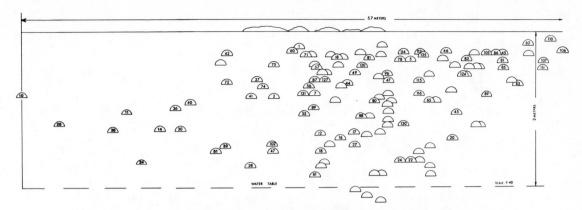

Figure 8.4. Side view, schematic, of excavated nest of *Atta sexdens rubropilosa* Forel
at San Lorenzo, Paraguay, June 1964.

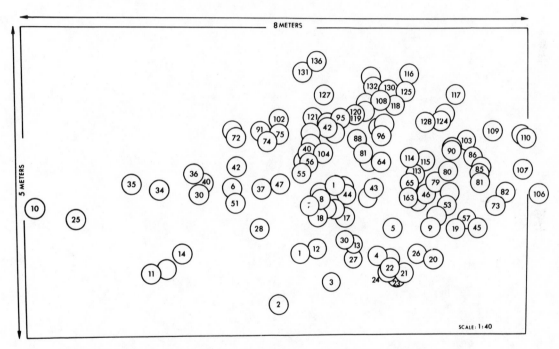

Figure 8.5. Top view, schematic, of excavated nest of *Atta sexdens rubropilosa* Forel
at San Lorenzo, Paraguay, June 1964.

IX. Some Plants and Animals in Guaraní and Guayakí Mythology

LEÓN CADOGAN

What attracts me now is the forest. . . A world of grasses, flowers, mushrooms, and insects leads there an independent life of its own, to which patience and humility are our only passports.

Lévi-Strauss*

Moon . . . is a pot-bellied man whose bluish intestines can be seen through his skin. His enemy is a spirit of death, the celestial Jaguar. Now and then the Jaguar springs up to devour him. . . Men, however, are afraid, and they beat their drums, strike their dogs, shout, and make all possible noise to . . . force him to relinquish his prey. . . Moon grows and again becomes a pot-bellied man. The eclipse is over.

Métraux**

Introduction

In the article *El culto al árbol y a los animales sagrados en la mitología y las tradiciones guaraníes,*[3] I drew attention to what are evidently traces of animal worship and a tree cult in Guaraní mythology. Since then I have obtained further information on this subject from among four Guaraní-speaking nations—Mbyá, Chiripá, Pâî-Cayuá, and Guayakí—the scattered remnants of which survive in eastern Paraguay. So when Dr. Gorham asked me to contribute a chapter to this book, it was a question of what material to select in order to give, in a short paper, a tolerably good idea of just what animals and plants represent in the *Weltanschauung* of our Indians.

After writing *El culto al árbol,* I read some of Dr. Otto Zerries' most interesting and fascinating work on animals and plants in South American mythology,[24] and exchanged some letters with him on the subject. The work of this eminent specialist, together with that of Haekel,[14] suffice to show how little is really known of Guaraní spiritual culture, in spite of the "cubic meters of literature" already published on the subject.

It will, I think, be admitted that to do justice to the subject, a fair-sized book would be necessary. But at the same time, access to bibliography is extremely limited in Villarrica (Guairá), so omissions, I trust, will be pardoned.

Animals

THE JAGUAR

With exception of "civilized" man, the jaguar is the Guayakí's most feared enemy. Countless taboos reflect the fear which this great cat inspires. A few of these follow.[7]

Do not eat monkey meat while lying down: the jaguar will rip your belly.

Whoever does not share his venison with his fellows will be mauled by the jaguar.

Young men should not eat the eyes of young carpinchos: they will not see the jaguar.

The ceremony called *kymatá tyrô* (= purification with *kymatá*) also reflects the fear in which the jaguar is held. *Kymatá* is a liana, probably the *timbó* used by other tribes to poison fish. Upon the termination of the seclusion and fast connected with the onset of menarche, a girl is ceremonially purified (= *tyró*) by being rubbed with an infusion of *kymatá* bark in water.[7]

We purify with *kymatá* to keep *bayjá* away; the jaguar loses itself, it goes away.

When the Guayakí has *bayjá,* all the jaguars come; the *bayjá* accompanying the Guayakí's body are the many jaguars, therefore we purify with *kymatá.*

It is therefore not surprising that a celestial jaguar should occupy a prominent place in their mythology.[7,16]

The jaguar mauled the sun, it devoured him, it gnawed his bones.

The men yelled hoarsely, the women shrieked, the growing children cried shrilly.

(They) made smoke with the wax of *choá* bees to chase the jaguar away.

They beat trees with their bows, they cleaved the earth with axes, they sent up to heaven the scent of *choá* wax.

The disembodied "heavenly" soul (= *ové, ovwé*) of the jaguar, like the human soul and the souls of other animals and birds, acquires the power of unleashing the elements upon ascending to Chingy-tý, the Guayakí paradise.[7]

*Lévi-Strauss, C. 1961. A world on the wane. Hutchinson, London. Quoted by permission of Atheneum Publishers and Georges Borchardt, Inc.

**Métraux, A. 1946. Myths of the Toba and Pilagá Indians of the Gran Chaco. American Folklore Society, Philadelphia. Quted by permission of the publisher.

*Baipú pichuaré ro chonó pirirí, bwytú pambú, kyraý ri verá
pirâ.*

Pichuá (= meteorological phenomena) of the jaguar are thun-
derclaps, roaring wind, in the sky red lightning.

It may be added that, in spite of the fear in which the
jaguar is held, its flesh is not despised, but rather is freely consumed by the Guayakí. One of my best informants
was a woman called Baipú (= jaguar), a name which is
proof that Baipú's mother ate some jaguar flesh just before her daughter was born.

Beliefs similar to those of the present-day Guayakí regarding the jaguar as the cause of eclipses were widespread
among the different Guaraní-speaking tribes at the time
of the Conquest. The *Vocabulário na língua brasílica,*
compiled during the first decades of the seventeenth century, states under the heading *Eclypse da lua:* "Regarding
an eclipse of the moon, they say that it is eaten by some
wild beast. Others, such as the Tupinambá, say a tiger.
The Tupí say it is a serpent." According to Montoya's
Tesoro de la lengua guaraní,[18] compiled about the same
time, an eclipse of the moon is *yací hoú yaguá,* the literal
meaning of which is "(the) dog ate (the) moon." The
word *yaguá,* however, which means "dog" in contemporary Guaraní, originally meant jaguar, even as it does up
to the present time in some mythical contexts. So it may
be assumed that all the Guaraní tribes whose dialects
were studied by Montoya, as a basis for his *Tesoro,* considered eclipses to be caused by a celestial jaguar. Is it a
coincidence that the ancient Peruvians also believed that
a celestial jaguar or tiger caused eclipses? [24]

A figure comparable to the celestial jaguar of the Guayakí is not mentioned in the Mbyá mythical texts. I have
not questioned the Chiripá or Pâî-Cayuá on the matter.
The same mythical monster still exists, however, in the
beliefs of other Guaraní remnants, as is pointed out by
Nimuendajú,[20] who quotes Nordenskiöld. The belief also
exists in the texts of the Apapokuva—a branch of the
Chiripá—studied by Nimuendajú.[20] An eternal bat, an
eternal jaguar, and an eternal boa are the guardians of the
heaven of Ñanderuvusú (= the creator).

In the lore of the Mbyá, Chiripá and Pâî-Cayuá Indians,
the jaguar is an incarnation of the "primitive beings" or
"primeval jaguars" that had devoured the mother of the
heavenly twins (Sun and Moon). The mother, gravid with
twins, was abandoned by the creator and, being unable
to follow his tracks, took the road which led her to the
home of the primitive beings or future jaguars. She was
devoured there, but it was impossible to kill the twins.
They were reared by the future jaguars whom they held
to be their uncles and aunts, and whose mother they
took for their grandmother. In the Mbyá myth, a parrot
(in other versions, a pheasant) tells the twins that their
mother had been killed and eaten by the future jaguars.
The twins then destroyed all of the future jaguars but
one, a pregnant female, that was able to escape. *Kuaraý*
(= Sun), enraged at the sight of his enemy escaping un-
scathed, uttered a curse which changed her into a "noisome being."

Noisome Being, sleep and awake; Being who renders noisome
the springs and the banks of the genuine (= flowing) waters,
fall asleep! Then awake (in the shape of a Noisome Being).

Those versed in tribal lore affirm that, had not Kuaraý
been so overcome with rage at the sight of his enemy escaping that he uttered the word *avaeté* (= noisome, fright-
ful), the primitive being would have been changed into
some harmless beast, and mankind would not have had
to contend with such a dangerous enemy as the jaguar.[4,5]

In the Pâî-Cayuá invocation, which is recited with the
object of keeping the jaguar away, the animal is addressed
as *che tutý* (= my uncle) and *takeresé marangatú* (the
first word is the secret or sacred name of the jaguar, the
second word means blessed or privileged).[10]

A Mbyá myth reminiscent of the Guayakí purification rite, *kymatá tyrô,* is the *i-vaí-kué jepotaá* (= he or
she who is possessed with the evil one—jaguar. The man
or woman so described is said to be unable to resist a
craving for raw meat. A complicated purification ritual
is resorted to in which the aid of Jakairá, the god of
spring and patron of sorcerers, is invoked. If the ceremony proves ineffectual, the possessed man or woman is
killed. In the mythical culture of some groups, the trans-
formation of the possessed person is more dramatic. His
canine teeth become enormous in size and he metamor-
phoses into a masculine, inhuman form called *jaguareté
avá* (= jaguar man), a counterpart of the European were-
wolf and the *luisón* of Paraguayan folklore.[12]

THE BIG WILD PIG

Called *chachú* in the Guayakí language, *tajasú* in Pâî-
Cayuá and Chiripá, and *tajachú* in Mbyá, the big wild pig
is another animal occupying a prominent place in Guaraní mythology. In the Mbyá language the female pig is
tajachú and the male is *karaveré.* In Chiripá the *karaveré*
is the big boar that leads the herd. The Guayakí celebrate
the capture of a *chachú* with ritual song, the soul of the
pig being surrounded in Chingy-tý (= heaven) with thunder, lightning and rain, as is the case with the souls of
other animals.[13] The three Indian groups consider the
pig to be a privileged animal. Both Chiripá and Mbyá
honor "Owner of the Pigs" and "True Father of the Pigs"
with ritual song and dance. Investigation would surely
prove that the Pâî-Cayuá do likewise. This true father of
the pigs for the Mbyá is Karaí Ru Eté, who lives in a land
situated beyond the sea. In Guaraní mythology the sea
separates the earth from the "promised land."[4,5] The
three Indian groups have a myth in which a young Indian,
obliged for some misdemeanor to marry a sow, follows
the herd to the abode of the true father of the big wild
pigs.

CELESTIAL SERPENTS

The Guayakí believe that the rainbow consists of two
enormous serpents, namely, Membó Ruchú (= Big Serpent) and Krijú Braá (= Black Boa):

They descend into the watercourse of the carpincho, into
the marsh.

One announces the probable death of an infant, the other warns that a member of the tribe may be mauled by a jaguar.[8] The eternal boa, guardian companion of Ñanderuvusú, the Apapokuva creator, was mentioned above. *Embó* is the Mbyá name for a large snake that inhabits the steep banks of streams. Embo-kwá or Hembo-kwá is what the Mbyá call a certain heavenly body, probably a nebula, the terms being reminiscent of the Apapokuva boa and the rainbow serpents of the Guayakí.[4,8]

THE TAPIR'S PATH

The tapir, too, has his path in the heavens, namely, the Milky Way, which is called Tapi'í Rapé and Moreví Rapé in the Guaraní dialects. This idea is certainly not unique to the Guaraní-speaking groups, rather the belief is widespread in South America.[24]

EARTHLY MONSTROUS PROTOTYPES

A fundamental belief about animals is that they are all "imperfect images of eternal animals" or, to put it another way, "earthly manifestations of an eternal cosmic being." But in addition to these "eternal animals," there are "monstrous earthly prototypes" of each animal species. Most of these, perhaps all, live alone or in pairs (but do not breed) in the densest forest and remotest mountain. Each kind is called by the name of the species it represents, followed by *jagua*, a word which originally meant "roaring one" and was applied to the jaguar, other felines, and some other carnivores, including the dog.

The Eirá-jaguá is one of these monstrous prototypes. The *eirá* is a small mustelid *(Tayra barbara)*, which is very fond of honey. But since *eí* or *eirá* is the Guaraní name for honey, the monster could be either the "spirit" of the carnivore or the bees or the honey. A point in favor of the bees is the Guayakí belief in *baiywá,* which are more or less dangerous maladies attributed to the "spirit" of different sorts of bees.

The Mbyá Eirá-jaguá is a monster in human form covered by scales impervious to arrows. The only vulnerable spot on its body is a small circle on the chest. This monster is the subject of several legends.[4,5] Proof that this myth of the earthly monstrous prototype is not limited to just one Guaraní-speaking tribe or group is provided by Paraguayan folklore in the names Mbói-jaguá (= monstrous water serpent) and Tejú-jaguá (= dragon or monstrous iguana).

ANIMAL ALTER EGO

According to Montoya's linguistic classic,[18] *tupichúa* means "familiar spirit," a spirit which counselled the Guaraní shaman. The term is translated the same way— *espírito familiar*—in the *Vocabulário na língua brasílica.* *Pichuá* in the Mbyá dialect is used in connection with the myth that the spirit of a jaguar may possess a person. The term is used by the Guayakí in connection with the meteorological phenomena surrounding the souls of human beings and animals. In Pâí-Cayuá, however, it is the name of the alter ego which takes the form of an animal visible only to the shaman, which accompanies a person throughout life, perched on his shoulder.

Some *tupichúa* are birds or other animals, some are good, others bad. The appetites of the *tupichúa* govern those of its host. Some ailments, such as sore eyes and toothache, are attributed to the *tupichúa.*[10] As Dr. Otto Zerries pointed out to me recently (personal communication), there is apparently a connection between the Pâí-Cayuá alter ego and the fact that all Guayakíes owe their names to birds, insects or other animals devoured by their mothers just prior to parturition. Probably there is also a relationship between the Pâí-Cayuá belief that *tupichúa* is the cause of some ailments and the fact that the Guayakí attribute most severe illnesses to the *iâvé* (= earthly spirit) of such animals as the coati and armadillo.

CELESTIAL ANIMAL PROTOTYPE

The only "animal" constellations mentioned in the Mbyá texts, in addition to the Tapir's Path and Embo-kwá (= Serpent's Cavern), are the Ostrich (= Gwyrá Ñandú or Ñandú Guasú) and the Pleiades (= Eichú), which will be referred to again below. However, every animal is the imperfect or earthly image of a "genuine" animal (*ha' eté'í va'é*—he who is the genuine one) which inhabits the outskirts of the creator's paradise.[4]

> The first being which soiled the earthly abode was the primeval serpent; It is only his image which now inhabits our earth; The genuine primeval serpent lives on the outskirts of our father's paradise.
>
> The first being which dug in the earthly abode was the armadillo; The one existing on our earth is not the genuine armadillo, but only his image. The genuine armadillo lives on the outskirts of our father's paradise.
>
> The first being to intone a song regarding the appearance of prairies, the first to express his joy at their appearance was the red partridge.
>
> The red partridge which sang a song about the appearance of the prairies is now on the outskirts of our father's paradise; The one inhabiting the earthly abode is merely its image.

Dr. Otto Zerries, unaware of the Mbyá texts which I have quoted, but basing his conclusions on his own field work and that of other investigators, describes the "master" or "father" of each animal species as follows: "It is an eternal cosmic being, and all the animals of its species are nothing but its earthly manifestations." Thus we have the same concept expressed first in the legend of the Stone Age Indian and then in the phraseology of the Atomic Age anthropologist.

PRIVILEGED BIRDS AND THUNDER BIRDS

According to the Mbyá texts, migratory birds at the end of autumn fly to Gwyrá Ru Eté Ambá, the abode of the genuine father of birds. These birds are referred to as Gwyrá Marangatú (= privileged or blessed birds). The Guayakí counterparts of these privileged birds are the Kwipirúgi and the Chonó Kybwyrá (= birds of thunder or the tempest). They unleash the tempest and hurl lightning at the tallest trees of the forest. Then they return to Chingy-tý

> To sleep with Thunder, their father.

When the ocotea plant renews its shoots at the beginning of spring, the birds of the tempest return to earth to lay their eggs.[4,8]

The following song of the Mbyá probably represents a link between the Guayakí birds of the tempest and the Mbyá privileged birds.[4]

> Come, vulture, opposite the *karandá*
> *(Prosopis sp.)* of brilliant foliage.
>
> When the true mother Tupâ (goddess of the storm) kneels, when she kneels
> her body flashes, her body flashes.
>
> When her body flashes, the sons of Tupâ
> move their bodies rhythmically,
> move their bodies rhythmically.
>
> When they move their bodies rhythmically,
> the Eternal Suruku'á *(Trogonorus rufus chrysochlorus)* sings his sad melody,
> sings his sad melody.
>
> When he sings his sad melody, and we,
> following the road, following the road,
> say, "My head aches,"
>
> The soul of the tree wounds us,
> wounds us.

In these verses, the wife of Tupâ, owner of the waters and goddess of the tempest, is teaching her sons the ritual dance. Lightning flashes from her body as she kneels and the boys move their bodies rhythmically. A vulture, another bird which in Guayakí lore has the power to unleash the tempest, precedes the approaching storm and takes refuge in the *karandá* tree of brilliant foliage (the fact that it is brilliant reveals that it is located in the heavenly regions). A *suruku'á* sings a sad song, and whoever ventures forth at such a moment risks being wounded by the soul of a tree, several of which are endowed with this malign power.

An interesting link between Apapokuva and Guayakí mythologies is a large scissor-tailed bird called *tapê* in Guaraní. According to Nimuendajú,[20] the *yvyra'ijá* (= messengers, subordinates) of Tupâ, the god of the storm, sometimes assumes the form of the *tapê* and attracts the rainclouds. This Tapê, called *pirá bwa kakô* by the Guayakí, is one of the birds of the tempest and is considered to be the father of fishes.[8]

One of the Guayakí birds of the tempest that also occupies a prominent place in Guaraní lore is Krumá, a hummingbird. In the Mbyá creation myth[4] this bird appears simultaneously with the creator

> In the midst of primeval darkness,

fluttering about among the flowers which adorn his headdress, and

> Nourishing him with products of the skies.

Both the Chiripá and the Pâí-Cayuá have ritual chants dedicated to the hummingbird.

> What news have you to impart, Hummingbird?
>
> Hummingbird emits lightning flashes,
> lightning flashes!
>
> Has the nectar of your flowers perchance
> befuddled you, Hummingbird?
>
> Hummingbird emits lightning flashes,
> lightning flashes!

In these verses, Hummingbird, bearer of news, partakes of the "nectar of the flowers," the religious name of the ritual *kawî* (= beer). He is surrounded by the lightning flashes which in both Guaraní and Guayakí mythology always surround heavenly beings. The verse

> "What news have you to impart, Hummingbird?"

signifies the mythical role of the hummingbird as messenger and counsellor to the shaman.

> *Ro ñe-mo-ñondeguá voí nte* Maino me.
>
> It is a fact that we allow ourselves
> to be led (counselled) by Hummingbird,

says the Chiripá *oporaíva* (= medicine man, singer), in agreement with the practice of his Mbyá and Pâí-Cayuá confreres. Thus the hummingbird is a bearer of messages from the celestial regions:

> He proceeds from the outskirts
> of our father's paradise
> to dance among the children
> in the earthly abode.

The messages he brings are all concerned with the welfare of the children of the tribe and must be interpreted by the tribal shaman.[5]

PARROT OF DISCREET SPEECH

In the Mbyá myth it was Parakáo Ñe'engatú (= the parrot of the discreet speech) that revealed to the heavenly twins, Sun and Moon, that their mother had been devoured by the Primitive Beings. To prevent Parakáo from revealing the secrets of fate to mankind, O-mbo-arakuaá (= impart knowledge of the universe), the older of the twins, banished him to the end of the earth and charged him with the custody of the rope or cable by which the human soul must cross the sea which separated earth from heaven.[4] According to the Pâí-Cayuá texts, the parrot (= Guyraju(a) Katu-râ) is the guardian of the paradise of Ñane Ramói (= grandfather).[21] The same bird is mentioned in the sacred song of a Pâí-Cayuá shaman who describes his ascent to the abode of Pa'í Kwará (= Owner of the Sun). This song was recorded by Egon Schaden, but unfortunately it has not been published.

ETERNAL BEES

In classical Guaraní the Pleiades are called Eichú, the name of a small bee. In referring to frost, the Mbyá sometimes say

Eichú *reviraó ho'á.* The Eichú's pollen is falling.

Mention is also made of the Eichú in the following Mbyá mythical text.[4]

Ñande Ru, our father, angered by the lack of piety in mankind, exclaimed:

I no longer see good thoughts in my sons.

Ñande Chy, our mother, answered:

I still see good thoughts in my children. Behold, on the outskirts of my abode I have gathered eternal baskets for my children to play with then they return to me.

Look! Among the tussocks which dot the meadows surrounding my abode I have caused Eichú Marane'ŷ (= eternal bees) to nest in order that my children, when they return to me, may rinse their mouths with honey.

FLAMING WASPS

The *kavendý* (= flaming wasps) guard the eternal palm (= Pindovy-jú) on the road to the Chiripá heaven. At the foot of this palm Charyi-piré awaits her grandchildren as they return to the heavenly abode. She has there the nest of *kavy apu'á* (= a small bee) which provides honey to refresh the grandchildren on their way to the outskirts of the house of Ñanderuvusú, the creator.[5]

ETERNAL WASP

Kavusú Ypý, the eternal wasp, is important in Guaraní mythology, and is the subject of a ritual dance by the Chiripá. The eternal wasp is called Kavy-jú by the Mbyá and Mberú Kaguá by the Pâí-Cayuá. It is, like the hummingbird, an ally and counsellor to the medicine man, bringing messages from the heavenly regions, which only the shaman is able to interpret.[5]

Plants

PLANTS AND THE INDIAN HEAVEN

For the Guayakí Indian, heaven is a vast grove of *chingý*[8] (*Ruprechtia laxiflora*).[17] To the Guaraníes studied by Schaden,[22] heaven is an endless orchard in which dwarf trees of all imaginable varieties provide a never-ending supply of delicious fruit. And there are cedar trees (*Cedrela fissilis*), too, which will be mentioned again later. Fruit and honey (usually from hollow trees) abound in the Apapokuva paradise.[20] The Chiripá paradise is Okavusú, a place where the eternal potato, the eternal cotton plant and other eternal cultivated plants abound.[5] Both Pâí-Cayuá and Chiripá myths have the *yrukú* plant (*Bixa orellana*) growing along the road to heaven. The mansion of Ñanderuvusú is usually described as being "situated beyond the eternal shrub." This designation may be related in some way to the annatto tree (*yrukú, urukú, Bixa orellana)* from which a ritual paint is made.

PINDÓ PALM

Arecastrum romanzoffianum is, or was, the most important plant in Tupí-Guaraní economy. Therefore, it is not surprising that five eternal *pindós* support the Mbyá universe, that the hero of the flood myth would save himself by creating a *pindó* palm in the midst of the waters, and that an eternal *pindó* towers above the fountain where Father of the Race was begotten.[4] This tree also figures in a Guayakí flood myth.[8] Our Grandmother awaits her children at the foot of Pindo-vy-jú, the eternal palm, on the road to the Chiripá heaven.

CEDAR TREE

Cedrela fissilis, among other trees, occupies the Guaraní heaven. The Mbyá have a sacred name for the cedar, Yvyrá Ñamandú (= tree, creator), but in all the Guaraní dialects the everyday name is *ygary* (= boat tree). The sacred name recalls a day when this tree must have been of great economic importance to the Indians. It may be inferred from the common name that the tree was economically important because it was used to construct boats. The Tupí-Guaraní Indians were formerly renowned as sailors, but nowadays boatmaking is a forgotten art and sailing is mentioned in just one myth, so far as I have heard, namely, the one already noted in which a young Indian follows a herd of swine to the abode of Karaí Ru Eté. The young man returned from there in a *ygá* (= boat) belonging to an alligator. From the wood of the *ygary* the Mbyá carve stools or benches which have an esoteric meaning. All the utensils connected with the ritual dance of the Chiripá are made of cedar wood.[5]

BAMBOO

A species of *takwá* (= bamboo) may be said to symbolize womanhood in Guaraní mythology. In the ritual dance the women beat time with a bamboo rod. The Mbyá sacred name for the human skeleton is *takua-ryva-'i-kâgâ* (= skeleton or bones of her who beat time or led the dance with the bamboo). In the Pâí-Cayuá epic poem recorded by Samaniego,[21] the ritual bamboo is referred to as *kamañy-tî* (= white *kamañy*). This word is not used in contemporary Guaraní dialects, but the *Vocabulário na língua brasílica* lists it as a species of cane, *"caña que tem nos." Takwá* is a sacred or secret name applied to woman by the Mbyá, Pâí-Cayuá, Chiripá and its branch the Apapokuva.[20] More significant still is the fact that the Pâí-Cayuá have a sacred song attributed to Takwá Rendy-jú Guasú (= Big Flaming Eternal Bamboo), who will be referred to below. In the Chiripá myth, the bamboo was brought from the east by *tajasú,* the big wild pig.[6]

MAIZE, TOBACCO AND *TIMBÓ*

Both Schaden[22] and Watson[23] refer to the divine origin of maize. In the Chiripá myth, it was found by Ñanderuvusú in the bamboo growing in a patch of forest which he was clearing for his plantation.[5] Tobacco and the pipe were created by Jakairá, the Mbyá god of spring and patron of medicine men, so that people could protect themselves against evil spirits, enemy sorcerers, and disease. Tobacco smoke is referred to in their texts as *tatachiná rekó achý* (*rekó achý* = mortal or earthly; *tatachiná* = the life-giving mist from which the universe and all living things are believed to proceed).[4]

TIMBÓ

This large liana used for poisoning fish was originally the son of Kuaraý (= Sun), the cultural hero. Whenever he wanted fish to eat, he told his son to wash his feet or take a bath in a stream, this being sufficient to provide him with all the fish he wanted. The son was changed into a *timbó* by Charía, a rival of Kuaraý. A fight between the two rivals developed in which Kuaraý was momentarily overcome, but he eventually won. This battle is re-enacted in the skies whenever an eclipse occurs.[4] Although the idea of plants being the embodiment of human beings is common throughout South America,[15] the story of *timbó* is the only instance of this belief which I have personally found in contemporary Guaraní mythology.

ORIGIN OF PLANTS

After the world had been destroyed by fire, Kuaraý sent the bird Piritaú to see what remained of the earth. Piritaú found a nightshade plant (*Solanum* sp.), called *ka'á eté'í,* among the roots of which the remains of the earth had begun to expand. Piritaú ate the berries of the *ka'á eté'í.* After passing through his body, the seeds sprouted and produced the *kurundi'ý (Trema micrantha).* The seed capsules of the *kurundi'ý* burst, and the seeds fell on the ground and sprouted, producing the *ygary* (the cedar, *Cedrela fissilis*). All sorts of trees and other plants emanated from the seeds of the *ygary* and the earth in due course became fit again for human beings to inhabit.[5]

In the Pâí-Cayuá creation myth, Ñane Ramói caused an infinitesimally small portion of earth (*he'ŷ mbaguáva rapichá* = similar to the wheel of a spindle) to appear and then to expand to become the abode of his future sons.[21] Upon the expanding earth the *para'ýry* (= sea-tree) appeared, each branch and twig of which was a different species of tree, shrub or plant. The only tree which appeared independently was the *yvyrá reakuâ* (= scented tree) or *yvyrá pajé* (= magic tree). The secret or sacred name of this tree is *pira-rý* (= *pirá* tree). This tree is the property of Pa'í Kwará (= Owner of the Sun). At the time of the Conquest, according to the *Vocabulário na língua brasílica,* the morning star was called *pirá panéma.*[10]

Our knowledge of Guayakí mythology is at present rather fragmentary. But it is fairly certain that the Guayakíes believe that a fruit consumed by a woman just before childbirth influences the "nature" or "condition" of her child.[7,8] In Mbyá lore all trees have souls, some of which are good, others bad. The soul of the evil tree wounds people, who then must be cured by the shaman.[4] The Guayakí belief and the Mbyá belief are in all probability somehow related.

SPURGE TREE

Kurupika'ý (Sapium longifolium) is a tree which poses an interesting problem. The literal meaning of the name is *y* (= tree) *ka'a* (= plant), i.e., tree which is the plant of the Kurupí. Bertoni[2] and other authors have established that Kurupí is a Guaraní satyr. Ample evidence of his amorous proclivities may be found in Paraguayan folklore. The satyrs of both Mbyá and Pâí-Cayuá mythology, however, have entirely different names, and there is no connection whatever between them and the *kurupika'ý.* The origin of the name and the evidence from Paraguayan folklore provide ample proof that the tree once "belonged" to an erotic sprite or satyr of some Guaraní-speaking group which inhabited Paraguay. Further information on this subject is given elsewhere.[3,9]

Animal and Plant Worship

ANIMALS AND GODS

Several years ago I ventured an opinion, based on information obtained exclusivly from Mbyá sources, that the name of Ñamandú, the Mbyá creator, was probably derived from *ñe'â* (= to strive after, to pray) and *andú* (= to perceive). Information obtained later obliged me to modify this opinion, offering as the etymology of the word *ñaguá* (= jaguar) with *û* (= black) and *nd* added for euphony.[6] Müller[19] suggested the possibility that the word is derived from *ñandú* (= spider) or *ñandú guasú* (= rhea). Now it appears that *ñaguá* is actually a contraction of *ñe-é haguâ* which means "something to talk about." The name of the Mbyá mother of gods, Jachuká Chy Eté, and the name of the Pâí-Cayuá lifegiving element, Jasuké, are probably of animal origin. The same may be said for the Mbyá god Karaí Ru Eté and the Pâí-Cayuá god Karavié Guasú.

In other words, the names of at least three of the principal Guaraní gods are derived from the names of animals. This conclusion is based on analysis of fieldwork by Nimuendajú,[20] Müller,[19] Schaden,[22] and Samaniego.[21] My contribution is mainly the interpretation of the word *jachuká.* According to my informants, *jachuká* is the Mbyá sacred name of a woman's headdress which formerly was used in the ritual dance. Müller agreed with my deduction that the word is derived from *ta-jachú* (= the big wild pig). It now seems, however, that the headdress is actually the wide part of a tumpline, which is placed on the forehead of the woman carrying an *ajaká* (= basket). Therefore, the true meaning of *che remi-mbojachukavá* (the sacred name of womanhood) must be "they whom I have provided with baskets."[11]

Although much painstaking field work needs to be done, the information thus far presented in this article suffices to show that what might be termed an "animal cult" still exists among the Guayakí Indians and formerly must have been widespread (to a certain extent still persists) among the Guaraní-speaking nations. Therefore, it would not be in the least surprising if the names of some of the principal Guaraní gods were linguistically related to the most feared animal, the jaguar, and the most useful animal, the big wild pig.

We should note that all Guayakí personal names are the names of animals. About 25 per cent of some 1,200 personal names of Guaraní Indians listed in the parochial registers of the Paraguayan missions are the names of animals. Many Guayakí, besides their genuine animal name, have a "familiar" name or nickname that recalls some characteristic of the animal to which they owe their by-kwá (= character or condition). Animal names are still used, to a limited extent, as sacred personal names by the Chiripá Indians.[5,6,16]

There is an intimate connection between this matter of animal cults and a statement by Watson[23] which refers to Guaraní seats: "Small, low wooden benches, carved from a single block of wood, sometimes, if not always, in the shape of animals." Apyká (apý = to sit; ha or ka, the instrument with which to do something), in the religious vocabulary of both the Mbyá and Paí-Cayuá, is the symbol of incarnation. Mbo apyká (= to provide with a seat or to cause the soul to incarnate) means in effect that the creator provides the soul with a seat on earth. Ñe-mbo-apyká means to incarnate, to embody, or to provide oneself with a seat on earth.[4]

In summary then we may state the following principal points of evidence: (a) The names of some of the principal Guaraní gods are probably of animal origin; (b) When the soul of a Guaraní Indian is sent to earth, he is said to take a seat which is sometimes, if not always, in the shape of an animal; (c) All Guayakí personal names are the names of animals; (d) Twenty-five per cent of the Guaraní converts chose for surnames the names of animals; and (e) The Chiripá still use, to a limited extent, the names of animals as sacred personal names.

BIG FLAMING ETERNAL BAMBOO

What has been said regarding plants in Guayakí and Guaraní mythology could be accepted as evidence of a sort of tree cult. I shall conclude this paper with a quotation from a document which, while showing the importance attributed to the plant world by the Guaraní, is at the same time proof of tree worship.

In 1956 General Marcial Samaniego requested my help in the translation of an epic poem which he had obtained from the Pâí-Cayuá Indians. Since at that time I was not conversant with the Pâí-Cayuá dialect, I enlisted the aid of four leaders of that tribe (Juan Bautista Ibarra, José Arce, Agapito López, Pablo Alfonso). Also, I had to analyse a mass of linguistical data before a tolerable translation of the poem could be achieved. Among these data I discovered Takwá Rendy-jú Guasú ñengareté (= the sacred chant of Big Flaming Eternal Bamboo), which originated as follows.

Ñane Ramói Jusú, the creator, accusing his wife of adultery, resolved to abandon her and return to heaven. But before leaving he sent a storm to either frighten or destroy his wife, who was called Ñande Jarí Jusú (= Our Big Grandmother) or Ñande Sy Eté (= Our Genuine Mother) or Takwá Rendy-jú Guasú. To placate her husband she sang a ñengareté (= sacred song) in which she referred to the time

In which the earth was not covered with forests,
in which the gods did not exist,
in which the foundations of the earth had not been laid
in which there were no souls,

implying that for all these blessings Ñane Ramói Jusú was to be thanked.

The following verses are transcribed from the ñengareté of Takwá Rendy-jú Guasú:

Aguyjé ne che Sy Eté arag'é,
o takwá rekýi vy araka'é,
o takwá rekýi gypý vy araka'é . . .

Karavié Guasú upe rañé ngatú
tape rosy katupyrý;

Pa'í Ñamói upe rañé ngatú
tape rosý katupyrý

Ararý Vusú upe rañé ngatú
tape rosý katupyrý;

Tanimbú Guasú upe rañé ngatú,
tape rosý katupyrý;

Japarié Guasú upe rañe ngatú,
tape rosý katupyrý . . .

Perfect must my Genuine Mother have been,
as she flourished her bamboo,
as she flourished her bamboo rod for the first time . . .

To Big Karavié, first, obediently
intone long ritual chants;

To Big Shaman Ñamói, first, obediently
intone long ritual chants;

To Big Ararý, first, obediently
intone long ritual chants;

To Big Tanimbú, first, obediently
intone long ritual chants;

To Big Japarié, first, obediently
intone long ritual chants . . .

Although Karavié, Pa'í Ñamói, and Japarié are, according to my informants, important figures of the Pâí-Cayuá Olympus, their functions have no bearing on the matter under consideration here. But one informant, Pablo Alfonso, speaking of Ararý Vusú and his lieutenant or helper, Tanimbú Guasú, says that

They care for little plants,
they care for plants in their totality,
throughout the whole extent of the earth.[10]

Ararý means "skytree" and is the Guaraní name of Calophyllum brasiliense which grows on Jasy Retá Island near Carmen del Paraná (Itapúa) and in the mountains of Amambay, this latter place being adjacent to the habitat of the Pâí-Cayuá Indians; tanimbú (= ashes) is Terminalia sp. and tanimbú yva (= ash tree) is Machaerium aculeatum.

The ritual chant of Takwá Rendy-jú Guasú, Big Flaming Eternal Bamboo, dictated to me by my Pâí-Cayuá friends, shows that a sui generis tree worship still exists among the sophisticated Guaraní remnants inhabiting eastern Paraguay, and makes patently clear that the language, mythology, and folklore of the Guaraní and Guayakí Indians have not as yet received the attention they deserve from men of science.

Literature Cited

1. Ayrosa, Plinio (Ed.). 1938. Vocabulário na língua brasílica. Bulletin no. 137 of the Faculdade de Filosofia, Ciências e Letras, Univ. of São Paulo. See also Drumond, Carlos. 1952. Etnografia e Tupi-guarani. 2d ed. Bulletin no. 23, Univ. of São Paulo.

2. Bertoni, Moisés S. 1946. Civilización guaraní. Parte II. Religión y moral. Editorial Indoamericana, Buenos Aires.

3. Cadogan, León. 1950. El culto al árbol y a los animales sagrados en la mitología y las tradiciones guaraníes. América Indígena (México) 10 (4): 327-333.

4. Cadogan, León. 1959. Ayvá Rapytá. Textos míticos de los Mbyá-guaraní del Guairá. Faculdade de Filosofia, Ciências e Letras, Univ. de São Paulo Bulletin no. 227.

5. Cadogan, León. 1959. Como interpretan los Chiripá (Ava Guaraní) la danza ritual. Rev. de Antropologia (São Paulo) 7 (2): 65-100.

6. Cadogan, León. 1959. Aporte al estudio de la onomástica guaraní. Bol. de Filología (Instituto de Estudios Superiores, Montevideo) 8 (55-57): 33-58.

7. Cadogan, León. 1960. Algunos textos guayakí del Yñaró. Bol. Soc. Cien. Paraguay 4 (4).

8. Cadogan, León. 1962. Baiô Kará Wachú y otros mitos guayakíes. América Indígena (México) 22 (1): 39-82.

9. Cadogan, León. 1962. Fragmentos del folklore guaireño. Cuadernos del Instituto Nacional de Investigaciones Folklóricas. Ministerio de Educación y Justicia, Dirección General de Cultura, Buenos Aires.

10. Cadogan, León. 1962. Aporte a la etnografia de los Guaraní del Amambái, Alto Ypané. Rev. de Antropologia. (São Paulo) 10 (1,2): 43-91.

11. Cadogan, León. 1962. The urgency of research on the Guayakí and Guaraní. Bul. Internat. Com. on Urgent Anthropol. and Ethnol. Research 5: 155-158.

12. Cadogan, León. 1963. Searching for the origins of *ojeó, jejarú* or *tupichúa.* Unpublished ms.

13. Cadogan, León, and Maxence de Colleville. 1963. Les Indiens guayakí de l'Yñaro (Paraguay). Bul. Fac. Let. Strasbourg 41 (8): 439-458.

14. Haekel, Josef. 1955. Zur Problematik des heiligen Pfahles bei den Indianern Brasiliens. Anais 31st Congr. Internac. Americanistas 1954: 229-243. (Editorial Anhembi, São Paulo).

15. Métraux, Alfred. 1948. Ensayo de mitología comparada americana. América Indígena (México) 8 (1): 9-30.

16. Métraux, Alfred, and Herbert Baldus. 1946. The Guayakí. *In* Steward, Julian H. (Ed.) Handbook of South American Indians. Smithsonian Inst. Bul. 143: 435-444.

17. Michalowski, Michael. 1960. Árboles y arbustos del Paraguay. Servicio Técnico Interamericano de Cooperación Agrícola, Ministerio de Agricultura y Ganadería, Asunción.

18. Montoya, Antonio Ruíz de. 1876. Tesoro de la lengua guaraní. Edición Platzman, Leipzig.

19. Müller, Franz. 1934-35. Beiträge zur Ethnographie der Guarani-Indianer im östlichen Waldgebiet von Paraguay. Anthropos (Wien) 29: 177-208, 441-460, 696-702; 30: 151-164, 433-450, 767-783.

20. Nimuendajú Unkel, Kurt. 1914. Die Sagen von der Erschaffung und Vernichtung der Welt als Grundlagen der Religion der Apapocuva-Guaraní. Z. Ethnologie 46: 284-403. (Trans. by Juan Francisco Recalde, São Paulo, 1944. Mimeographed.)

21. Samaniego, Marcial. 1956. Ñane Ramói Papa ye papa. Asunción. Mimeographed.

22. Schaden, Egon. 1954. Aspectos fundamentais da cultura guarani. Faculdade de Filosofia, Ciências e Letras, Univ. de São Paulo Bul. no. 188.

23. Watson, James B. 1952. Cayuá cultural change. Amer. Anthropologist 54 (2), part 2, memoir 73: 1-144.

24. Zerries, Otto. 1959. Las constelaciones como expresión de la mentalidad cazadora en Sudamérica. Rev. Estudios Americanos (Sevilla) 88-89: 1-18.

Author's address: Mr. León Cadogan
                   Villarrica, Guairá
                   Paraguay

X. Colonization and Agriculture in the Paraguayan Chaco

ROBERT C. UNRUH

The Chaco is a huge outwash plain built up of sediments derived mainly from the eastern Andes flanks. At least locally, sedimentation took place under lacustrine conditions. Due to the arid climate, primary minerals and soluble salts are abundant. . . The heavy-textured sub-soils make the area very susceptible to inundation during the wet season in the summer.

Beek and Bramao*

The Chaco is not very suitable for agriculture, although almost all of the native peoples are familiar, to some degree, at least, with the practice of growing edible plants, much influenced, of course, by Europeans.

Zerries**

Climate

This paper does not refer to the entire Chaco, since the writer has not had opportunity to make observations over the whole area. It is confined, rather, to that part of the Chaco settled and developed by the Mennonites (see Smith and Smith 1950, and Fretz 1953). The settlement is composed of three contiguous colonies located about 280 miles northwest of Asunción. The colonies lie between 22 and 24 degrees latitude and 58 to 61 degrees longitude, and cover an area approximately 78 by 102 miles.

TEMPERATURE

The climate of the area is characterized by extreme variations of temperature and rainfall (see also Chapters 3 and 4). Temperatures of 110 F have been recorded for the summer months (December, January) and a low of 26 F for the winter months (July–September). Perhaps the most disagreeable weather occurs during the winter when strong north winds of 30–40 miles per hour commonly raise the temperatures into the 90 to 100 degree range. Then a strong cold front moves up out of Argentina and the temperature drops as much as 40 degrees in two or three hours. The lowest temperatures of winter are brought in by these cold fronts. But the effects of the cold fronts usually last only four or five days.

RAINFALL

Records kept in the colonies show that the average yearly rainfall for the period 1932–1951 was 31 inches. Most of the rain comes in the months of November through May. There are, however, intermittent periods of drought during the growing season. The drought may last up to two months, followed by a period of a week or two during which 8 to 10 inches of rain may fall. In addition to this, the rate of evaporation is very high. Records kept at the Experimental Farm near Filadelfia in the state of Boquerón show that the relative humidity drops consistently to between 20 and 30 per cent during the day, and at times even goes down to 10 per cent. These conditions necessitate planting immediately after a rain, for experience has shown that in three or four days after a heavy rain the top soil is too dry to insure germination of the seed. This is especially true when the skies are clear and a brisk wind blows, as is often the case. Prevailing winds are from the north and the south, with occasional winds from the northeast and southeast.

SOILS

Soils in this region vary from very light sand in the open areas to heavy silt loams in the forested areas. The light sandy soils were comparatively easy to clear and have therefore been under cultivation since the arrival of the first settlers in 1927. In spite of the fact that the colonists have used no fertilizer of any kind, these soils have remained fairly productive. But because of their light nature and the fact that no effort on the part of the colonists has been made to provide a cover crop for the winter months, there has been a good deal of erosion by the strong north winds. In a few cases, farmers have abandoned fields because they were unable to cope with this problem. Tests show that these soils have become strongly acid (pH 3.5–4.0) and contain very little organic matter. Experiments conducted at the Experimental Farm, using the legumes as green manure, show that the fertility

*Beek, K. J., and D. L. Bramao. 1968. Nature and geography of South American soils. *In* Fittkau, E. J., *et al.* (eds.). Biogeography and ecology in South America. Dr. W. Junk, The Hague. Quoted by permission of the publisher.

**Zerries, O. 1968. The South American Indians and their culture. *In ibid.* Quoted by permission of the publisher.

of such soils can be markedly improved. Hubam clover *(Melilotus alba annua),* an annual white clover, has been found to be very well adapted as a winter cover crop for the Chaco soils.

The forest or "bush" soils, as they are commonly called, were largely neglected until 1954–55. This was due mainly to the difficulty encountered in attempting to clear and work the land, and also because of the common belief that these soils were too heavy to be of much use for farming. This picture has been completely changed in the past ten years due to the following factors: The purchase of bulldozers by the colonies for clearing the land; demonstration by the Experimental Farm of the disc-plow and tractor for initial plowing of cleared land; and introduction of adapted grasses by the Experimental Farm.

Vegetation

The best adapted and most widely accepted of the introduced grasses is Buffel grass *(Pennisetum ciliare)*, with Blue Panic *(Panicum antidotale)* also used but to a lesser extent. Today one sees large areas of land being cleared, and planted to these grasses. This has helped to stimulate interest in dairy farming, and it has also opened new possibilities for the development of beef cattle. While it normally required 3 to 4 years on native pastures to produce a steer weighing 770 to 880 pounds, it is now possible to produce a steer of that weight in only two years on introduced grasses. It is interesting to note that International Products Corporation of Paraguay is going ahead with a plan to clear 7400 acres on their ranch near Puerto Pinasco, basing their decision on the success of land clearing operations in the Mennonite colonies.

The vegatation native to the area is predominantly a thorny scrub forest surrounding comparatively small, open areas of grassland. Settlers say that at the time they came these grasslands contained a good deal of "sweet" grass (that is, palatable to livestock), but today one sees espartillo grass *(Elyonurus adustus)* almost exclusively where grassland still exists. This espartillo grass has a bitter flavor and is grazed by livestock only when they are on the verge of starvation. The pattern of settlement has contributed largely toward the elimination of the native grasses.

OVERGRAZING

Open areas were chosen for settlement because of the relative ease of clearing and preparing the land for cultivation. Settlement was made in villages, the size of the village depending upon the size of the open area of grassland. The number of farms in a village varies from 3 to 48, but the average is closer to 12 farms per village. This concentration of population also brings with it a concentration of livestock, with resultant overgrazing and consequent elimination of palatable grasses.

Another result of this overgrazing has been the invasion of the grasslands by various species of thorny brush, the most important of which are *algarrobo* and *vinal (Prosopis* sp.), and *aromita (Acacia* sp.). These are leguminous plants that produce many seeds each year. These seeds are eaten by livestock and pass through the digestive tract whole, without any effect on germinative properties of the seed. This, of course, scatters the seed effectively and widely with the end result that many areas which were once open grasslands are now completely overgrown by brush. Land clearing followed by seeding to grass can again restore the grassland, but these procedures must be accompanied by good management practices if the land is to remain in grass.

There are indications that at one time there was an abundance of useful legumes in the light, sandy soils of the open grassland. In pastures at the Experimental Farm, where grazing has been controlled, I have noted four different species of legumes that are coming back in. It is my opinion that these could prove a valuable asset to the agriculture of the colonies if they were cultivated and put to proper use.

Crops
COTTON

In the early days of the settlements, the principal cash crop was cotton. The sorghums were grown for grain and a few peanuts provided the family's supply of oil. Because of problems with disease, especially *Fusarium* wilt, and soil fertility, the production of cotton seems to be decreasing. More acres are planted now, but the yield per acre is dropping. It is possible that with the use of disease-resistant varieties of cotton and good land management, this situation might improve; but little effort is now being directed toward this end.

PEANUTS

This crop has become increasingly important for the colonists, and it will continue to be important. The installation of equipment for processing peanuts for oil has done much to promote the production of this crop.

INSECT PESTS

There is apparently an increase in insects destructive to both cotton and peanuts from year to year. This is especially true of the cotton leafworm *(Alabama argillacea)*, cotton aphid *(Aphis gossypii),* red spider mite *(Tetranychus telarious),* and the lesser cornstalk borer *(Elasmopalpus lignosellus).* The indiscriminate use of modern insecticides, which kill all insects—beneficial as well as destructive—has undoubtedly been a contributing factor in the increase of pest insects.

CASTOR BEANS

These have been grown successfully for a number of years but interest is waning due to low prices paid for the seed. There is currently no equipment in the colonies for the processing of this crop.

SORGHUM

At first this crop played only a small part in the agricultural picture of the colonies. The grain was used principally for horse feed. However, with the opening of the Trans-Chaco road in 1962, the opportunity for marketing poultry and poultry products materialized and, since then, production of poultry has increased tremendously. This in turn requires the production of more grain to feed the poultry, thus acreage in sorghum is increasing.

WHEAT

This grain is comparatively new to the colonies. The Experimental Farm, with the help of STICA (Servicio Técnico Interamericano de Cooperación Agrícola), began working with wheat in 1951. However, it was not until 1961 that a large acreage was planted. The acreage has since increased consistently and it now appears that the colonies will be able to produce enough wheat for their own flour consumption in a normal year. Flour milling equipment has been installed by the colonies so that now wheat can be milled locally, and the by-products used as feed for livestock.

Wheat is grown as a winter crop. The present practice is to seed it on land that was used for peanuts the previous summer. It is doubtful that this practice can be continued for any extended length of time due to the resultant decrease in soil fertility, although no significant reduction in yields has been noted thus far. Before wheat was grown, the land lay idle and was allowed to grow up in weeds during the winter months. It is probable that the wheat requires no more moisture or soil minerals than do the weeds, but neither wheat nor weeds are soil builders; so, undoubtedly, the time will come when other management methods will have to be used.

VEGETABLES

The vegetable-growing season in the Chaco is relatively short, April through August. High temperatures and/or lack of moisture prohibit vegetable culture during other months of the year. Early attempts by the settlers to grow vegetables resulted in failure, but the Experimental Farm has successfully demonstrated that with proper ground preparation, fallowing during summer months to conserve moisture, and the use of adapted varieties, vegetables can be successfully grown. Vegetable varieties from southern Texas, Florida, and California are found to be well adapted to the climate of the Chaco.

FRUITS

A number of both fruit and shade trees have been introduced into the colonies. In the early years of the settlement the Carlos Casado Company operated a small agricultural experiment station from which the colonists obtained citrus trees. The citrus fruit produced in the Chaco is excellent, but the trees often suffer from the intermittent drought periods and therefore yields are not consistent from year to year. The date palm *(Phoenix dactylifera)* has been planted by some colonists and yields are good; but expanded plantings have been limited by lack of equipment for processing and packaging the dates for market. Some guava *(Psidium guajava)* trees have been planted, but only enough to produce fruit for jam and jelly for home use. There are some wild fruits that grow in the "bush" and are eaten by the Indians, but no attempt has been made to utilize these.

TREES

The most widely planted shade tree is the chinaberry *(Melia azedarach).* It is used for both shade and lumber, producing a good-sized log in 12 years. This wood is used almost exlusively for the making of furniture. The trees do well when planted in a single row, but attempts at planting in larger woodlots have been unsuccessful because, for some unknown reason, the trees simply do not develop. Thus far the colonists have relied on the lumber that they have been able to get out of the bush. Most of this is quebracho *(Schinopsis* spp.), used for building construction. In certain areas all the good trees have been felled. The time is at hand when reforestation work ought to be begun, but so far no attempt at this has been made.

Literature Cited

Fretz, J. S. 1953. Pilgrims in Paraguay. Herald Press, Scottsdale, Pennsylvania.

Smith, Willard H., and Smith, Verna G. 1950. Paraguayan interlude. Herald Press, Scottsdale, Pennsylvania.

Author's address: Mr. Robert G. Unruh
                   c/o Mennonite Central Committee
                   Casilla de Correo 166
                   Asunción, Paraguay

XI. The People of Paraguay: Origin and Numbers*

GUILLERMO T. BERTONI AND J. RICHARD GORHAM

One of the most serious challenges to human destiny in the last third of this century will be the growth of the population. Whether man's response to that challenge will be a cause for pride or despair in the year 2000 will depend very much on what we do today.

Nixon 1969

The Amerind Population

In view of the incompleteness of archeological information from Paraguay and adjacent portions of Brazil, Argentina and Bolivia, it is pointless at this time to try to make any generalizations about when the first Amerinds arrived in Paraguay.

Very little is presently known about the occupants of Paraguay from the time the first Indians arrived until the time the first Spaniards arrived (Métraux 1963c). During the years 1888 to 1890, Dr. Moisés S. Bertoni worked a site at Yaguarasapá (Alto Paraná), which he called the Altoparanense Culture. The artifacts that he collected are reported to be in the Ethnographic Museum of the Scientific Society of Paraguay. Another ancient site in the Misiones Province of Argentina, just across the Río Alto Paraná from Paraguay, was worked by Menghin (1955–56). Other ancient materials have been recovered from the bottom of Lake Ypacaraí, located 40 kilometers east of Asunción.

The Spanish explorers encountered numerous Indian tribes in Paraguay, most of which are listed in Tables 11.1 and 11.2. Just in their expeditions alone the Spanish accounted for the presence of many thousands of Indian men, including both their Guaraní allies and whichever tribe they happened to be fighting. From this it would not be too generous to describe the Indian population as "abundant" or "numerous." But no one really knows just how many Indians were present in Paraguay in 1500 or, for that matter, how many are present today. One estimate (Steward and Faron 1959) puts the population density of Indians in the year 1500 at 0.5 per square mile for the Paraguayan Chaco (at least the eastern half of it) and 0.7 for eastern Paraguay. Using the present dimensions of these territories, the population would have been 47,669 for the Chaco and 43,265 for eastern Paraguay.

This total of 90,934 falls short of Steward's (1963) estimate of 100,000 in 1500, but, of course, Paraguay was a much bigger country in 1500 than it is today. The 1947 estimate (Steward 1963) of 60,000 Indians in both the Paraguayan Chaco and eastern Paraguay in 1940 is at least grossly in accord with Belaieff's (1963) estimate of 68,000 Indians in the entire Gran Chaco (Paraguayan, Argentine, Bolivian, but excluding all of eastern Paraguay) in 1946. The Indian population of Paraguay was estimated to have been 35,000 in 1962 (Statistical Office of the United Nations 1968).

Discovery and Exploration

A detailed statement of the comings and goings of the Spanish explorers and the intricacies of their politicking in Paraguay is not required here (for information on these points, see Chapter I, and the works of Warren 1949 and Service 1954). It is appropriate, however, to very briefly outline the first faltering steps in the collision course

---

*Before his death in 1963, Professor G. T. Bertoni had indicated to me his intention to use the pertinent parts of his "Geografía Económica Nacional y Comparada de Paraguay y América" (1952) as the basis for this essay on the population of Paraguay. He had already traced the history of population development from pre-Colonial times to the 1950 census. It was my first intention to simply translate the appropriate sections of his "Geografía" and include them in the present volume. However, the "Geografía" was written in a detailed, didactic style for the benefit of university students, a style which turned out to be very lengthy in the English version. Then there was the matter of updating the material to include the 1962 census and more recent statistics. Therefore, I have had to enter the matter much more deeply than I envisioned in 1963. I trust that the resulting essay, being a condensed, revised and updated version of Bertoni's earlier work, will meet the standards that he himself would have applied. Since I cannot speak for Bertoni, I use the first person singular throughout. But in deference to the enormous labor which Bertoni expended in assembling the basic data, the senior authorship of this essay must be his. (J.R.G.)

between the cultures of European and Amerindian in the circum-Plata region.

SOLÍS

Juan Díaz de Solís, during the course of optimistic probings of the South American coast in the year 1516, started things off rather badly by walking blindly into a fatal ambush by the Charrua Indians on the Uruguayan side of the Plata estuary. Having lost their leader and their will to persevere, the remaining members of the Solís expedition set sail for home.

GARCIA

The Solís expedition was not yet done with misfortune. One of the ships foundered near Santa Catarina Island and, while 18 survivors struggled ashore, the other two ships sailed on toward Spain. What happened in the next few years was a sort of preview of events during the next thirty years. The survivors, including a Portuguese sailor named Aleixo Garcia, were well received by the Indians, in this case the Tupinambá. Although there are no specific historical documents to support this assertion, I think it is safe to assume that the mixing of the races—European and Indian—began at this point and continued energetically throughout the Colonial Period in both Brazil and Paraguay. With children sired and a new language acquired, Aleixo Garcia began to understand some of the stories told by the Indians, especially the ones about the white king and the Land of the Grandfather far away to the west.

In 1524 we find Aleixo Garcia about to begin his Bolivian odyssey—his search for the Land of the Grandfather and the vast treasures that were reported to occur there—an odyssey that for Garcia, at least, was cut short on the return trip by the arrows or clubs of the Payaguá near the Río Paraguay.

It might be asked at this time just why were the survivors of the 1516 shipwreck so well treated, and just how did Aleixo Garcia manage to persuade a large contingent of Tupinambá to accompany him to Bolivia, and even to add to his entourage en route a sizable band of Guaraní (some 2,000 Carios) from the Paraguay Valley? The Charruas ate Solís, but the Tupinambá treated Garcia with *chicha,* women and song.

Without wishing to slight in the least the intrepidity of Aleixo Garcia, the answer, I believe, lies entirely with the Indians—their attitudes and beliefs were the controlling factors, not any special attributes on the part of the Europeans. The Indians killed whomever they felt it was propitious to kill. They welcomed in their midst whomever they believed it propitious for them to welcome. They undertook long journeys only when the spiritual elements in their environment indicated that it was propitious for them to do so.

As to the initial welcome of the shipwrecked sailors on Santa Catarina Island, it would appear that the Tupinambá considered the sailors to be some species of messianic messenger and therefore treated them with great respect. Freyre (1966) puts it this way: "The women

were the first to offer themselves to the whites, the more ardent ones going to rub themselves against the legs of these beings whom they supposed to be gods." Other explorers (Columbus, for example) had similar experiences in some other parts of the Americas.

Whatever other reasons they may have had, the Indians had already undertaken extensive migrations in pursuit of the elusive Land of the Grandfather. The Tupinambá had migrated to coastal Brazil, displacing the more primitive inhabitants (Métraux 1963d). Other elements of the Tupi-Guaraní family had occupied central Paraguay, possibly as late as 1400 A.D. The Chiriguano, also members of the Tupi-Guaraní linguistic group, moved from coastal Brazil and from Paraguay across the Chaco to Bolivia in several waves, beginning in 1471, always in search of the Land of the Grandfather (Métraux 1963e). Aleixo García, it appears, was permitted to join the migratory wave of 1521, a wave that carried him to Bolivia and to death (Nordenskiöld 1917).

CABOT

In 1526 Sebastian Cabot ascended the Río de la Plata and eventually entered the Río Alto Paraná. He met bands of friendly Guaraní and traded trinkets for food. Cabot dropped back to the confluence of the Paraná and Paraguay rivers and turned up the latter. A large force of canoe-borne Agaces (= Payaguá) attacked the Cabot party, and were summarily defeated. The Carios, no doubt watching the whole affair from the eastern shore, were apparently much impressed by this victory over the notoriously competent Agaces. The Carios received the Cabot party in a friendly manner. Some of the Carios from this region (corresponding to the environs of present-day Asunción) had probably made the trek to Bolivia with Aleixo Garcia the previous year, so it was not surprising that Cabot found Incan silver in their possession.

AYOLAS

Ten years after Sebastian Cabot departed from the Plate Region, Pedro de Mendoza entered the estuary of La Plata and encamped near the present site of Buenos Aires. The Charrua were on hand, also the Querandí, first with friendly offers of food, but later disastrously hostile to the Spanish intruders. Juan de Ayolas, a member of the Mendoza party, was sent upstream on a foraging-exploratory mission. He traded trinkets for food with the Carios around Asunción Bay.

The next historical incident somehow seems out of place in the context of the otherwise remarkably amicable relations between the Spanish and the Guaraní. It would appear that the Spaniards encountered a pocket of resistance to their intrusions at Lambaré, an important Cario stronghold: Ayolas and company presumably captured Lambaré. With that bit of unpleasantness out of the way, the more normal and peaceful pattern of events reappears, with the Carios presenting six young women to Ayolas as a peace offering. We may assume that the mixing of the races in Paraguay began in earnest at that point, but Ayolas and his companions did not live to see their offspring (if there were any). The Ayolas party was wiped out in 1538 at the end of an otherwise successful expedition across the Chaco to the Land of Incas.

In 1537 Gonzalo de Mendoza and Juan de Salazar de Espinoza (also members of the Pedro de Mendoza expedition) decided to build a fort on the shores of a quiet bay of the Río Paraguay, a site that eventually became the capital of Paraguay. Both wives and supplies were acquired from the Cario population of the region, a pattern that persisted throughout the exploratory period.

IRALA

Domingo de Irala assumed command of Spain's interests in Paraguay in 1539. Asunción became the center of operations for future expeditions to the Inca territories. The Spaniards were largely dependent on the Carios. Even with their muskets and cannon, the Spaniards could scarcely have long resisted attack by the overwhelming numbers of Carios. It is true, of course, that the Carios had been harassed by Chaco tribes, and that Cabot had demonstrated what the Spaniards could do to some very competent warriors. It is difficult nevertheless for me to believe that the Carios accepted the Spaniards only because they would be useful as allies against the Chaco tribes. The Carios had previously held their own against the Chaco tribes without Spanish help. Far from being hard-pressed and in danger of extinction, the Carios were a flourishing group, expanding both in population and territory before the Spaniards arrived.

The Carios accepted the Spaniards on the same terms that the Tupinambá had accepted Aleixo Garcia and company. The Spaniards' great interest in the territories to the west fit in very well with the Carios' own interpretation of their destiny, an interpretation that seemed to draw them, as it had done the Chiriguanos, toward the west. Cario women willingly became the wives and concubines of the Spaniards, and supplied them, as good Cario wives were supposed to do, with all the necessaries of life. Such informal and amicable arrangements became well established during the next 20 years of the exploratory period.

In 1540 Irala sent two Carios on an errand to the Brazilian coast. This mission was successfully completed. Their presence on the coast happened to coincide with the arrival of Alvar Núñez Cabeza de Vaca, newly appointed governor of Paraguay. The governor was guided overland to Asunción by these same two Indians during the years 1541 and 1542. The fact that two Carios could make such a journey indicates that the Carios must have had close linguistic and cultural affinities with many of the Indian groups along the route of their journey, or that they were wonderfully adept at avoiding potential enemies.

The year 1548 was a dismal one for Irala and his fellow conquistadores. Having laboriously reached the Altiplano, Irala learned that the Incan Empire had already been conquered, and that the conquerors were in no mood to share the wealth with any latecomers from Paraguay.

Colonization

An event in 1553 brings out two important points in the history of Spanish-Indian relations. One of these points is that the Portuguese even at this early date were already firmly committed to slavery as their only means of economic survival in the new colony of Brazil (the first African slaves had been taken to Brazil in 1533, according to Kirkpatrick 1967).* Guaraní chiefs from the Guayrá region (near Guairá Falls on the Río Alto Paraná) had complained to Irala about Portuguese-instigated slave raids by the Tupí and had requested his assistance in the defense of their territory and people. In 1553 Irala commanded an expedition which temporarily achieved this end. This brings up the second point, which is that this was the first military operation directed toward preserving the colony, rather than for seeking treasure. In other words, the Spaniards had finally started thinking of themselves as resident colonizers rather than transient treasure-seekers. The end of the exploratory period and the beginning of the colonial period were demarcated by the establishment of the encomienda system in 1556 (see Service 1954 for details of this system).

Language and Culture

Paraguay is well-known for its bilinguality (Spanish and Guaraní), and this feature alone has been the object of considerable interest and study (see Rubin 1968). The remarkable persistence of the aboriginal Indian language in Paraguay naturally leads one to ask what other cultural contributions, if any, were made by the Guaraní? Opinions on this subject have been offered by both Paraguayan and non-Paraguayan scientists, with considerable divergence among the several views.

Some non-Paraguayan opinions are similar only in their extreme position. Service and Service (1954) suggest that the Guaraní language is the only Indian cultural remnant still extant in present-day Paraguay (see Cadogan 1956 for a criticism of this position by a Paraguayan anthropologist). On the other hand, Bilden (1931) believed that in Paraguay "the European element is at best a veneer."

Prof. Bertoni (1952) took a much more moderate and, I believe, much more defensible position on this subject. He believed that, excepting the African influence, the outcome of cultural collision in Paraguay was very similar to that of Brazil, and he cited the work of Freyre (1966) to support this position.

Freyre says next to nothing about Paraguay—his first love is obviously Brazil, and he describes its cultural history with enormous candor. It remains for a Paraguayan scholar (or, failing that, a non-Paraguayan perfectly fluent in Guaraní) to follow Freyre's lead and subject the cultural history of Paraguay to the same sort of analysis that Freyre applied to Brazil. Many of Freyre's comments may be applied wholesale to Paraguay, but when he deals with specific cultural remnants of Indian origin, allowance has to be made for the probable existence of autochthonous variations between the largely Brazilian Tupí

*1538 is the date given by E. B. Barnes, 1970, in A history of Brazil, Columbia University Press, New York.

and the largely Paraguayan Guaraní. In any case, a few of Freyre's comments which appear to be particularly germain to the cultural question are reproduced below (Freyre 1966):

> The lustful inclinations of individuals without family ties and surrounded by Indian women in the nude were to serve powerful reason of State, by rapidly populating the new land with mestizo offspring.
>
> This was wholly physical love, a taste for the flesh and from it resulted offspring whose Christian fathers were at little pains to educate them or bring them up in the European manner, under the wing of the Church.
>
> A society was organized that was Christian in superstructure, with the recently baptized native woman as wife and mother of the family, who in her domestic life and economy made use of many of the traditions, experiences, and utensils of the autochthonous folk.
>
> The native woman must be regarded not merely as the physical basis of the Brazilian family, upon whom, drawing strength from her and multiplying itself, rested the energy of a limited number of European settlers; she must also be considered a worth-while cultural element, at least so far as material culture goes, in the formation of Brazilian society. Thanks to her, Brazilian life was enriched . . . with a number of foods that are still in use today, with drugs and household remedies, with traditions that are bound up with the development of the child, with a set of kitchen utensils, and with processes having to do with tropical hygiene—including the frequent or at least daily bath, which must greatly have scandalized the sixteenth-century European, who was so filthy in his own personal habits.
>
> From the *cunhã*, or Tupí-Guaraní woman, has come the best of our indigenous culture. Personal neatness. Bodily hygiene. Corn. The cashew. *Mingua*, or porridge.
>
> As for the knowledge of seeds and roots and other rudimentary agricultural lore, this was transmitted to the Portuguese not so much by the warrior male as by the Indian woman, who in addition to the household work also labored in the fields.
>
> In the popular dress of rural and suburban Brazilians—the poor who live in huts or native shacks—as in their diet, their intimate life, their domestic arts, and their attitude toward sickness, the dead, new-born children, plants, animals, minerals, the stars, etc., there remains a large trace of fetishistic, of totemistic influence, of the beginnings of astrology, and Amerindian taboos.

Without specifically referring to either Freyre or Bertoni, Ribeiro (1970) in effect sums up their positions by saying that "Only the Paraguayans and, to a lesser extent, the Brazilians of some regions still preserve clearly recognizable cultural and linguistic traits from the indigenous Tupi-Guarani heritage."

INDIAN LABOR

The Crown's attitude toward Paraguay seemed to be one of ambiguous disinterest. The failure of the search for El Dorado in Paraguay had effectively removed that colony from the monarch's list of important things to think about. Yet there were Indians there who could work, so it was only right that they should do so. But the Pope had decided that Indians were human after all, so they really should not be mistreated while they work. And since they were human, it really was necessary to Catholicize them, too. Royal ordinances were duly promulgated to cover all these dreary matters (see Service 1954).

The conquistadores-turned-colonists had very limited options regarding their future. Those few who might have left independent sources of wealth in Spain could have returned to the homeland. For the rest, home was Paraguay. It was subsistence living, with polygyny being the only noteworthy luxury, and that was not enjoyed by every Spaniard. Governors Irala and Cabeza de Vaca both recognized the indispensability of the Indians and both made rules prohibiting their mistreatment (Service 1954). Apparently there were lapses in the enforcement of these rules, accompanied by excesses on the part of some of the Spaniards, situations which led to several uprisings by the Guaraní, the first of which occurred in 1545 (the revolt of 1539 failed in the planning stage).

Before the encomienda system of 1556 was established, colonial life in Paraguay was largely a family affair, with the Indians' loyalty and service rendered through familial channels, the Spaniard being considered sort of a chief or at the very least the head of a household. With the coming of the encomienda, relationships became more impersonal and exploitative and the lives of the Indians much more regimented. By the time the Crown got around to making rules about the conduct of the exploitation, the new Paraguayans had already grown accustomed to doing things pretty much as they pleased. In any case, two sorts of encomiendas evolved in Paraguay—the *originario* and the *mitayo* (Service 1954). The *originario* Indians lived and worked permanently on a Spaniard's land. The *mitayo* Indians lived in their own villages or in towns created by the Spaniards and ruled by the Spanish administrators, but worked a third of a year or more on the estate of a Spaniard. The evolution of agrarian systems in other parts of Spanish America differed in many details from that of Paraguay (Weeks 1947).

POPULATION TRENDS

There were three distinct trends in the population of Paraguay during the colonial period: the numbers of Spaniards dwindled to zero; the number of Indians, especially in the vicinity of Asunción, decreased sharply; and the number of mestizos increased greatly. Although the Spaniards had not been famous for inhibited dispositions, the mestizos, on the whole, were much more willful lot. As would-be encomenderos increased in number, there was heightened competition for the smaller number of available Indians, and each Indian was required to work longer and harder.

SLAVERY

The Portuguese in Brazil had already discovered that the life expectancy of an Indian slave was frustratingly short. Freyre (1966) says it this way:

> If the Indians with such an appearance of good health broke down once they had been incorporated into the

economic system of the colonizer, this was for the reason that the passage from a nomadic to a sedentary way of life, from sporadic to continuous activity, had been too abrupt for them...As a result, the Indian was to prove to be a sorry worker and an indolent one, and the Negro had to be substituted for him.

However, before the Portuguese turned completely to the Negro solution for the problem of a failing source of slaves, they beat the bushes of the backlands in an effort to round up more Indians. Uncounted thousands of Indians were carried to the plantations for sacrifice upon the altar of greed, both personal and national. The infamous mamelukes reached into Guaraní (Paraguayan) territory, especially the Guayrá region, to capture slaves—and expanded Brazil's frontiers in the process. This last fact—and perhaps a possible genuine concern for the welfare of the Indians—stimulated the Crown to action: the Jesuits were ordered to Brazil and Paraguay.

To the Guaraní the Jesuits brought a message of hope for both temporal and eternal salvation. The Indians were to be segregated and protected from further exploitation by the Paraguayans; they were to be organized into an army to defend themselves from attacks by the mamelukes (and at the same time halt Portuguese encroachments on Spanish territory); and they would, of course, be Catholicized. Freyre (1966) describes how the activities of the Jesuits affected Indian culture.

> It was to free him [the Indian] from the tyranny of the plantation that the missionary segregated him in villages, another method, if a less violent and more subtle one, of exterminating the Brazilian native: by preserving him in brine, but not allowing him to preserve his own proper and autonomous life.
>
> . . . the Jesuits wished . . . in the hothouse atmosphere of . . . the Guaraní missions, to make unnatural individuals out of the aborigines, individuals who not only had no bond with the moral traditions of their own culture, but who were, in addition, cut off even from the colonial environment and the social and economic realities and possibilities of that environment.
>
> The attentions of the Brazilian Jesuit were most advantageously directed to the native child. Advantageously from the point of view by which the padre of the Society of Jesus was governed: that of dissolving in the savage, in as short a time as possible, any native value that was in serious conflict with the theology and morality of the Church. The eternal oversimplified criterion of the missionary, who never perceives the enormous risk involved, seeing that he will be incapable of repairing or finding a substitute for all that he destroys.

Jesuit efforts were mainly concentrated among the Guaraní of the Alto Paraná Valley, Indians that had been untouched or only lightly touched by Spanish influence. Some other tribes peripheral to the Guaraní were also contacted, but with much less success. The first mission town was founded in Guayrá region in 1609. By 1700 there were some thirty towns with a combined Indian population on the order of 70,000 to 100,000. Additional population figures for the Jesuit missions are given in Table 11.3.

Quite apart from their altruistic motives and achievements, the Jesuits created a micro-empire of such economic, political, and military significance that it became the envy (and the alleged enemy) of both the Crown and colonists: the Jesuits were expelled from Paraguay in 1767, and their "empire" promptly fell into disarray.

EARLY POPULATION DATA

The influx of Europeans to Paraguay during the period 1537 to 1580 amounted to approximately 2,000 persons, the great majority being of Spanish nationality. The Pedro de Mendoza expedition, which led to the founding of Asunción and the temporary occupation of Buenos Aires, contributed about 1,000 men and at least one woman (Kirkpatrick 1967 comments on the uncertainty of the number). There must have been considerable attrition in that population; with the abandonment of Buenos Aires in 1541 and the transfer of its personnel to Asunción, the colony numbered only about 350 Europeans, including four women. Alonso Cabrera arrived in La Plata with 200 men in 1538. How many of these stayed in Buenos Aires and how many went on to Asunción is not clear; in any case, they were included in the total of 350 in 1541.

The arrival of the Cabeza de Vaca party brought the European population of the colony to 600 in 1542. Survivors of the Diego de Sanabria expedition added a dozen men and seven women in 1552. Small additions to the population were made by the men accompanying Nufrio de Cháves in 1550 and Martín de Orué in 1555. In 1556 Irala assigned encomiendas to 320 Spaniards, and there were 359 voters in the election of 1558.

The last significant European contribution to the population of Paraguay was made by the 500 members of the Juan Ortíz de Zárate expedition of 1571. The population of Spaniards dwindled rapidly thereafter, but the actual figures are few and unreliable. Precise counts of conquistadores did not much concern the early chroniclers of colonial Paraguay. Spanish *encomenderos* numbered approximately 400 in 1574 (López de Velasco 1894), but twenty years later not a single living Spaniard was to be found in the land. Apparently a few more arrived later—Azara (1904) counted 193 in 1785.

INDIAN POPULATION DECLINE

The population of Guaranís also decreased markedly during the early history of the colony. In 1556, 20,000 Indians in the vicinity of Asunción were divided among 320 *encomenderos* (Irala 1939). By 1600, only 3,000 Indians could be found within a radius of 21 miles from Asunción (Métraux 1963c). In view of the great demand for Indian labor, it would not have been unnatural for those Indians unattracted by servitude to seek refuge beyond the reach of the *encomenderos*. Also, in that day and time, a newborn was likely to be a mestizo rather than a full-blooded Indian. The privilege of being fully exploited belonged only to the fullblood Indian (and the occasional Negro).

Exodus of Indians from Asunción and the mestizo

population explosion accounted for some of the decrease in the Indian population. Disease did its part. An estimated 100,000 Indians died in the smallpox epidemic of 1558 or 1560, according to López de Velasco (1894). This same reporter quoted a figure of 400,000 Indians in the vicinity of Asunción in 1574, a figure that seems grossly inflated even if it did include Chaco Indians as well.

On the eastern fringe of Paraguay in the region of Guayrá (now Brazilian territory), thousands of mission Guaraní were killed or captured by the mamelukes during the years 1620 to 1640. Their insecurity was so great that they completely abandoned Guayrá and fled, with their Jesuit leaders, to the safety of southern Paraguay. In 1785 Azara (1904) estimated that there were 33,752 Indians in the Paraguayan Chaco: Guaná (19,000), Mbayá (1,300), Mocoví, Pilagá, and Abipón (13,000), Payaguá (350), and unnamed remnants comprised of 102 souls.

MESTIZOS

From 1557 (or thereabouts) onwards, mestizos came to play ever more important roles in the life of Paraguay. They eventually became superior in both influence and numbers in Paraguayan affairs. The Crown's disinterest had spawned a spirit of self-reliance and independence in the new Paraguayans that, only 274 years after the founding of Asunción, found its best expression in the establishment of Latin America's first republic.

The most significant type of miscegenation in Paraguay was the European (mainly Spanish) male with the Guaraní female, the offspring being called mestizo. The cross between European female and Indian male must have been very rare, if indeed it occurred at all. After the production of the first generation of mestizos, then crosses of mestizo with mestizo and mestizo with Indian (especially mestizo male with Indian female) accounted for more offspring than any other combination.

Several other combinations were possible, but probably not very important in the formation of the Paraguayan "race": castizo (white male + mestizo female), octavón (white male + castizo female), pachuela (white male + octavón female) (Warren 1949). Criollos (born in America of European parentage) were scarce in Paraguay. The term criollo or creole was (and still is) variously used. In Brazil it meant a Negro slave born in America. Azara (1904) had a category in his census called Indian creoles, by which he apparently meant the offspring of mestizos and Indians (another cateogry was Spanish Americans, the product of European + Indian) (Table 11.4).

NEGROES

The Negro population of Paraguay never constituted more than a small fraction of the total. In contrast to Brazil, where miscegenation of white and Negro was so significant for the future of that country, the results of unions between whites and Negroes contributed very little to the national character. The most probable combinations were white and Negro yielding mulatto, and Indian and Negro yielding zambo. Mestizo-Negro and mestizo-mulatto crosses must have occurred as well.

The disadvantages and deficiencies of Indian labor caused colonial officials in Asunción to ask the Crown for permission to import Negro slaves (Service 1954). How these requests were answered, I do not know, but for one reason or another Negroes did find their way to Paraguay. There was an estimate of 6,667 mulattoes and free Negroes in Paraguay in 1740 (Warren 1949). Some of these settled in Emboscada (Cordillera) where they worked as farmers and quarriers.[1] (Even today, Emboscadans have a distinct melanistic cast to the complexion.) Azara (1904) counted 10,469 Negroes and mulattoes in 1785, all of whom were eventually absorbed into the mestizo population. Slavery persisted to a limited extent in Paraguay until 1869 when the Triumvirate decreed the abolition of slavery) (Warren 1970, personal communication).

RACIAL INTEGRATION

The mixing of the races in Paraguay did not occur uniformly either geographically or temporally, but happened in two distinct phases (Bertoni 1952). The first phase of miscegenation took place during the years 1537 to 1803 and was largely limited to the non-mitayo towns in Azara's census list (Table 11.5). During this first century and a half, in addition to the 44 towns just mentioned, the rest of the population of Paraguay was composed of scattered wild Indians, mission Indians in towns, and mitayo Indians in towns. Both the mission and the mitayo Indians were more or less protected from contact with Spaniards and Paraguayan mestizos. These populations therefore entered into the mixing of the races in only a very limited way.

When the Jesuits were expelled from Paraguay in 1767, some of the mission towns became mitayo towns and their isolation from the "other Paraguay" continued. The abolishment of the encomienda system in 1803 ushered in a period of national integration and internal migration which was fairly complete by the time the Triple Alliance War began in 1865. That this was a largely national and internal affair, rather than an international one, was due to the fact that the dictator Francia sealed the borders of the country from 1816 to 1840. In this second phase of miscegenation the major crosses were mestizo with Indian and mestizo with mestizo. A population (often referred to as the Paraguayan "race" or "nationality") thus evolved that was genetically more Indian than Spanish, and culturally more Spanish than Indian.

Population Growth and Distribution

The census of 1962 was the most accurate one yet done in Paraguay. Previous censuses (see Table 11.6) were deficient in both procedure and accuracy; in a few cases the population figures were deliberately inflated in a misguided effort to make them more impressive. The population has steadily increased since 1785, with the notable exception of the period associated with the War of the

---

[1] "Un gobernador que en 1740 se vió muy acosado de los indios albayas, sacó del amparo a muchos negros y mulatos; y libertándolos del tributo, fundo con ellos el pueblo de la Emboscada, obligándoles a hacer el ejercicio militar que no habían entonces" (Azara 1847).

Triple Alliance. Paraguay lost some 330,000 citizens in the few short years of that war.

Intercensal population growth has been variable rather than steady. The first half of the present century was characterized by a slow-down of natural population growth. The Chaco War contributed to this, but the main causes were chronic political instability, civil wars, and mass emigration for political reasons.

HIGH-DENSITY AREAS

Ever since the conquistadores chose to build a fort on the site of present-day Asunción, the population of Paraguay has clustered around the capital city. As a result, Paraguay is very unevenly populated (Table 2.1). Some areas, of course, are simply not suitable for agriculture, which always has been and still is the major industry of Paraguay. But a more direct cause of this tendency to cluster in one area, while good land in other areas goes begging, is an underlying tradition which tends to keep successive generations tied to ancestral lands. These lands are divided and subdivided as subsequent generations of inheritors come along, until profitable farming becomes impossible on such small pieces of land, a situation called minifundial agriculture. The owner of one of these "microfarms" usually has only two alternatives: subsistence living on the farm, or retreat to the big city (usually Asunción).

The provinces *(departamentos)* of greatest population density are Central, Paraguarí and Cordillera. Those parts of Guairá and Caazapá adjacent to the main highways and the railroad also fit in this category (Table 11.7). In some cases the size of the overpopulated area is smaller than the area of the province; this is because those portions of the province that are unsuitable for agriculture (extensive stands of forest, and the marshy bottom-lands of Caañabé Creek and Lake Ypoá) were deducted from the total. This overpopulated region then comprises only 4.5% of the total area of Paraguay, or 11.5% of the area of eastern Paraguay, but contains 60% of the population.

MINIFUNDIA

This region demonstrates what is meant by minifundia: 2.8 hectares per person or 14 hectares per family. In Paraguay 20 hectares is considered the absolute minimum size for a one-family farm to make just a small profit; 25–30 hectares is much better, permitting better management and surer profits. Smith (1967) believes that the creation of one-family farms, with ready credit to support mechanization, operated by middle class farmers, should be a major goal of agricultural development programs in South America.

The STICA (Servicio Técnico Interamericano de Cooperación Agrícola) census of 1942–1944 recorded 94,498 farms in Paraguay. Average farm size was 16.4 hectares. There were 1,185 farms of 50–100 hectares, 1,215 farms of 100–1,000 hectares, and 154 farms of more than 1,000 hectares. Considering for the moment only those farms located in the overpopulated regions listed in Table 11.7, and only those of less than 100 hectares, the STICA census showed that 75% of the farms were 7 hectares or smaller (Table 11.9). The situation has scarcely improved; in 1960, 86% of the farms were less than 20 hectares (Table 11.9).

LOW-DENSITY AREAS

Several regions of Paraguay may be described as underpopulated, that is, having already a considerable population but capable of supporting a larger one. This category is apt for the states of Concepción, Itapúa, Misiones, and Ñeembucú, and parts of San Pedro (especially the districts San Pedro, Nueva Germania, Rosario, Itacurubí del Rosario, and parts of San Estanislao), Caaguazú (districts of Coronel Oviedo, San José, Carayaó, Dr. Cecilio Báez, San Joaquín), and Caazapá (districts of Caazapá in part, Yuty, San Juan Nepomuceno, Yegros, Maciel) (see Table 2.1 for population densities in these provinces).

There are still large uninhabited areas and regions only sparsely populated. The Paraguayan Chaco has the lowest population density of any region of Paraguay (Table 2.1). In eastern Paraguay, especially in the heavily forested highlands, the population is very small: the states of Alto Paraná and Amambay, parts of Caaguazú (especially Yhú, Curuguaty, Igatimí, and Ypejhú), Caazapá (especially Dr. Moisés S. Bertoni and Tabaí) and San Pedro (especially Nueva Germania in part, San Estanislao in part, and Tacuatí) (Table 2.1).

The Chaco will probably never support a dense population on a self-sufficient basis on account of its peculiar physical characteristics, but those areas of eastern Paraguay just mentioned are capable of supporting much larger populations, but at the cost, at the very least, of extensive deforestation, a price that may be too high to pay (Sternberg 1969). In any case, the government of Paraguay is actively encouraging agricultural settlements in some of these areas (see Pincus 1968 for a detailed history of land use in Paraguay).

AGRICULTURE

The predominance of agriculture in Paraguayan life is borne out in the census data of 1962. Among those persons included in the "economically active" category (52.5% of the population 12 years of age and older), 54.7% were employed in agricultural pursuits (including farming, ranching, lumbering, hunting and fishing). Paraguay has a larger percentage (46.8 in 1962) of self-employed persons than any other American nation. This high percentage is explained by the fact that 62.2% (Instituto Interamericano de Estadística 1959–60) of those persons engaged in agriculture, forestry, hunting and fishing are self-employed, mostly as farmers of small plots.

Comparative Demography

Population and vital statistics data of Paraguay are compared with those of neighboring states, Latin America in general, and major world regions in Table 11.10. The population of Paraguay in 1950 and 1962 is grouped by age and sex in Table 11.11, and by age, sex, and rural or urban location in Table 11.12.

MARITAL STATUS

Some statistics relating to marital status were gathered during 1950 and 1962 (Table 11.13). The data indicate that there is a higher percentage of never-married persons in Asunción than in the interior, and conversely, a higher percentage of married persons in the interior than in Asunción. This is probably a reflection of a trend that began about 1940, namely that increasing numbers of young, never-married persons have given up the rural life for the presumably greater opportunities of the capital city. Many of the young men who come to Asunción as military conscripts choose to remain there when their tour of duty is over. Consensual union is common and widely practiced in Paraguay (23.7% of the marriages are of this kind), as it is in other Latin American countries (e.g., Haiti, 38.9%; Guatemala, 40.9%; El Salvador, 25.2%).

IMMIGRATION

Like neighboring Brazil and Argentina, Paraguay has been selected as the "promised land" by several organized groups from various parts of the world. In isolated Paraguay they have had the opportunity to work out their own peculiar destinies as a demonstration of the validity of the political, social, religious, or racial foundation upon which they chose to build a new life, uninhibited (or at least tolerated) by the host government (for example, see Fretz 1962, Hack 1958, Souter 1968, and Stewart 1967). Many individuals and families have immigrated to Paraguay (Table 11.14).

MIGRATION

The population of interior Paraguay, that is, excluding Asunción and Central province, was 1,212,818 in 1950. This figure, however, included the interior cities and towns as well as the rural areas. The actual rural population in 1950 was 868,726. Six years later the Agricultural Census recorded a rural population of 884,000. The fact that this was such a small increase may be accounted for in two ways: attrition of the rural population due to emigration (mainly for political reasons) and migration to the cities; and, the 1950 census used a much broader definition of "rural," while the 1956 census counted only those who were distinctly rural in habitation and occupation. The 1962 census brought to light the great differences in growth rates between urban and rural populations. For urban populations the intercensal increase was 215%; during the same period rural populations increased 4% (Table 11.12).

EMIGRATION

Besides being a major buyer of Paraguayan products, Argentina has been a market for excess Paraguayan labor and a haven for political exiles. Rivarola (1967) has tabulated the records of movement from Paraguay to Argentina, and has associated surges of emigration with unemployment and political strife (Table 11.15).

LIFE EXPECTANCY

Life expectancy at birth has increased steadily during the last 75 years in Paraguay and each of her neighboring states (Table 11.16). This statistic has interesting and useful correlations with many other biostatical and economic indicators (Anon. 1964). Sauvy (1963) has graphically illustrated the striking correlation between life expectancy and per capita income (1959 data). Argentina, with 5.4 times the per capita income of Paraguay, had an additional decade of life expectancy. Bolivia, with 7/10 the per capita income of Paraguay, lagged behind Paraguay by about 10 years in life expectancy. The correlation does not hold so well for Brazil: life expectancy was the same as that of Paraguay, but per capita income was 2.7 times greater, according to Sauvy's (1963) graph. In general, literacy levels appear to be directly proportional to levels of per capita income (Table 11.17).

BIRTH RATES

Cho (1964) included Paraguay and its neighbors in his estimates of fertility (Table 11.18). The basic figures required for calculating the crude birth rate are published from time to time by the Paraguayan government (e.g., Dirección General de Estadística y Censos 1969). These figures may be accurate, but they are also inadequate in that they reflect only registered births. Calculations based on the published statistics produce values that are too small (see Table 11.17). The crude birth rate based on registered births is about 24.6; a rate of 45 is much closer to reality (Vidal 1969).

EXPLOSIVE GROWTH

All indications are that the Paraguayan population has great potential for continued explosive growth (Tables 11.19 and 11.20). It might be argued that such growth is in fact healthy in a country with a population density of 4.5 persons per square kilometer and vast uninhabited or sparsely inhabited territories. This argument, however, is vitiated by facts. The vastness of vacant lands is more relative than real. The adjacent state of Mato Grosso, Brazil, is, for example, three times bigger than the entire country of Paraguay. In short, Paraguay's horizons are finite. Some areas of Paraguay simply cannot support dense populations; forcing these regions to accept many more people will result in radical and unfavorable alterations of their ecosystems, leading to soil impoverishment or demineralization (Schwabe 1969), soil erosion, deforestation (Sternberg 1969), and interference with hydrologic systems (especially ground water and evapotranspiration).

The impact, in terms of sheer numbers, of Paraguay's population on the population of Latin America is not proportionate to the impact of Latin America's population on world population (Table 11.21). Paraguay still enjoys a comparatively small population, and there is still some room for population expansion.

DEMOGRAPHIC TRANSITION

Another advantage apparent in Paraguay's present situation concerns demographic transition. Of the several South American countries for which estimates of demographic transition are available (Bogue 1969), only Argentina (84.3%) and Chile (55.4%) (and probably also Uruguay) have completed more of the process of demographic transition than Paraguay (43.6%) (Table 11.18).

The casually and easily achieved portion of demographic transition in Paraguay is past. It is very unlikely that any further progress will be achieved by chance alone. It is very likely that further progress in demographic transition can be made when fertility control becomes a national goal, pursued with vigor by the leadership of Paraguay and its individual citizens. Since public education must play a significant role in any progress in the achievement of fertility control, the current level of support for education (about 15% of the national budget) (see Table 11.17) seems inadequate (Carleton 1967, Stycos 1967, Dandekar 1967).

OPTIONS

A continued annual growth rate of 3.5% and a population doubling time of 20 years will drastically alter the present situation. The social and economic changes and the governmental responsibilities associated with rapid population growth have been forcefully presented by many authors (e.g., Jones 1962, Dedrick 1965, Urquidi 1967, Bogue 1969, Borgstrom 1969, Olivos 1969, Ehrlich 1970). The enormous advantages of slowing population growth are well-known and predictable (Enke 1969, 1970). The means of slowing population growth are numerous, slow, and only partially effective (Davis 1967). The application of these means for slowing population growth must have highest national and personal priority if any success is to be achieved. Paraguay now faces the choice of capitalizing on its present advantages by slowing and eventually stabilizing population growth or joining the growing list of nations that are proving that overpopulation means poverty at best.

Paraguayan Demography

Paraguay, as a member of the Latin American and the world communities, is mentioned incidentally in numerous works that deal with general demography and specific subtopics thereof (Arriaga 1968, Bogue 1969, Carleton 1968, 1969, Dedrick 1965, Dunn et al. 1945, Durand 1967, Elizaga 1969a, Miró 1964, 1969, Mortara 1964a, 1964b, Sauvy 1963, Smith 1960, 1964, 1967, Stolnitz 1967).

General and regional economic or economic-demographic studies also often mention Paraguay (Anon. 1964, Benko 1967, Brown 1966, Chackiel 1969, Elizaga 1969b, Gaslonde 1969, Olivos 1969, Urquidi 1967, van den Boomen 1967).

Paraguayan demographic data are represented in collections of statistical facts (e.g., Departamento de Asuntos Sociales n.d., Instituto Interamericano de Estadística 1959-60, 1967-68, 1970, Inter-American Statistical Institute 1969, Population Branch, Bureau of Social Affairs 1955, Roberts 1968, Statistical Office of the United Nations 1968).

Demographic activity relating directly to Paraguay has consisted mainly of collecting and reporting census figures (Dirección General de Estadística y Censos n.d., 1964, 1966, 1968, 1969). Pincus (1968) and Warren (1946) included much demographic information in their detailed studies of the economy of Paraguay. Vidal (1969) computed population projections for 5-year intervals between 1969 and 2000. The recent series of studies sponsored by the Paraguayan Center for Sociological Studies (Kostianovsky 1970, Mendoza 1970, Rivarola 1967, 1970, Rivarola and Heisecke 1970) indicate an awakening of interest in Paraguayan demography by Paraguayan scientists.

This chapter on the population of Paraguay is not intended to be a thorough demography of Paraguay; such a study would require demographic capabilities far exceeding mine. My hopes are that this cursory treatment (1) will show that considerable demographic data are available, and that it (2) will encourage competent demographers to undertake thorough studies of all aspects of this fascinating population.

Bibliography

Anderson, W. H. 1966. World population. Prospects and problems. Chamber of Commerce of the United States, Washington, D.C.

Anonymous. 1964. The economic development of Latin America in the post-war period. United Nations, New York.

Arriaga, E. E. 1968. New life tables for Latin American populations in the nineteenth and twentieth centuries. Institute of International Studies, University of California, Berkeley.

Azara, F. de. 1847. Descripción e historia del Paraguay y del Río de la Plata. Sanchiz, Madrid.

Azara, F. de. 1904. Geografía física y esférica de las provincias del Paraguay y misiones guaraníes. Anales del Museo Nacional, Montevideo.

Belaieff, J. 1963. The present-day Indians of the Gran Chaco. In Steward, J. H. (Ed.). Handbook of South American Indians. Vol. 1. The marginal tribes. Cooper Square, New York. Reprint of 1946 edition.

Benko, F. 1967. Economic progress, investment and population growth in the developing countries. In (see Carleton 1967).

Benítez, M. 1901. El Paraguay. Estudio comparativo de su población. Imprenta "El País," Asunción.

Bertoni, G. T. 1952. Geografía económica nacional y comparada de Paraguay y América. Editorial Cultura Guaraní, Asunción.

Bilden, R. 1931. Race relations in Latin America with special reference to the development of indigenous culture. Institute of Public Affairs, University of Virginia, Charlottesville.

Bogue, D. J. 1969. Principles of demography. Wiley, New York.

Borgstrom, G. 1969. Too many. A study of the earth's biological limitations. Macmillan, London.

Bourgade La Dardye, E. de. 1892. Paraguay: The land and the people, natural wealth and commercial capabilities. Philip, London.

Brown, R. T. 1966. Transport and the economic integration of South America. Brookings Institution, Washington, D. C.

Cadogan, L. 1956. Breves consideraciones sobre algunos aspectos del folklore paraguayo. Rev. Antropol. (São Paulo) 4 (1): 63-66.

Campos, D. 1888. De Tarija a la Asunción. Expedición boliviana de 1883. Peuser, Buenos Aires.

Carleton, R. O. 1967. The effect of educational improvement on fertility trends in Latin America. In Department of Economic and Social Affairs. Proceedings of the World Population Conference. Vol. 4. Selected papers and summaries: Migration, urbanization, economic development. United Nations, New York.

Carleton, R. O. 1968. Crecimiento de la población y fecundidad diferencial en América Latina. Centro Latinoamericano de Demografía, Santiago, Chile.

Carleton, R. O. 1969. Aspectos demográficos de la infancia y de la juventud en América Latina. Centro Latinoamericano de Demografía, Santiago, Chile.

Carrasco, G. 1905. La población del Paraguay antes y después de la guerra. H. Kraus, Asunción. Originally published in *La Nación* of Buenos Aires.

Carroll, T. F. 1961. The land reform issue in Latin America. *In* Hirschman, A. O. (Ed.). Latin American issues. Twentieth Century Fund, New York.

Chackiel, J. 1969. América Latina: Participación de la actividad económica por sexo y grupos de edades, 1960. Centro Latinoamericano de Demografía, Santiago, Chile.

Cho, L. J. 1964. Estimated refined measures of fertility for all major countries of the world. Demography 1: 359-374.

Dandekar, K. 1967. Effect of education on fertility. *In* (see Carleton 1967).

Davis, K. 1967. Population policy: Will current programs succeed? Science 158 (10 Nov.): 730-739.

Dedrick, C. L. 1965. 600 million Latin Americans in the year 2000? *In* Moran, W. E. (Ed.). Population growth—threat to peace? Kenedy, New York.

Departamento de Asuntos Sociales. n.d. Datos básicos de población en América Latina. Unión Panamericana, Washington, D.C.

Dirección General de Estadística y Censos. n.d. Anuario estadístico de la República del Paraguay, 1954-1959. Ministerio de Hacienda, Asunción.

Dirección General de Estadística y Censos. 1964. Población, educación, bio-estadística, inmigración. Bol. Estad. Paraguay 7 (19/21): 15-42.

Dirección General de Estadística y Censos. 1966. Censo de población y vivienda 1962. Ministerio de Hacienda, Asunción.

Dirección General de Estadística y Censos. 1969. Anuario estadístico del Paraguay 1960-1965. Ministerio de Hacienda, Asunción.

Dirección General de Estadística y Censos. 1969. Demografía. Ministerio de Hacienda, Asunción.

Du Graty, A. 1865. La République du Paraguay. Librairie Européenne de C. Muquardt, Brussels.

Dunn, H. L., H. T. Eldridge, and N. P. Powell. 1945. Demographic status of South America. Ann. Amer. Acad. Polit. Soc. Sci. 237: 22-33.

Durand, J. D. 1967. World population estimates, 1750-2000. *In* Department of Economic and Social Affairs. Proceedings of the World Population Conference. Vol. 2. Selected papers and summaries: Fertility, family planning, mortality. United Nations, New York.

Ehrlich, P. R. 1970. Ecology and the war on hunger. War on Hunger 4 (12): 1-3, 18.

Elizaga, J. C. 1969a. Población económicamente activa. Centro Latinoamericano de Demografía, Santiago, Chile.

Elizaga, J. C. 1969b. Urban-rural pattern of population distribution in Latin America. Centro Latinoamericano de Demografía, Santiago, Chile.

Enke, S. 1969. Birth control for economic development. Science 164 (16 May): 798-802.

Enke, S. 1970. Economic benefits of slowing population growth. War on Hunger 4 (3): 12-17.

Fretz, J. W. 1962. Immigrant group settlements in Paraguay. Bethel College, North Newton, Kansas.

Freyre, G. 1966. The masters and the slaves. A study in the development of Brazilian civilization. Knopf, New York. 2nd English-language edition, revised. Quoted by permission of the publisher.

Gaslonde, S. 1969. El crecimiento de la población y sus repercusiones sobre el desarrollo social, económico y cultural. Centro Latinoamericano de Demografía, Santiago, Chile.

Hack, H. 1959. Primavera, a communal settlement of immigrants in Paraguay. Department of Cultural and Physical Anthropology, Royal Tropical Institute, Amsterdam.

Hernández, P. 1913. Organización social de las doctrinas guaraníes de la Compañía de Jesús. Gili, Barcelona.

Instituto Interamericano de Estadística. 1950-1960. La estructura demográfica de las naciones americanas. Unión Panamericana, Washington, D.C.

Instituto Interamericano de Estadística. 1967-1968. América en cifras 1967. Unión Panamericana, Washington, D.C.

Instituto Interamericano de Estadística. 1970. América en cifras 1970. Unión Panamericana, Washington, D.C.

Inter-American Statistical Institute. 1969. Statistical compendium of the Americas 1969. Pan American Union, Washington, D.C.

Irala, D. de. 1939. Relación breve con parecer de Domingo de Irala, Gobernador de la provincia del Río de la Plata, por su Majestad para el ilustrísimo señor Marqués de Mondejar de Consejo de las Indias (abril de 1556). *In* (see Lafuente Machain 1939).

Jones, J. M. 1962. Does overpopulation mean poverty? Center for Economic Growth, Washington, D.C.

Kirkpatrick, F. A. 1967. The Spanish conquistadores. Black, London.

Kostianovsky, O. M. de. 1970. Historia y evolución de la población en el Paraguay. *In* (see Rivarola and Heisecke 1970).

Lafuente Machain, R. de. 1939. El Gobernador Domingo Martínez de Irala. Bernabé, Buenos Aires.

López de Velasco, J. 1894. Geografía y descripción universal de las Indias. Fortanet, Madrid.

Lowrie, R. H. 1963. The southern Cayapó. *In* (see Belaieff 1963).

Mason, J. A. 1963. The languages of South American Indians. *In* Steward, J. H. (Ed.). Handbook of South American Indians. Vol. 6. Physical anthropology, linguistics and cultural geography of South American Indians. Cooper Square, New York. Reprint of 1950 edition.

Mayntzhusen, F. C. 1924-1926. Guayaki-Forschungen. Zeit. Ethnol. 57: 315-318.

Mendoza A., R. 1970. Desarrollo y evolución de la población paraguaya. *In* (see Rivarola and Heisecke 1970).

Menghin, O. F. A. 1955-1956. El Altoparanaense. Revista Ampurias 17-18: 171-200.

Métraux, A. 1963a. Ethnography of the Chaco. *In* (see Belaieff 1963).

Métraux, A. 1963b. The Caingang. *In* (see Belaieff 1963).

Métraux, A. 1963c. The Guaraní. *In* (see Belaieff 1963).

Métraux, A. 1963d. The Tupinambá. *In* Steward, J. H. (Ed.). Handbook of South American Indians. Vol. 3. The tropical forest tribes. Cooper Square, New York. Reprint of 1948 edition.

Métraux, A. 1963e. Tribes of the eastern slopes of the Bolivian Andes. *In* (see Métraux 1963d).

Métraux, A. 1963f. Tribes of eastern Bolivia and the Madeira headwaters. *In* (see Métraux 1963d).

Métraux, A., and H. Baldus. 1963. The Guayakí. *In* (see Belaieff 1963).

Miró, C. A. 1964. The population of Latin America. Demography, 1: 15–41.

Miró, C. A. 1969. The influence of population changes in Latin America. Centro Latinoamericano de Demografía, Santiago, Chile.

Mortara, G. 1964a. Appraisal of census data for Latin America. Milbank Mem. Fund. Quar. 42 (2, part 2): 57–85.

Mortara, G. 1964b. Characteristics of the demographic structure of the American countries. Pan American Union, Washington, D.C.

Nixon, R. 1969. The population challenge. War on Hunger 3 (9): 2–3.

Nordenskiöld, E. 1912. Les Indiens du Chaco. Rev. Géog. 6: 1–278. Also published as Indianerleben. El Gran Chaco (Südamerika). Bonnier, Leipzig.

Nordenskiöld, E. 1917. The Guaraní invasion of the Inca Empire in the sixteenth century: An historical Indian migration. Geog. Rev. 4: 103–121.

Olivos, L. 1969. 2000: A no-space odyssey. Américas 21 (8): 15–21.

Pincus, J. 1968. The economy of Paraguay. Praeger, New York.

Population Branch, Bureau of Social Affairs. 1955. The population of South America 1950–1980. Report 2. Future population estimates by sex and age. United Nations. New York.

Ribeiro, D. 1970. The cultural-historical configurations of the American peoples. Cur. Anthropol. 11 (4–5): 403–434.

Rivarola, D. M. 1967. Migración paraguaya. Centro Paraguayo de Estudios Sociológicos, Asunción.

Rivarola, D. M. 1970. Factores histórico-sociales en la evolución de la población en el Paraguay. In (see Rivarola and Heisecke 1970).

Rivarola, D. M., and G. Heisecke. (Eds.). 1970. Población, urbanización y recursos humanos en el Paraguay. Centro Paraguayo de Estudios Sociológicos, Asunción. 2nd ed.

Roberts, C. P. (Ed.). 1968. Statistical abstract of Latin America 1967. Latin American Center, University of California, Los Angeles.

Rubin, J. 1968. National bilingualism in Paraguay. Mouton, The Hague.

Samoza, J., and L. Llano. 1968. Bolivia: Proyección de la población. Centro Latinoamericano de Demografía, Santiago, Chile.

Sauvy, A. 1963. La population des pays d'Amérique Latine. Population 18 (1): 49–64.

Schwabe, G. H. 1969. Towards an ecological characterisation of the South American continent. In Fittkau, E. J., J. Illies, H. Klinge, G. H. Schwabe, and H. Sioli. (Eds.). Biogeography and ecology in South America. Vol. 1. Dr. W. Junk, The Hague.

Service, E. R. 1954. Spanish-Guaraní relations in early colonial Paraguay. University of Michigan Press, Ann Arbor.

Service, E. R., and H. S. Service. 1954. Tobatí: Paraguayan town. University of Chicago Press, Chicago.

Smith, T. L. 1960. Latin American population studies. University of Florida Press, Gainesville.

Smith, T. L. 1964. The population of Latin America. In Freedman, R. (Ed.). Population: The vital revolution. Doubleday, Garden City, New York.

Smith, T. L. 1967. The process of rural development in Latin America. University of Florida Press, Gainesville.

Souter, G. 1968. A peculiar people. The Australians in Paraguay. Angus and Robertson, Sydney.

Statistical Office of the United Nations. 1968. Statistical yearbook 1967. Publishing Service, United Nations, New York.

Sternberg, H. O. 1969. Man and environmental change in South America. In (see Schwabe 1969).

Steward, J. H. 1963. The native population of South America. In Steward, J. H. (Ed.). Handbook of South American Indians. Vol. 5. The comparative ethnology of South American Indians. Cooper Square, New York. Reprint of 1949 edition.

Steward, J. H., and L. C. Faron. 1959. Native peoples of South America. McGraw-Hill, New York.

Stewart, N. R. 1967. Japanese colonization in eastern Paraguay. National Academy of Sciences, National Research Council, Washington, D.C.

Stolnitz, G. 1967. Recent mortality declines in Latin America, Asia and Africa: review and some perspectives. In (see Durand 1967).

Stycos, J. M. 1967. Education and fertility in Puerto Rico. In (see Carleton 1967).

Susnik, B. 1964. El Guaraní en la vida socio-económica colonial. Rev. Paraguaya Soc. 1 (1): 30–48.

Susnik, B. 1965. El indio colonial del Paraguay. Vol. 1. El Guaraní colonial. Museo Etnográfico "Andrés Barbero," Asunción.

Susnik, B. 1966. El indio colonial del Paraguay. Vol. 2. Los trece pueblos guaraníes de las Misiones (1767–1803). Museo Etnográfico "Andrés Barbero," Asunción.

Susnik, B. 1968. Chiriguanos. Dimensiones etnosociales. Museo Etnográfico "Andrés Barbero," Asunción.

Urquidi, V. L. 1967. Population growth and economic development in Latin America. In (see Carleton 1967).

Van den Boomen, J. 1967. Population and labour force growth in selected Latin American countries. In (see Carleton 1967).

Vidal, L. J. 1969. Paraguay: Proyección de la población, por sexo y grupos de edades, 1960–2000. Centro Latinoamericano de Demografía, Santiago, Chile.

Warren, C. A. 1946. Paraguay. Emancipación económica americana. Ceibo, Montevideo.

Warren, H. G. 1949. Paraguay. An informal history. University of Oklahoma Press, Norman.

Weeks, D. 1947. The agrarian system of the Spanish American Colonies. J. Land Pub. Util. Econ., May 1947, pp. 153–168.

Author's address: Dr. J. Richard Gorham
Department of Biological Sciences
University of Alaska
Fairbanks, Alaska 99701

Table 11.1. Indians of the Paraguayan Chaco*
Compiled by
DR. BRANKA J. SUSNIK
Director, Andrés Barbero Ethnographic Museum
Asunción, Paraguay

Linguistic Family	Tribe	1500–1800	1800 onward	Physical Type	Comments
Guaicurú	1. Mbayá = Eyiguayeguí				
	a. Southern Group = Yiqui	Located between Pilcomayo and Verde Rivers; circa 1700, decimated by smallpox; joined the norteños.			
	b. Northern Group = Yegi	An equestrian tribe situated along the Río Paraguay from the Río Verde northward; 1647—made raids into eastern Paraguay and established settlements between the Jejuí and Miranda rivers; from 1790, migrated northward toward Brazil.	Gradual migration to Albuquerque (Brazil); since 1800 the tribal remnants have been known as Caduveos.		The chieftan class was maintained ethnically pure as a result of endogamous marriage; the other social classes commonly mixed with slaves and captives.
	2. Payaguá = Evuevis				
	a. Southern Group = Agaz, Agaces	Located along the Río Paraguay from the Pilcomayo River southward; 1740–settled around Tacumbú (a barrio of Asunción), where they became known as Tacumbúes.	Cultural accommodation: bartered for manufactured items, and served the Paraguayan government as canoe-borne guards on the Río Paraguay; main settlements in Chacarita (barrio of Asunción), Limpio (Central), and Tacumbú; extinct by 1943.		Ethnography associated with canoe culture; from 19th century onward crossed with mestizos and mulattos.
	b. Northern Group = Siacuá	Located along the Río Paraguay between the Pilcomayo and Verde Rivers; in 1790 their principal site was near Asunción; both Agaz and Siacuá were canoe-borne river pirates.			
	3. Toba = Ntokowit			Pámpid	
	a. Emok	Located between the Pilcomayo and Bermejo Rivers; circa 1780, entered the Melodía Mission (Villa Hayes, Presidente Hayes)	Located today around Villa Hayes and Rosario (San Pedro) where they are hunters, traders, and ranch hands; acculturated.		Extensive crossing with the Lengua-Maskoỹ and Paraguayan mestizos.
	b. Takshik	Situated near Río Bermejo.	In 1860 migrated from Formosa, Argentina to Puerto Casado (Boquerón) where they now work as manual laborers.		Interbreeding with the Lengua and Sanapaná.

Group	No. Tribe	Location / History	Acculturation	Physical type	Physical group
Guaicurú	4. Yaperú	Hunters; located just west of the middle Río Paraguay; died out during the 17th century.			
	5. Guatata	Canoeists and fishermen located along the Río Pilcomayo opposite Asunción; absorbed by the Payaguá during the 17th century.			
	6. Mocoví and 7. Abipón	Equestrian tribes located in the Argentine provinces of Chaco and Santa Fé; carried out many raids across the Paraguay and Paraná Rivers during the 17th and 18th centuries.	A few acculturated Mocoví still exist around Quitilipi in the Argentine Chaco. It is possible that a few Abipón still exist in the vicinity of Santa Fé, Argentine Chaco.		
Maskoy	8. Machicuy = Mascoi, Maskoy	From the 17th century, located along the Río Aguary-guazú (Presidente Hayes) the central Paraguayan Chaco.		Of varied physical type due to crosses with captive women of other tribes; ancient connection with the Gorgotoqui of Chiquitos, Bolivia. Intensive crossing with Paraguayan mestizos.	Pampid
	9. Lengua = Enthlit	Located between the Verde and Montelindo Rivers (Boquerón), well back from the Río Paraguay.	Since 1850, contacts (bartering) with Spanish Americans; acculturated—work as ranch hands, drivers, and manual laborers.	Extensive mixing with Chamacoco (Tomárxa) women; population was about 800 in 1954.	
	10. Sanapaná	Located during the 18th century between Galván Creek and Salado Creek on the upper Paraguay River.	Contacts with Paraguayans since 1860; acculturated—laborers around Puerto Sastre (Boquerón).	Interbreeding with the Sanapaná; population about 500 in 1954.	
	11. Angaité	18th century—located along Yacaré Creek (Boquerón), well away from Río Paraguay.	Acculturated—laborers around Puerto Pinasco (Boquerón).	Variable physical type due to mixing with the Chané-guaná.	
	12. Kaskihá	Located during 18th century along Alegre Creek (Boquerón), well back from Río Paraguay; vassals of Mbayá and Chané-guaná.	Located today along Yacaré Creek; prefer working their own farm plots to hiring out as manual laborers.		
	13. Sapuquí	Located in central Paraguayan Chaco during the 18th century.	Absorbed by the Sanapaná.		
Mataco	14. Chulupí = Ashluslay, Churupí	Known as Nohaague; located along north bank of Pilcomayo River, especially around marshes; partial fusion with Guentusé.	First observed in 1883 (Campos 1888); culturally adaptive; now working as ranch hands and seasonally migratory workers; located near San José de los Esteros (Presidente Hayes) and Guachalla (Boquerón).	Interbreeding with Paraguayan mestizos. Belaieff (1963) estimated that there were still 6,000 Chulupí in 1946.	Paraguid
	15. Guisnay = Mataco	During 17th century located along Río Pilcomayo, especially in the vicinity of present-day Fortín Ballivián (Boquerón).	Acculturated; frequently move from place to place on both sides of the Pilcomayo.	Prehistoric fusion with an Amazonid people.	
	16. Chorotí	During the 17th century located along the Río Pilcomayo, especially near present-day Fortín Guachalla; slaves of the Chiriguano and the Chané of Tarija (Bolivia).	Unstable settlements; some acculturated, others located near Fortín Oruro (Boquerón).	Interbreeding with the Chulupí and the Tapieté. Belaieté (1963) judged that the Chorotí population was about 3,000 in 1946.	

Table 11.1. (Continued)

Linguistic Family	Tribe	1500–1800	1800 onward	Physical Type	Comments
Enimagá	17. Lengua = Juiadjé, Ouajadgé	Migrated to the Paraguayan Chaco during the 17th century and settled between the Confuso and Verde Rivers (Presidente Hayes); equestrian; decimated by smallpox and absorbed by the Enimagá in 1794.		Pampid	Possess same physical characters as the Pampid Huárpido; physical type does not correspond to that of their language group, indicating that they may have adopted a new language.
	18. Enimagá = Cochaboth	Equestrians; migrated to Paraguayan Chaco in 17th century and settled around the Verde River; retreated to central Chaco about 1790.			
	19. Guentusé	Farmers; migrated to Paraguayan Chaco in 17th century; partially fused with the Chulupí in 1790.			
	20. Maká = Macá	Probably represent ancient Enimagá.	Designated "Maka" at time of first contact with whites in 1923; a large group moved in 1940 to a colony (called "Bartolomé de Las Casas") founded for them near Asunción by General Belaieff.		Estimated 1,000 Maká still living in 1946 (Belaieff 1963). Physically similar to the Enimagá; very little miscegenation with non-Indians. Probably represent combined remnants of Lengua, Enimagá, and Guentusé.
Zamuco	21. Zamuco	Located in Chaco Boreal, especially around Río Tímane; "reduced" by the Jesuits in 1726 and moved to Chiquitos, Bolivia.	Absorbed by the acculturated Chiquito of Chiquitos, Bolivia.		
	22. Caipotorade	Located in Chaco Boreal; moved to Chiquitos, Bolivia (see Chamacoco).	Extinct.		Prehistoric interbreeding with Amazonid groups of Chiquitos, Bolivia.
	23. Timinahá	Located in Chaco Boreal, especially around Zamucos Creek (Olimpo) (see Tomárxa).			
	24. Morotoco	Located in Chaco Boreal; most moved to San José mission, Chiquitos, Bolivia in 1717.	Extinct.		
	25. Chamacoco = Ishira				
	a. Ebidoso = Horio Ebitoso	Possibly (?) ancient Caipotorade.	Located since 1802 along Río Paraguay, especially around Puerto Leda and Bahía Negra (Olimpo); acculturated—woodcutters and ranch hands; associated with Catholic and Protestant missions of the region.		Extensive interbreeding with the Tomárxa and with whites; at least 75% of mixed origins; slaves of the Mato Grosso Mbayá during the 19th century. Chamacoco numbered about 1,500 in 1954.
	b. Tomárxa = Tómarha, Tumerehã	Possibly (?) ancient Timinahá.	Acculturated, but less so than the Ebidoso; located from Puerto Sastre west into the Chaco.		Genetically "purer" than the Ebidoso, in spite of ancient crosses with the Sanapaná.

Language family	Group	Origin	Location / History	Physical type	Notes
Zamuco	26. Ayoreo = Moro, Ayoweo	Possibly (?) derived from ancient Morotoco or Guarañoca.	Located in Chaco Boreal, especially around Ingavi and San Miguel (Boquerón); aboriginal culture intact; only sporadic contact with whites. (See Fig. 11.1.)	Pampid	Population estimated at about 500 in 1954.
	27. Tsirakuá	Possibly (?) derived from ancient Satieño.	Located today around Cerro Guaraní (Boquerón); aboriginal culture intact; no contacts with whites.		Both the Moro and the Tsirakuá may represent remnants of the Guarañoca.
Chané-Arawak	28. Layaná = Guaná	Located along the upper Río Paraguay, especially around Alegre Creek (Boquerón); vassals of the Mbayá; became part of the colonies of Lima and Tacuatí (San Pedro).	Expelled from Paraguay in 1840; relocated around Miranda (Mato Grosso, Brazil); extensive interbreeding with Brazilian mestizos.	Amazonid	Predominantly of Amazonid physical type, but varied due to interbreeding with the Mbayá and captive women of other tribes.
	29. Chararaná = Echoaladi	Situated along Río Paraguay just south of Fuerte Olimpo.	Moved in 1808 to a colony at San Juan Nepomuceno (Caazapá); absorbed by Paraguayan mestizos.		
	30. Tereno	An equestrian and farming people located north of Fuerte Olimpo.	Several remnants were settled around Concepción until 1830; these migrated to Brazil where they now constitute the only survivors of the Chané-Arawak linguistic group.		
	31. Kinikinao	Hunters and canoeists inhabiting the west bank of the upper Río Paraguay.	Migrated to Brazil and eventually disappeared.		
Tupí-Guaraní	32. Tapieté	Located between the Pilcomayo and Parapetí Rivers; enslaved by the Chiriguano.	During the 19th and 20th centuries located mainly around Fortín Guachalla, Fortín Oruro, and Nueva Asunción (Boquerón); influenced by cultural contacts with Paraguayans, but some aboriginal culture retained.	Pampid	Belong to the Pampid physical type called "mataco"; language acquired during slave period from the Chiriguano. Estimated 2,000 extant in 1946 (Belaieff 1963).

*Principal sources: Mason 1963, Métraux 1963a, e, f; other sources: Belaieff 1963, Campos 1888, Nordenskiöld 1912, 1917, Susnik 1968. This table was translated from the Spanish and edited by J. R. Gorham.

Table 11.2. Indian Tribes of Eastern Paraguay*
Compiled by
DR. BRANKA J. SUSNIK
Director, Andrés Barbero Ethnographic Museum
Asunción, Paraguay

Linguistic Family	Tribe	1500–1800	1800 onward	Physical Type	Comments
Tupí-Guaraní	ANCIENT TRIBES			**Amazonid**	Intensive miscegenation with non-Indians from the 16th century onward; white-Indian crosses were most important, but crosses with free Negroes and mulattos also occurred; even though pure-blooded Indians were scarce in the mitayo towns, the Paraguayan mestizos referred to the "town" Guaraní as "indios." Miscegenation intensified after the "liberation" of 1848, leading to the gradual disappearance of the distinction between the "biological mestizo" and the "socio-biological mestizo." The process of acculturation and fusion with the Paraguayan mestizo population was temporarily slowed by the onset of the Triple Alliance War of 1864–1870.
	1. Cario	Located between Tebicuary River and Manduvirá River (Cordillera); nucleus of Spanish colonization; gathered during the 16th century into the mitayo towns of Itá (Central), Yaguarón (Paraguarí), and Altos (Cordillera).	All of these tribes were controlled by the colonial government in Asunción; the concentration of the Indians in mitayo towns led to their rapid acculturation; these towns were open to white contacts from 1800 onward; Guaraní Indians began serving in the Paraguayan army in 1830; 4,200 "town" Guaraní were counted in 1845; the organized towns of hispanized Guaraní were disbanded in 1848; the Indians dispersed to the countryside where they became indistinguishable from rural Paraguayan mestizos.		
	2. Tobatin	Situated along Río Manduvirá and the forests of San Joaquín (Caaguazú); gathered into the mitayo town of Tobatí during the 16th century; moved southward during the 17th century.			
	3. Guarambaré	Located between Ypané and Apa Rivers (Concepción); brought together in the mitayo towns of Ypané, Guarambaré, and Arecayá (Concepción) during the 16th century.			
	4. Yvyturusu-ense	Located between the Yvyturusú Hills (Guairá) and the Río Tebicuary; gathered into the mitayo towns of Caazapá and Yuty (Caazapá) during the 16th century.			
	5. Mbaracayu-ense	Located in Guayrá, east of the Río Alto Paraná; 16th century—united in mitayo towns, e.g. Terecañý (= Igatimí) (Caaguazú); dispersed during the 17th century.			

Tupi-Guaraní

Amazonid

No. & Name	Location and history	Mission history	Physical type
6. Itatín	Originally located in the Itatí region of Mato Grosso between the Apa and Miranda Rivers; some migrated in 1476, 1513–1518, and 1564 to Bolivia where they became known as Guarayú and Pauserna; others "reduced" by the Jesuits and moved to Misiones (Paraguay) during the 17th century.	These tribes had been under the influence of the Jesuit system; some of the Indians left the mission towns; some settled nearby as independent farmers or returned to the forest; in 1845 there were still some 6,000 Indians living in the mission towns; in 1848 C. A. López ordered the remaining Indians out of the mission towns; some of the Indians sought new land in Argentina; the Triple Alliance War effectively scattered the last hold-outs in the mission towns.	The Jesuit policy of strict segregation of mission Indians from the Paraguayans permitted only few instances of miscegenation before 1767. The regimented life of the mission towns profoundly altered the aboriginal culture. The expulsion of the Jesuits in 1767 opened Indian lands to colonization and the Indians themselves to miscegenation. Many of the ethnically "purer" Indians retreated to the forests where they gathered in numerous small enclaves during and after the Triple Alliance War.
7. Guayrá	Located between the Paranapanema and Piquiri Rivers (Paraná, Brazil); one group moved to Misiones (Paraguay) in 1630.		
8. Tapé	Situated during the 16th and 17th centuries in the Serra dos Tapés, Serra Geral, and other parts of the Brazilian state of Rio Grande do Sul; Jesuits established missions there in 1632–35; attacks by mamelukes forced priests and Indians to abandon the Tapé region and resettle between the Paraná and Uruguay Rivers in Argentina.		
9. Yacuiense	Located between the Paraná and Uruguay Rivers; Catholicized during the 17th century.		
10. Paraná	Occupied the territory between the Alto Paraná and Tebicuary Rivers (Neembucú); Catholicized during the 17th century.		
11. Mondayense	Situated in the vicinity of the Río Monday, Río Acaray, and Río Yguazú; "reduced" in 1630; moved to Misiones (Paraguay) in 1650.		
12. Taruma	Located between the San Joaquín Hills and the Yhú River (Caaguazú); concentrated in the towns of San Joaquín (Caaguazú) and San Estanislao (San Pedro) in 1740.		
13. Mbyá = Chiriguano	Several Guaraní factions, including representatives of the Guayrá, Tapé, and Mondayense, migrated to the eastern slopes of the Bolivian Cordillera in several waves during the last quarter of the 15th century and the first half of the 16th; highly resistant to missionary efforts of Jesuits, Franciscans, and Augustinians, but many mission towns were established—and many were abandoned or destroyed; relatively few Chiriguano masters ruled several thousand Chané serfs.	Franciscan missionaries established several towns and were successful in attracting many Indians to them; the missions became secular towns in 1929 and some of the Indians migrated to Argentina; the total Chiriguano population was estimated to be about 20,000 in 1928 (Métraux 1963e); the Chaco War of 1932–35 was extremely disruptive for the Chiriguano and no doubt stimulated many more of them to move to Argentina.	Interbreeding with the vassal Chané-Arawak was intense; this, however, did not greatly alter the physical characteristics of either group since both were of the same Amazonid stock; miscegenation with whites began in the 19th century.

Table 11.2. (continued)

Linguistic Family	Tribe	1500–1800	1800 onward	Physical Type	Comments
Tupí-Guaraní	14. Guayakí = Aché	Located during the 17th century in the vicinity of San Joaquín (Caaguazú), and the Monday and Alto Paraná Rivers; some attempts to Catholicize the Guayakí were made during the 17th century; occasional Indians were settled in the town of Jesús (Itapúa).	One group near Ñacunday (Alto Paraná) contacted by Mayntzhusen (1924–26); since then the group near San Juan Nepomuceno (Caazapá) has had contacts with whites; the more isolated groups retain their aboriginal culture, but those in contact with whites have undergone some acculturation.		The Guayakí speak a dialect of the Guaraní language, but their origins are obscure; physical features correspond to both Amazonid and Lagid "races."
	15. Kaynguá = Cainguá Monteses, Caagua	Located during the 18th century in the province of Alto Paraná and the forests around San Joaquín (Caaguazú); most of these Guaraní retreated to the forests, avoiding both Jesuits and encomenderos; one group was "reduced" and settled at Itapé (Guairá); the Kaynguá were comprised of three groups: Mbyá, Carima, and Taruma.	As late as the first half of the 19th century, the Kaynguá still occasionally attacked yerba harvesters, whom they considered intruders in their territory; retaliatory raids by the Paraguayans resulted in occasional captive Indians who were then brought to Asunción where they were called "Kaynguá."	Amazonid	There is no doubt that the basic physical type of both ancient and modern Guaraní is Amazonid; there are, however, certain variations which indicate that some interbreeding with some other group must have occurred even during prehistoric times. With this consideration in mind, it is possible to speak of the "mbyá variant" and the "cario variant" –the latter being closer to the Amazonid prototype.
	MODERN TRIBES				
	16. Apapocuva	Possibly represent remnants of the ancient and dispersed Guayrá.	The ancestral home of the Apapocuva was around the Iguatemí River in the most southerly sector of the State of Mato Grosso, Brazil; a small group remained in that locality until 1922; a major portion of the tribe undertook migrations in 1870, 1880, 1890 in search of the "Land-Without-Evil," which brought them eventually to localities in the States of Paraná and São Paulo, as well as Mato Grosso.		
	17. Tañyguá	Derived from ancient Carima and Mbyá.	Originally lived near the confluence of the Alto Paraná and Iguatemí Rivers; competition for their territory by the Ingain caused the Tañyguá to migrate to the Atlantic Coast (Paraná, Brazil) in 1820.		
	18. Oguauíva	Possibly derived from the ancient and dispersed Mbaracayuense.	Formerly located in the Cordillera de Mbaracayú (between the Mato Grosso and the Paraguayan state of Alto Paraná) and its extension, Serra de Mbaracayú, into the Brazilian state of Paraná; harassment by the Mbyá-Guaraní and their urge to find the Land-Without-Evil caused them to migrate, as the Apapocuva and Tañyguá had done, to the Atlantic Coast in 1830; now extinct.		

	Entry	Location / History	Physical type	
Tupí-Guaraní	19. Cheiru	Remnants of ancient Carima and Mbyá.	Located near Guairá Falls (Alto Paraná) and near the mouth of the Iguatemí River in Brazil; partial fusion with other Guaraní tribes.	The Mbyá represent the "mbyá variant" of the Amazonid physical type; the Apyteré group has experienced some miscegenation with whites.	**Amazonid**
	20. Mbyá = modern Cainguá	These were the Monteses who occupied the forests from the Cordillera de Mbaracayú southward to the province of Itapúa and carefully avoided contacts with Spanish Americans.	Encroachments by the Caingang and even by some of their own relatives, the Chiripá, began about 1820, forcing the Mbyá to seek other unclaimed territories; the Mbyá cling to their aboriginal culture and isolate themselves in small enclaves in the forests.		
	a. Mbyá-Apyteré	Derived from ancient Taruma; some gathered into a mission town near Ycuá Mandyyú (San Pedro) in the 18th century.			
	b. Mbyá-Mondayense	Remnants of ancient Mondayense, Acarayense, and Yguazuense.			
	21. Chiripá = Avá-katú-eté	Remnants of ancient Guayrá and Mbaracayuense.	Territorial encroachments by the Ingain, a Caingang subtribe, caused the Chiripá to move southwestward to the forests around the Caaguazú towns of Igatimí, Curuguaty, and Yhú; the Chiripá are the most acculturated of the Guaraní groups.	The Chiripá were formerly good examples of the "cario variant" of the Amazonid physical type, but recent and numerous crosses with Paraguayan mestizos have produced a heterogenous physical type.	
	22. Pañ = Terenōhẽ	Remnants of ancient Itatin and Guarambaré; possibly some interbreeding with the Nu-guara.	Located north of the Río Jejuí-guazú (San Pedro and Caaguazú); undergoing acculturation, but attempting to accommodate aboriginal culture with new conditions of life.	Not definitely either the "mbya" or the "cario" variant, but rather an intermediate type possessing characteristics of both; considerable miscegenation with Paraguayan mestizos.	
Ge-caingang	23. Guayaná, a Caingang subtribe a. Piquiryense b. Mondayense	Located during the 16th century in isolated forest retreats near the confluence of the Piquiri and Alto Paraná Rivers; in the 17th century, located southward from the Río Monday along the Río Alto Paraná; many Guayaná taken into the Guaraní mission towns during the 18th century; some entered the short-lived San Francisco de Paula mission in 1784.	Displaced eastward in Brazil. Abandoned the mission town in 1810 and then settled along Pirapytá Creek near Irala (= Villa Azara) (Alto Paraná); the process of integration with Guaraní in 5 mission towns began in 1830; adopted Guaraní culture and language.	Originally typical of the Lagid physical type, but since the 18th century have crossed with the Guaraní so that characteristics of both Amazonid and Lagid stocks now appear in these Indians; more recently there have been some instances of miscegenation with Paraguayan mestizos.	**Lagid**

Table 11.2. (continued)

Linguistic Family	Tribe	1500–1800	1800 onward	Physical Type	Comments
Gê-caingang	24. Ingain = Tain, Yvytirocay	Located on the west bank of the Alto Paraná River from Yvytirocay Creek northward to Guairá Falls; encroached upon the territory of the Carima and the Mbyá-Monteses during the 18th century.	Retain aboriginal culture; occupy both sides of the Río Alto Paraná near Guairá Falls.	Lagid	Typical of the Lagid physical type.
	25. Guetris = Ñu-guara	Members of the southern Cayapó; occupied the region just north of Río Apa (the boundary between Mato Grosso, Brazil, and Concepción, Paraguay); some entered the town of Pericó (Concepción) during the 16th century; adopted Guaraní culture and language during the 17th century.	Extinct.		Represented an intermediate type resulting from crosses between Amazonid and Lagid stocks.

*Principal source: Métraux 1963c; other sources: Lowrie 1963, Métraux 1963b, d, e, Métraux and Baldus 1963, Mayntzhusen 1924–1926, Susnik 1964, 1965, 1966, 1968. This table was translated from the Spanish and edited by J. R. Gorham.

Table 11.3. Number of Guaraní in Several Curacies
of the Society of Jesus in Colonial Paraguay

Year	Number of Curacies	Number of Indians
1614	10	28,714
1682	15	48,491
1702	–	48,018
1716	–	66,367

Source: Hernández 1913.

Table 11.4. Ethnic Components in the Population of Paraguay
in 1785 (Azara 1904)

Ethnic Category	Number
European	193
"Spanish American"	49,901
"Creole Indian"	3,913
Originario Indian	752
Mitayo Indian	27,761
Negro and mulatto	10,469
Total	92,989

Table 11.5. Azara's Censuses of Paraguay

Town or District	Date Founded	Census of 1785 (Azara 1904)	Later Census (Azara 1847)
		Population	
Acaai	1783	–	858
Aguay		1,519	–
Ajos	1758	–	715
Arroyos	1781	–	1,227
Asunción	1536	6,285	7,088
Bobí	1789	1,432	427
Caacupé	1770	–	1,066
Caapucú	1787	–	659
Campo Grande		568	–
Capiatá	1640	3,624	5,305
Caraiy	1770	–	654
Carapeguá	1725	1,006	3,346
Carimbatai	1760	–	372
Concepción	1773	670	1,551
Cordillera		10,251	–
Cuarepotí	1783	–	540
Curuguaty	1715	4,094	2,254
Emboscada	1740	750	840
Frontera	1718	–	2,187
Itaguá	1728	3,268	2,235
Lambaré	1766	4,329	825
Laureles	1790	–	621
Limpio	1785	–	1,769
Ñeembucú	1779	765	1,730
Paraguarí	1775	935	507
Pirayú	1769	2,811	2,352

Table 11.5 (Continued)

Town or District	Date Founded	Population Census of 1785 (Azara 1904)	Census of 1796 (Azara 1847)
Piribebuy	1640	–	3,595
Quiindy	1733	2,517	1,894
Quinquió	1776	–	1,136
Quyquyó		2,606	–
Remolinos	1777	160	453
San Lorenzo	1775	–	1,720
San Roque	1770	–	733
Tabapi	1538	–	644
Tacuaras	1791	–	520
Tapuá (Luque)	1635	5,933	3,813
Villarrica	1577	7,432	3,014
Villeta	1714	3,702	3,098
Yaca-guazú	1785	–	866
Ybitimiri	1783	–	620
Ybycuí	1766	–	1,500
Ybytymí		571	–
Yguamandiyú (Ycuá Mandyyú)	1784	–	949
Yhaty (Hiati)	1773	–	1,232
Mitayo towns			
Altos	1538	743	869
Areguá	1538	–	200
Atisá (Iois)	1538	–	972
Atyrá		890	–
Belén	1740	373	361
Caazapá	1607	705	725
Candelaria	1627	1,748	1,514
Corpus	1622	2,574	2,267
Guarambaré	1538	258	368
Itá	1536	929	965
Itapé	1673	67	124
Itapúa	1614	2,889	1,049
Jesús	1685	1,302	1,185
Loreto	1555	1,459	1,519
San Cosme	1634	1,111	1,036
San Estanislao	1749	723	729
San Ignacio Guazú	1609	867	864
San Ignacio Miri	1555	798	806
San Joaquín	1746	854	854
Santa Ana	1633	1,747	1,430
Santa María de Fe	1592	1,062	1,144
Santa Rosa	1698	1,237	1,283
Santiago	1592	1,215	1,097
Tobatí	1536	818	932
Trinidad	1706	1,097	1,017
Yaguarón	1536	1,597	2,093
Ypané	1538	223	278
Yuty	1610	475	674
"Españoles parroquianos de los pueblos de indios no comprendidos en sus padrones"		–	5,533
Totals		**92,989**	**96,803**

Table 11.6. Summary of Population Censuses, Estimates and Projections
Paraguay, 1785 to 2000

Year	Kind of Measure	Source	Population	Comments or Figures Regarding Indian Population
1785	Census	Azara 1904	92,989	33,752
1785	Estimate	Bertoni 1952, based on Azara 1904	150,000	not included
1796	Census	Blas Garay, based on Azara 1847, cited by Mendoza 1970	97,480	
1796	Census	Azara 1847	96,803	
1796	Censuses	Based on Azara 1847 and 1904	113,208	not included
1828	Estimate	Bally, cited by Carrasco 1905	250,000	not included
1852	Estimate	Du Graty, cited by Carrasco 1905	300,000	
1857	Estimate	Du Graty 1865	800,000	
1857	Estimate	Du Graty 1865	1,337,439	
1861	Estimate	Martínez, cited by Carrasco 1905	1,300,000	
1865	Estimate	Carrasco 1905	525,000	
1865	Estimate	Rodolfo Ritter, cited by Bertoni 1952	560,000	120,000
1872	Estimate	De Schutterer, cited by Bertoni 1952	231,000	
1886	Census	Carrasco 1905	239,774	
1886	Estimate	José Jacquet, cited by Carrasco 1905	263,751	
1887	Census	Jacquet, cited by Carrasco 1905	329,645	
1890	Estimate	Bourgade La Dardye	500,000	100,000
1899–1900	Census	Carrasco 1905	490,719	
1899–1900	Census plus Estimate	Juan Asencio Roa, cited by Carrasco 1905	635,571	100,000
1900	Estimate	Bertoni 1952	493,821	
1900	Estimate	Benítez 1901	643,852	
1914	Family Census	Bertoni 1952	650,562	
1920	United Nations' Estimate	Cited by Smith 1960	660,806	
1924	Agricultural Census	Bertoni 1952	828,698	
1935	Census	Alfonso B. Campos, cited by Bertoni 1952	992,420	
1936–1937	Census	Dunn et al. 1945	931,799	
1941	Estimate	Dunn et al. 1945	1,040,420	
1950	Census	Boletín Estadístico del Paraguay, December 1964	1,328,452	39,213
1960	Estimate	Roberts 1968	1,768,448	68,000
1962	Census	Dirección General de Estadística y Censos 1966	1,819,103	35,000
1967	Estimate	Rivarola 1969	2,161,200	
1968	Estimate	Boletín Estadístico del Paraguay, December 1968	2,243,400	
1969	Estimate	Rivarola 1969	2,303,500	
1970	Estimate	Instituto Interamericano de Estadística 1970	2,386,000	
1980	Projection	Vidal 1969	3,456,284	
1990	Projection	Vidal 1969	4,859,872	
2000	Projection	Vidal 1969	6,618,861	

Table 11.7. Overpopulated Regions of Paraguay

Departamento (Province)	Total Area (hectares)	Overpopulated Areas (hectares)	Population		Number of Hectares in Overpopulated Areas			
					Per Person		Per Family	
			1950	1962	1950	1962	1950	1962
Central	285,500	285,500	359,742	512,962	0.79	0.56	4.0	2.8
Paraguarí	851,100	592,700*	150,542	203,444	3.9	2.9	19.5	14.5
Cordilleras	494,800	494,800	145,232	188,657	3.4	2.6	17.0	13.0
Guairá	320,200	225,954*	90,308	115,531	2.5	2.0	12.5	10.0
Caazapá	949,600	245,780*	73,051	92,266	3.4	2.7	17.0	13.5
Totals	**2,901,200**	**1,844,734**	**818,875**	**1,112,860**	**2.3**	**1.6**	**13.5**	**8.0**

*Estimates.

Table 11.8. Farm Size in Several Overpopulated Areas of Paraguay
Based on the STICA Farm Census of 1942–44

Locality	1–2 ha.	%	2–3 ha.	%	3–5 ha.	%	5–7 ha.	%	7–10 ha.	%	10–20 ha.	%	20–50 ha.	%	50–100 ha.	%
Villeta	878	13	1,302	19	1,882	27	1,277	19	541	8	752	11	172	2	544	0.5
Central	811	17	1,101	21	1,416	29	781	16	309	6	353	7	129	3	9	0.2
Paraguarí	1,537	12	2,238	12	3,285	18	2,343	26	960	19	1,458	8	599	12	95	9
Quiindy	1,051	15	1,533	16	1,914	25	1,083	28	509	16	179	5	62	8	98	3
Caazapá	1,308	12	1,638	13	1,728	16	724	22	1,748	17	603	7	101	17	70	6
Guairá	881	11	950	11	1,238	16	958	22	528	16	921	9	520	15	56	9
Caraguatay	1,501	11	2,431	11	5,510	16	3,181	25	1,268	22	2,050	9	615	10	191	4
Totals	**7,997**	**11**	**11,193**	**18**	**17,018**	**27**	**10,347**	**17**	**5,863**	**9**	**6,316**	**10**	**2,198**	**4**	**1,075**	**0.9**

Table 11.9. Distribution of Landholdings in Latin America and Paraguay

Size of Farm (hectares)	Percent of Farms		Percent of Land Area, Latin America, 1950a
	Latin America, 1950a	Paraguay, 1960b	
0–20	72.6	86.3	3.7
20–100	18.0	10.5	8.4
100–1000	7.9	2.3	23.0
1000+	1.5	0.9	64.9

aCarroll 1961. bPincus 1968.

Table 11.10. Comparative Demographic Data from Selected Countries and Regions

Region or Country	Population (millions)				% Increase in Population 1940–70	1970 Crude Birth Rate	1970 Crude Death Rate	Annual Growth Rate (%) circa 1970	Population per Square Kilometer circa 1970
	circa 1940	1950	1960	1970					
Africa	191.0	222.0	273.0	346.0	81.2	45	21	3.0	11
Asia	1,244.0	1,381.0	1,651.0	2,298.588	84.8	35	15	2.0	68
Europe	380.0	392.0	425.0	462.117	21.6	17	10	0.8	91
USSR	195.0	204.0	214.0	242.612	24.4	19	7	1.3	11
Latin America	130.0	163.0	212.0	283.251	117.9	39	10	2.9	13
Argentina	13.517	17.070	20.85	24.0	77.5	23	9	1.5	8.6
Bolivia	3.495	3.012	3.453	4.9	34.9	44	19	2.4	4.4
Brazil	42.533	51.944	69.72	92.3	117.0	42	10	3.0	11
Paraguay	1.041	1.397	1.816	2.379	128.5	45	11	3.5	5.8
United States	133.203	152.271	180.684	204.766	53.7	17	9.5	1.0	22

Sources: Numerous sources, including Anderson 1966, Bogue 1969, Departamento de Asuntos Sociales n.d., Dunn et al. 1945, Durand 1967, Gaslonde 1969, Instituto Interamericano de Estadística 1970, Inter-American Statistical Institute 1969, Roberts 1968, Samoza and Llano 1968.

Table 11.11. Population of Paraguay by Age and Sex, 1950 and 1962

Age Group	Males				Females				Total				% Change 1950-62
	1950	%	1962	%	1950	%	1962	%	1950	%	1960	%	
0-4	110,735	17.1	159,393	17.8	106,905	15.7	152,526	16.5	217,640	16.3	311,919	17.1	43.3
5-9	99,979	15.4	148,372	16.6	96,208	14.2	141,782	15.3	196,187	14.8	290,154	16.0	47.9
10-14	86,284	13.3	119,144	13.3	81,229	12.0	113,506	12.3	167,513	12.6	232,650	12.8	38.9
Less than 15	296,998	45.8	426,909	47.7	284,342	41.9	407,814	44.1	581,340	43.6	834,723	45.9	43.5
15-19	63,162	9.7	91,009	10.2	65,577	9.7	93,814	10.1	128,739	9.7	184,557	10.1	43.4
20-24	58,248	9.0	68,765	7.7	64,276	9.5	76,151	8.2	122,524	9.2	144,916	8.0	18.3
25-29	46,784	7.2	51,541	5.8	52,230	7.7	57,699	6.2	99,014	7.5	109,240	6.0	10.3
30-34	36,943	5.7	52,776	5.9	39,974	5.9	56,436	6.1	76,917	5.8	109,212	6.0	42.0
35-39	31,830	4.9	43,655	4.9	38,817	5.7	48,400	5.2	70,646	5.3	92,055	5.1	30.3
40-44	24,235	3.8	37,690	4.2	28,576	4.2	40,653	4.4	53,111	4.0	78,343	4.3	47.5
45-49	20,776	3.2	29,174	3.3	24,264	3.6	34,285	3.7	45,040	3.4	63,459	3.5	40.9
50-54	18,081	2.8	26,504	3.0	20,729	3.0	29,470	3.2	38,810	2.9	55,974	3.1	44.2
55-59	14,905	2.3	18,076	2.0	16,608	2.4	21,187	2.3	35,513	2.4	39,263	2.2	10.6
60-64	15,060	2.3	16,736	1.9	16,236	2.4	19,616	2.1	31,296	2.4	36,352	2.0	16.2
65 and over	21,787	3.4	31,174	3.5	27,714	4.1	39,553	4.3	49,501	3.7	70,762	3.9	44.9
65-69	10,407	1.6	10,657	1.2	11,225	1.6	12,333	1.3	21,632	1.6	22,990	1.3	6.3
70-74	6,080	0.9	9,389	1.1	7,566	1.1	10,911	1.2	13,646	1.0	20,300	1.1	48.8
75 and over	5,300	0.8	11,128	1.2	8,923	1.3	16,309	1.8	14,223	1.1	27,437	1.5	92.9
Age unknown			155				127				282		
Totals	648,809	—	894,164	—	679,343	—	924,939	—	1,332,451	—	1,819,103	—	36.5

Sources: Bol. Estad. Paraguay, December 1964; Dir. Gen. Estad. Cen. 1966; Inst. Interamer. Estad. 1970.

Table 11.12. Rural and Urban Population of Paraguay by Age Group and Sex, 1950 and 1962

Age Group	Urban						Rural						Urban, Both Sexes %*	Rural, Both Sexes %*
	Males			Females			Males			Females				
	1950	1962	%*	1950	1962	%*	1950	1962	%*	1950	1962	%*		
0-4	12,069	47,536	293.9	11,598	45,359	291.1	98,666	111,857	13.4	95,307	107,167	12.4	292.5	12.9
5-9	10,844	45,688	321.3	10,891	45,102	314.1	89,095	102,684	15.2	85,317	96,680	13.3	317.7	14.3
10-14	11,655	40,152	244.5	12,274	42,885	249.4	74,629	78,992	5.8	68,955	70,621	2.4	247.0	4.2
15-19	15,078	38,846	157.6	12,866	39,175	204.5	48,084	52,163	8.5	52,771	54,373	3.0	179.2	5.6
20-24	11,218	24,013	114.0	12,607	31,410	149.1	47,030	44,752	-4.8	51,669	44,741	-13.4	132.6	-9.3
25-29	8,373	17,754	112.0	9,955	22,734	128.4	38,411	33,787	-12.0	42,275	34,965	-17.3	120.9	-14.8
30-34	6,220	18,730	201.1	7,526	22,553	199.7	30,723	34,046	10.8	32,448	33,883	4.4	200.3	7.5
35-39	5,634	15,753	179.6	7,057	19,336	174.0	26,196	27,902	6.5	31,760	29,064	-8.5	176.5	-1.7
40-44	4,644	13,213	184.5	5,290	16,311	208.3	19,891	24,477	23.1	23,286	24,342	4.5	197.2	13.1
45-49	3,619	10,909	201.4	4,643	13,942	200.3	17,157	18,265	6.4	19,621	20,343	3.7	200.7	5.0
50-54	2,778	10,017	260.6	3,516	12,381	252.1	15,303	16,487	7.7	17,213	17,089	-0.7	255.9	3.2
55-59	2,107	6,787	222.1	2,740	8,991	228.1	12,798	11,289	-11.8	13,868	12,196	-12.0	225.5	-11.9
60-64	1,876	5,907	214.9	2,647	8,229	210.9	13,184	10,829	-17.9	13,589	11,387	-16.2	212.5	-17.0
65-69	1,186	3,763	217.3	1,884	5,307	181.7	9,221	6,894	-25.2	9,341	7,026	-24.8	195.4	-25.0
70-74	692	3,157	356.2	1,201	4,786	298.5	5,388	6,232	15.7	6,365	6,125	-3.8	319.6	5.1
75+	588	3,709	530.8	1,318	7,158	443.1	4,712	7,319	57.4	7,605	9,151	20.3	470.1	34.5
Age unknown	152			124			3			3				
Totals	98,621	306,086	210.4	108,013	345,783	220.1	550,488	588,078	6.8	571,390	579,156	1.4	215.5	4.0

*Change 1950 to 1962.
Sources: Boletín Estadístico del Paraguay, December 1964; Dirección General de Estadística y Censos 1966.

Table 11.13. Marital Status, Paraguay, 1950* and 1962**

| | Location | | | | | | | | |
| | Asunción | | | Interior | | | Paraguay | | |
Marital Status	Ratio†	1950 (%)	1962 (%)	Ratio	1950 (%)	1962 (%)	Ratio	1950 (%)	1962 (%)
Never-married	d/a	52.8	52.8	e/b	45.9	46.8	f/c	47.1	47.9
Married	g/a	28.7	33.1	h/b	34.3	37.9	i/c	33.3	37.0
Consensual union	j/a	13.9	10.2	k/b	14.8	11.8	l/c	14.7	11.5
Widowed	m/a	3.8	3.3	n/b	3.9	3.1	o/c	3.9	3.2
Divorced or separated	p/a	0.8	0.5	q/b	1.0	0.3	r/c	0.9	0.4

*Population less than 15 years old excluded.   **Population less than 12 years old excluded.
†Legend for ratio symbols:

	Total	Never-married	Married	Consensual Union	Widowed	Divorced or Separated
Asunción	a	d	g	j	m	p
Interior	b	e	h	k	n	q
Paraguay	c	f	i	l	o	r

Table 11.14. Numbers of Immigrants

Regional, National, or Religious Affinity	1882–1907	1908–1915	1918–1959	1960–1965	Total
Argentine	890	819	2,555	2,392	6,643
German, Central and Northern European	2,486	367	7,234	727	10,814
Brazilian	197	36	627	905	1,765
Other Latin American	743	519	542	318	2,122
Eastern European	157	1,712	1,752	81	3,702
Polish	–	–	14,226	606	14,832
Mennonite*	–	1,500	6,164	–	7,664
British	461	27	374	72	924
Japanese, Chinese	–	–	4,891	2,333	7,224
United States and Canada	203	–	587	460	1,250
Southern European	5,846	1,855	2,748	474	10,923
Unspecified	1,117	619	4,890	696	7,322
Totals	12,100	7,451	46,590	9,064	75,205

*Not tabulated as a separate category since 1960.
Source: Bertoni 1952; Dirección General de Estadística y Censos 1968.

Table 11.15. Paraguayans in Argentina

Year	Number	Related Events
1940 and earlier	46,800	
1941–1945	11,600	
1946	2,500	
1947–1950	34,000	1947–1957: Civil war of 1947 and its aftereffects
1951–1955	21,000	
1956–1960	33,700	1957–1960: Decline in agricultural production; political strife
1963	25,800	
1964	34,700	
January to June, 1965	14,500	

Source: Rivarola 1967.

Table 11.16. Expectation of Life at Birth in Argentina, Bolivia, Brazil and Paraguay[a]

Year	Argentina	Bolivia	Brazil	Paraguay
1870			27.1–27.6	
1880			27.3–27.9	22.0–23.4
1890			27.5–28.2	23.4–24.8
1900		25.2–25.7	29.1–29.7	25.5–26.9
1910		28.1–28.8	30.1–31.1	27.7–29.2
1914	45.2–47.5[b]			
1920		31.1–32.1	31.4–32.5	30.3–31.8
1930		34.1–35.3	33.4–34.6	33.6–35.1
1940		38.1–39.5	36.1–37.3	37.3–40.1
1945–1950	61–62[c]	39.25[e]		
1947	56.9–61.4[b]			
1950		42.2–44.0	42.1–43.9	44.8–46.8
1955–1960	64–66[c]	42.25[e]		
1957	61.4–66.9[b]			
1959–1961	63.1–68.9[b]			
1960			54.0–57.0	52.6–55.4
1960–1965		43.75[e]		55.4–59.3[d]
1965–1970		45.25[e]		57.4–61.3[d]
1970–1975		46.75[e]		59.4–63.8[d]

[a]Data from Arriaga 1968 unless otherwise specified. [b]Bogue 1969. [c]Dedrick 1965. [d]Vidal 1969. [e]Samoza and Llano 1968.

Table 11.17. Indicators of Progress in Paraguay and Neighboring Nations

Statistic	Argentina		Bolivia		Brazil		Paraguay	
	c. 1960	c. 1970	c. 1960	c.1970	c. 1960	c. 1970	c. 1960	c. 1970
Per Capita Gross National Product (U.S. dollars)	649[a]	780[b]	105[a]	160[b]	165	240[b]	159	200[b]
Per Capita Gross Domestic Product (U.S. dollars)	511	635[c]	93	150[c]	166	200[c]	139	205[c]
% Annual Increase in Gross Domestic Product	–	1.6[e]	–	55.8[e]	–	4[c]	–	4[e]
% of Total Population Economically Active	38	38	46[d]	–	33	33	32	34
% of Economically Active Population Devoted to "Primary Activities"	22	–	68	–	54	–	56	–
% of Total Population under 15 Years	31	29	42	43	43	42	46	46
Urban Population (%)	73.7	73.8	29.0	34.2	46.3	46.3	35.8	35.7
% of National Budget Spent on Education	9.7	15	–	27.5	6.4	7	16.5	15
Literacy Rate (%)	91	–	31	54	39	60	25	68
% of National Budget Spent on Health	–	5	–	2.8	–	3	–	4
Infant Mortality Rate	62	61[d]	90	77	170	170	89[c]	91[b]

[a]1961; [b]1969; [c]1966; [d]1964; [e]1961–1966. Primary source: Departamento de Asuntos Sociales n.d.

Table 11.18. Estimated Fertility Rates for Paraguay and Adjacent Countries [a]

Country	Crude Birth Rate	Fertility Rate		Age Specific Fertility Rate							Number of Children Less Than 5 Years Old/1000 Women 15–49 Yrs.[e]		Per Cent of Demographic Transition Completed [f]
		General	Total	15–19	20–24	25–29	30–34	35–39	40–44	45–49	1960	1969	
Argentina	23.2	89.9	2,962	59	133	181	116	70	26	7	417	392	84.3
Bolivia	43.6[b]	177.8	5,629	75	203	281	252	197	96	22	688	728	36.1
	41.5[c]	170.7	5,403	74	207	274	239	182	86	19			
Brazil	44.6	183.7	5,768	92	232	284	248	191	88	20	716	692	31.0
Paraguay	39.8	162.5	5,077	96	230	242	208	158	68	14	766	793	43.6
	24.6[d]	111	3,600	60	170	174	141	114	51	10			

[a]Data from Cho 1964, unless otherwise specified. [b]High estimate. [c]Low estimate. [d]Calculated from Dirección General de Estadística y Censos 1966, and Instituto Interamericano de Estadística 1970. [e]Departamento de Asuntos Sociales n.d. [f]Bogue 1969.

Table 11.19. Population Growth Ratings Applied to Paraguay

Rating [a]	Annual Rate of Growth [a] (%)	Population Doubling Time [a] (years)	Population Growth Rates–Paraguay	
			Period	Rate
Stationary population	no growth	—	—	—
Slow growth	0.5	139	1924–36	0.98
Moderate growth	1.0	70	1872–86	1.2
Rapid growth	1.5	47	1828–65	1.9
			1796–1828	1.9
			1900–14	1.9
Very rapid growth	2.0	35	1936–41	2.2
			1914–24	2.4
Explosive growth	2.5	28	1950–62	2.6
			1941–50	2.7
			1886–1900	2.8
Explosive growth	3.0	23		
Explosive growth	3.5	20	1962–70	3.5
Explosive growth	4.0	18		

[a]Bogue 1969.

Table 11.20. Résumé of the Population Growth of Paraguay, 1796–1970

Date	Population	Intercensal Period (years)	Intercensal Change (%)	Annual Intercensal Growth Rate (%)	Approximate Doubling Time (years)
1796	131,604				
1828	250,000	32	89.9	1.9	34 (1796–1830)
1865	525,000	38	110.0	1.9	35 (1830–1865)
1872	231,000	7	−56.0	−11.1	
1886	329,645	14	42.7	1.2	
1900	493,821	14	49.8	2.8	
1914	650,562	14	31.7	1.9	
1924	828,698	10	27.4	2.4	
1936	931,799	12	12.4	0.98	
1941	1,040,420	5	11.6	2.2	76 (1865–1941)
1950	1,328,441	9	27.7	2.7	
1962	1,819,103	12	36.9	2.6	
1970	2,395,614	8	31.7	3.4	26 (1941–1967)

Table 11.21. Relative Growth of the Populations of Paraguay and Latin America

Year	Paraguay: % of Latin American Population	Latin America: % of World Population*
1900	0.87	2.7
1920	0.89	4.9
1940	0.80	5.5
1950	0.85	6.1
1960	0.86	6.9
1970	0.84	7.6
1980	0.91	8.3
2000	1.06	9.5

*Smith 1964.

Figure 11.1. Moro (Ayoreo) Indians, Fortín Teniente Martínez, Boquerón, Paraguayan Chaco, 28 June 1962. The Moros are capable of living off the land, but they have a long history of sporadic contacts (both friendly and unfriendly) with "civilization." These photographs were taken on the occasion of a friendly visit (indicated by the presence of women) to a remote military outpost. Some of the Indians donned articles of clothing given to them by the soldiers. The Indian skirts, shoulder bags and sandal straps are handwoven from the fibers of Chaco plants. The sandal soles are made from rubber tires, discarded during the days of oil exploration in Moro territory. Photographs by Constantino Cáceres.

XII. Human Nutrition in Paraguay

PABLA DUARTE DE STORNI

> *La Naturaleza ha sido desde tiempos inmemoriales la proveedora de todas las necesidades materiales para la humanidad.*
>
> Acosta-Solis 1968

> *La infraproducción, el subconsumo alimentario, el bajo nivel dietético del país y el deficiente nivel de ingresos de la mayoría de los "grupos familiares" de la población, son el nexo que se establece entre los sindromes "pluricarenciales" y de "malanutrición" con las causas que lo han producido, originándose así, como epifenómeno, la subalimentación, el hambre crónica, específica y global, y, a la vez, los otros fenómenos sociales y culturales desfavorables en que se desenvuelve y vegeta el hombre paraguayo; todos constituyen las trabas para el desarrollo económico y social del país.*
>
> Montalto 1962

Introduction

Before considering human nutrition in Paraguay, it is necessary to discuss briefly certain aspects of the nutritional situation in the whole of Latin America. The importance of human nutrition in the present and future of Latin America is obvious. Inadequate nutrition is one of the most serious problems affecting a large part of the population of this region. It is a tragic fact that malnutrition is robbing the health and energy of thousands of people, and hundreds die simply because they do not receive aliments of even minimal quantity and quality.

Dr. José A. Mora (1959), Secretary of the Organization of American States, said that the solution of the problem of hunger in America cannot wait. The population of Latin America increases annually by about 3 per cent (Mashbitz 1967). Food production increases at approximately the same rate. But since food production is inadequate in the first place, the net result is an improperly-nourished population.

By way of comparison, it may be noted that the population of Europe increases annually by about 0.7 per cent, while food production increases by about 3 per cent (Paz 1959). Many Latin Americans consume less than 2,500 calories per day. Several countries find themselves in an unfavorable position with regard to balance of payments because they must import basic foodstuffs purchased with money that would otherwise be used to buy and import manufactured articles.

The combination of inadequate food production and increasing population points up clearly the necessity of building up food production to properly feed the expanding population. According to a United Nations report, food production in Latin America must increase by 45% in order to accommodate the projected population of the region 20 years hence. It is important to point out that some Latin American countries have initiated positive measures of broad scope designed to improve the lot of certain improperly nourished sections of their populations.

The papers presented during the 1958 symposium in Cali, Colombia, and La Paz, Bolivia (Rothman 1959), pointed out that continued undernourishment of our peoples is the cause of a large share of infant mortality and morbidity. The overall mortality rate for Latin America is about 75 to 105 per 1,000 (for Europe it is 20 to 30 per 1,000). Furthermore, undernourishment limits productivity and shortens the life span, the latter being definitely shorter than the United States average.

Nevertheless, the progress being made by the various international organizations in the struggle against hunger is a great stimulus for Latin America. The three special agencies—FAO, WHO, and UNICEF—of the United Nations have made very evident contributions to the solution of important nutritional problems.

The government of Paraguay, in collaboration with international organizations, is initiating the great task of national development that will eventually lift each citizen to a more "human" level of life. With regard to human nutrition, the government and the international agencies have taken the first steps to determine the cultural, social, and economic factors which influence the production, distribution, and consumption of foodstuffs. These

Dr. de Storni's original manuscript of 156 pages was translated to English by Mr. Warren L. Armstrong, whose assistance is gratefully acknowledged. After careful consideration of both the Spanish and English versions, the editor has attempted to reduce the length of the paper while preserving the essential message of Dr. de Storni's essay. (J.R.G.)

facts are absolutely necessary in order to plan a proper program of nutritional improvement for the people of Paraguay.

Nutrition in Paraguay

HISTORY OF GOVERNMENTAL PARTICIPATION

The Department of Nutrition, an agency under the Ministry of Public Health and Social Welfare, is specifically concerned with the problems of nutrition in Paraguay. This agency began functioning in 1942 and continued active until 1949. The department was reactivated and reorganized in June of 1956 under the direction of Dr. Henri Teulon, a United Nations consultant in charge of the FAO Experiment in Nutrition in Paraguay.

Considering the scope of its activities and responsibilities, the Department has at present a very small staff—the director, a secretary, an office aide, and three statistical aides. At one time, however, the Department had 15 investigators and three dieticians.

From 1945 to 1948 about 20 dieticians graduated from the Escuela de Idóneos en Alimentación (a subdivision of the Escuela Dr. Andrés Barbero). Budget limitations permitted the hiring of only a few of these dieticians by the Ministry of Health. The rest of the graduates are involved in activities unrelated to their special training in dietetics. In the final part of this work I will discuss the activities of the Department of Nutrition during the second phase of its existence.

Since the solution on a national scale of the complex problems of nutrition depends on a joint and coordinated effort invovling several different ministries, the National Council on Nutrition was created (Executive Decree No. 2628 of 4 April 1957) to unify and intensify the study of nutritional problems and to plan an appropriate remedial program. The Minister of Public Health is the president of the Council, and the director of the Department of Nutrition is the secretary. Other members of the Council are the Minister of Treasury, Minister of Agriculture, Minister of Education and Worship, Minister of National Defense, Minister of Industry and Commerce, and the president of the Banco Central del Paraguay.

CURRENT STATE OF PROBLEM

So far as its nutritional problems are concerned, Paraguay is in no better situation than the majority of the countries of Latin America (Montalto 1956). There is still much to learn about the nutritional state of our population. With the exceptions of the National Alimentary Survey and certain isolated studies of limited scope, there has been no systematic study which could provide sufficiently complete data to properly evaluate the nutritional condition of the people in general, or yield specific information on the incidence of deficiency diseases, the nutritive value of our foods, or the cultural, social and economic factors related to improper nutrition.

Such studies as have been made were isolated and private in nature and generally incomplete. Some very good studies were done years ago, but these data are no longer applicable to current conditions in Paraguay. In order to be most useful, such studies must have the continuity which permits the evaluation of changes occasioned by the application of improvements in the production and use of foodstuffs.

Nevertheless, it is important to emphasize the valuable studies done by Dr. F. A. Montalto (1956). As director of the Department of Nutrition, he came very close to the heart of our nutritional problems. Many of the problems which he pointed out in his book continue unchanged to the present; others have been solved in part or completely; and still others have worsened.

It is true that during the last 20 years the country has experienced considerable progress, especially in the realm of public health: for example, the installation of a potable water system and two milk pasteurization plants in Asunción, the fluoridation of the Capital water supply, iodized salt, two major food and nutrition surveys, and the establishment of a food science laboratory and a national technical training institute. On the other hand, very little has been done up to the moment to raise the standard of living for the working classes, especially the rural population. These peoples are still entangled in the vicious circle of low production-poverty-malnutrition-disease.

The modern science of nutrition is still very new in our milieu, and, unfortunately, there may still be observed a certain indifference or even resistance to recognizing the great importance of nutritional factors in general pathology and especially public health. It is true that the combating of infectious diseases has a certain priority in the health program of a country. On the other hand, it does not seem prudent to continue to relegate nutritional problems to a lower level of importance. What success can the physician have, even using abundant medications, in curing a patient suffering from both infectious disease and malnutrition? Certainly the latter works considerable disadvantage to both the patient and the physician. The tendency on the part of the physician to disregard or belittle nutritional factors in individual and public health is perhaps simply a reflection of his professional training at the National University of Asunción, where there is neither professor of nor course in human nutrition.

The slight importance granted by many physicians to nutritional problems may be due simply to indifference or to a failure to recognize the magnitude of these problems. This latter is reflected in the vital statistics of the country in which figures for morbidity and mortality due to infectious diseases are relatively high, but show practically nothing in the way of cases of malnutrition other than a very few cases of avitaminosis. The fact is that improper diet or malnutrition is a serious problem in Paraguay and this must soon be admitted by all concerned with the health of the nation. It often happens that when the physician fails to find patent signs of malnutrition, he rules out nutritional factors as being contributory to the condition of the patient. But specific clinical signs of malnutrition are, at best, few, and the most frequent cases are those of incipient multiple deficiency in which the signs are vague or subclinical.

The lack of interest in or comprehension of the problem by the physician usually means that he fails to give the patient and his family adequate dietary instructions. Thus the malnutrition or deficiency disease follows its inexorable course and the price which must ultimately be paid is always high: either a long and costly hospitalization, or the death of the patient due to an overwhelming infection to which he could muster only token defense.

ECONOMICS OF NUTRITION

It is important to emphasize the fundamental role which nutrition plays in the economics of a country. It is well known that the smaller the income of a family, the greater is the relative amount spent on food. The acquisition of food holds first place among the several indispensables of life, it being directly related to the health and vigor of the individual and the preservation of the species. The priority of food over the other necessities of life which require the expenditure of energy for their acquisition takes on special importance for those persons employed as manual laborers. This type of unskilled labor brings in the least amount of money and at the same time requires a relatively greater caloric intake in order to support it. By inference then it may be concluded that the smaller the family income, the more difficult it is for the family to enjoy a proper diet.

The planning of a program of nutrition improvement (Rothman 1959) requires that certain basic information be available concerning the production and distribution of foodstuffs, the consumption of foodstuffs (dietary habits, nutritional value of foods), the nutritional state of the population, and the economic situation of the people. Each of these points will be commented upon in some detail in order to show that in Paraguay sufficient information already exists which might permit a more exact estimation of the nutritional state of the population than any such estimate made thus far.

The Production of Foodstuffs

Production is the first link in the long chain of events leading to food consumption. This subject will be briefly analyzed on the basis of the most important factors that affect production: the physical and biological aspects of the country, money, and manpower.

THE PRODUCTION OF FOODSTUFFS

The surface area of the republic amounts to some 406,752 km² or 157,047 mi². The climate is healthy. The average annual temperature is 22 C and the average annual rainfall is 1,500 mm (Warren 1946). Paraguay is composed of two principal regions ("Oriental" and "Occidental") separated by the Río Paraguay. The headwaters of this river lie far to the north in the Brazilian state of Mato Grosso. The river flows at an average rate of 3 km per hour, and has an average width of 500 meters, an average depth of 5 meters, and a total length of 2,500 km. The physical and economic characteristics of the two regions of Paraguay are quite different (see Chapter 2 for additional geographic details). The Río Alto Paraná separates Paraguay from Argentina and Brazil. It flows at an average velocity of 8 km per hour, has an average width of 400 meters, an average depth of 30 meters, and an overall length of 4,500 km.

PARAGUAY ORIENTAL

This region of the country has a surface area of 159,827 km² or 39,392,710 acres. It is abundantly supplied with natural waters in the form of some 3,000 rivers and streams. It is the agricultural region *par excellence* of Paraguay. The region is blessed with an extraordinary hydrodynamic potential capable of irrigating all of the tillable lands in the eastern region and of supplying electricity to the entire country. Forests cover some 19,273,800 acres, at least half of which remain unexploited. Grasslands, some 16,061,000 acres in extent, support about 2 million head of livestock. Tillable land, according to a 1957 survey, amounts to some 4,139,420 acres. Only 22% of this was being utilized in 1957; that represents about 0.94% of the total area of Paraguay (Tables 12.1 and 12.2).

PARAGUAY OCCIDENTAL, OR THE CHACO

This region has a surface area of 246,925 km² or 61,015,168 acres. About 60% of the Chaco consists of lowlands subject to inundation during the rainy season. The extensive grasslands support some 3 million head of cattle and horses. At least some of the land is tillable, as the Mennonites, with no little effort, have proved (see Chapter 10). Forests of palms and other trees, especially *quebracho,* are fairly extensive. Fresh water is one of the great limiting factors in the exploitation of the Chaco (rainfall is discussed in Chapter 4). Much of the ground water and most of the surface waters are brackish. The Río Pilcomayo runs across the Chaco, but the other "rivers" are more or less limited to the littoral of the Río Paraguay.

Economics of Food Production

POPULATION

According to the official census, 1,819,103 people lived in Paraguay in 1962 (see Chapter 11). This figure does not include some 30,000 more or less nomadic Indians. The Chaco which comprises 60% of the total surface area of the country, has only 4.1% of the population. About 35% of the Paraguayan population is urban. Some 50% of the urban population is concentrated in Asunción. 51% of the population over 12 years of age (31% of the total population) is referred to as "economically active." The population is comparatively young: about 44% of the people are less than 14 years old.

SOILS

The soils are generally fertile and productive in the eastern region. The land is well-suited to a wide variety of crops of good nutritive value—cereals, root crops, legumes, vegetables, and fruits. Some impoverished and eroded soils occur in central eastern Paraguay; deforestation has contributed to this situation, as well as lack of technical know-how to cope with it. By its very nature—extensive, rich, and virtually unutilized lands, favorable climate, adequate and well-distributed rainfall, and long growing season—Paraguay could well become the garden of America. However, in the 15 years covered by Tables 12.1 and 12.2, the amount of land, especially cultivated land, devoted to agriculture did not change in any significant way.

DISTRIBUTION OF RURAL PRIVATE PROPERTY

The land, especially as it is used in agriculture, is the base upon which rests the nutrition of the people of Paraguay. How that land is distributed in terms of ownership, along with other factors which will be mentioned below, gives an explanation for several socio-economic phenomena which bear directly and importantly on the question of nutrition. Table 12.3 shows that 43% of farm and ranch land is owned by only 25 landowners, each of whom owns at least 100,000 hectares. 50.2% of farm and ranch land is the property of 1,526 landowners. 98.7% of the landowners own but 6.7% of the land. From these figures it is obvious that the natural riches of Paraguay belong neither to the nation nor to the majority of people of the country. Some of the larger properties are operated by local representatives of absentee landlords. This situation is largely the result of the Law for the Sale of Public Lands, dated 16 July 1885, fifteen years after the end of the War of the Triple Alliance. The government sold huge tracks of land, especially in the Chaco, at truly bargain prices to various foreign speculators. Some of these estates have remained more or less intact to the present and are largely unproductive. From all of this I conclude that although Paraguay has the potential for agricultural development, the land largely remains poorly distributed and utilized.

CAPITAL

Capital, the result of human labor on the land, is deeply involved in the production of foodstuffs. According to Montalto (1956), Paraguay is semicolonial so far as its capital is concerned. It is colonial because the money which transforms the basic natural resources of the country into energy and credits is largely foreign in origin. Thus the country is *semi*colonial because Paraguay is economically dependent on foreign capital but is nevertheless politically autonomous. Paraguay must recognize this situation as it actually is and strive to recover as well its economic independence, which was also lost during the War of the Triple Alliance (1864–1870).

The *"gran capital"* has been and continues to be malutilized, in the sense that its objectives are not oriented toward the high necessities of the nation and that negligible amounts of the profits are reinvested within the country with the object of benefiting the community. In other words, "big money" has not produced those goods and services most needed by Paraguay, such as the production of foodstuffs. Rather the prime object of investment has been an easy and comfortable profit through the exploitation of the natural riches of the country—lumber, yerba mate, etc.—with no thought given to the renewal of those resources.

Only "small capital" is really representative of the nation, but it has been largely subordinated to foreign capital, which fact more or less explains why Paraguay is still one of the "emerging nations." Small private capital, often invested without guarantees, simply has not been able to produce economic benefits on the scale required. Private investors have avoided financial involvement in food-producing schemes, either because of unattractive returns or because of political instability.

Besides those drawbacks, there is the ever-increasing out-flow of monetary reserves that began at the end of World War II. These monetary reserves must be spent to make up the difference between the costs of imports and exports. The prices of exportable commodities have decreased while the price of required imports, such as machinery, have steadily increased. Then to the foregoing list, I must add inflation and the associated devaluation of currency. Under these circumstances, investors cannot even recover their investments, let alone profit enough from them to make new investments.

Static, unproductive capital, such as that involved in usury and exorbitant rents, is the kind least likely to contribute to the social and economic progress of the country. Laws prohibiting usury and exorbitant rents are just as necessary as laws protecting investment.

Do not forget that money for equipment and physical facilities is not the only factor in increasing production; also required is "human capital," the money required to educate and train people to do the many tasks required to achieve economic stability and a higher standard of living. But this is a very slow process. Paraguay has an abundance of manual labor, but even this valuable male resource is not efficiently utilized.

This great resource could be most effectively used in agriculture, but here, too, we often see idleness and inefficiency. It is important to note that in the United States of America and in Japan, agricultural investments have frequently brought the highest returns. This is because the most advanced techniques for improving production are utilized, such as modern implements, fertilizers, pesticides, improved seeds, all of which cost considerable money. Paraguayan farmers do not have that kind of money. Therefore they have no hope of improving techniques and production without a system of loans and credits for small farmers.

All of the negative factors cited above only serve to emphasize the urgent need for the establishment of corrective measures.

LABOR

Labor derives its dynamic character from man, the primary force in agricultural production.

The Paraguayan population emerged mainly from a cross between the Spanish conquistadores and Guaraní Indian women. Just after the Triple Alliance War (1864–1870), during which a very large proportion of the male population died, a wave of non-Spanish European migrants arrived in Paraguay. The people of Paraguay emerged with their own cultural and "racial" characteristics. A great variety of cultural and racial types went into the make up of the Paraguayan nation, but in spite of this the typical mestizo that emerged bore no trace of racial prejudice. The creation of this feeling of equality has been traditionally ascribed to the influence of the ancestral Guaraní matriarchs. Be that as it may, Mengüal has observed that "the Paraguayan, especially the farmer, is closely tied to tradition and the soil, has well-developed feelings of dignity and patriotism, is strong, patient, self-denying, hospitable, intelligent, and, finally, is generous, valiant and noble, both in peace and war."

But this "man of yesterday," the farmer, often subjected to conditions more than just hostile, living in extreme poverty, undernourished, physically weak, and without means of doing hard farm labor, cannot fulfill the requirements of the human factor needed for agrarian development.

Unfortunately, since the War of 1864–70, this manpower has been under-estimated by governments which have subjected it to ignorance and exploitation. As a result of this policy "The peasant is unstable because he lacks his own land, he wanders from job to job, is ignorant and backward, and for these reasons does not know how to take advantage of the land nor make the most of his work, nor manage the fruit of his labors; and what is worse, he cannot obtain from the land the food he needs for a balanced diet" (Mengüal 1962).

CONDITIONS OF WORK

The economy of Paraguay has been based up until now on farming and forestry. It is important to point out then the conditions required for the development of the agricultural population on the basis of natural products of the country.

TENANCY

According to the data provided by the Censo Agropecuario of 1956 (Table 12.4), 44% of the occupants of the land are squatters—lack title of ownership. This high percentage of squatters will convey some indication of the large numbers of people who just "vegetate" on the land. They have no interest in annual crops, let alone ones that require several seasons (sugar cane) or many years (fruit trees) to mature. Peasants and day laborers are hardly likely to volunteer for projects to improve someone else's land.

Knowing that agricultural production is the primary source of human and animal foods, and realizing that agricultural production has been very lethargic in Paraguay, it is easy to explain our present situation and to imagine what the future holds if this situation is not promptly corrected.

MINIFUNDIA

Table 12.5 indicates that 66.5% of the total farms censused had an area of 1 to 7.49 hectares. This small parcel of land is not big enough to give its occupants a useful return. An average of 5.7 persons lives on each farm. It is estimated that, under present conditions of production, a farmer requires at least 25 to 30 hectares to support his family and to make his efforts worth while in terms of profits.

On the other hand, of farms of 100+ hectares (representing 1.5% of all the farms of the nation), it is estimated that less than 5% are dedicated to agriculture. The rest are either used for cattle-grazing or not used at all. These farms (representing 53.1% of the total land under consideration) are in the hands of 1.6% of all the farmers censused.

The central zone of the country (within 150 km of Asunción) contains 70% of the agricultural population and is so compressed and overpopulated that it cannot accommodate any further agricultural development. This area, nevertheless, is responsible for 65% of the agricultural production or approximately 25% of the national income.

The foregoing introduces two great national problems: minifundia (farms that are too small) and latifundia (farms that are too large). I consider the second to be less serious; expropriation can solve it. The low productivity associated with minifundia is the more serious problem. At a conference sponsored by the National Agricultural Society, José J. Marqüez Vaz reported the results of a study of minifundia and pointed out its negative economic aspects—low net production, low per capita income, low family income, negligible working capital, and inefficient labor. This study was done at Yaguarón in the central zone of Paraguay; there was an average of 5 hectares per farm of the 1,400 farms that made up the 7,000 hectares of the study area. The average annual income per capita was Gs 6,844 ($54.32), about one-fifth the Latin American average ($250) and one-fortieth the United States average ($2,500).

Table 12.6 summarizes the results of this study and demonstrates the great difference between the two groups of farms. The farmer in the lower income group, far from getting a return for his capital, annually loses Gs 12,900, a net loss of 44%. Table 12.7 clearly shows the inefficiency of labor; even in the higher income group the farmer works only 137 days per year, when theoretically he should work 300 days. This means a great underutilization of available manual labor, with resultant low standard of living. Table 12.8 relates to the living conditions of farmers and reveals the predominance of one-room houses with walls of adobe or sticks, thatched roofs, and dirt floors. These data on living conditions in Yaguarón are very similar to those compiled by Reh (1946) and to those gathered in the national census of 1950 (Table 12.9).

The data on nutrition are scarcely more encouraging than those relating to housing. Simply stated, the people eat too little animal protein and too much food derived from root crops. Table 12.10 indicates how very small is the income derived from cultivated crops. In the case of Yaguarón, this low income results from several factors:

soil fertility, efficiency of labor (human and animal), efficiency of equipment, the type of crop, the market, and many other factors. With a few exceptions, the situation in Yaguarón is indicative of the conditions of farmers in the rest of the country. Other farming communities have been described by Service and Service 1954, Fretz 1962, and Stewart 1967.

CREDIT

If the fundamental factors of our economy are forestry, cattle-raising, and agriculture, then agriculture is certainly the factor most in need of help. In most parts of the nation, agriculture production has stagnated at low levels during the last three decades; in some cases there has been decreased production, and in a few regions very small production increases have occurred. The supply of agricultural credits to the farming community has been insufficient to say the least (Table 12.11), in spite of the fact that farming is the main activity of 65% of the nation's population. A credit of $2,900,000 from the International Development Bank and administered by the National Development Bank was specifically earmarked for the small farmer. But this will benefit only 3% of the small farmers. This sum seems small when one realizes that 156,700 families (about 50% of the national population) need help. Moreover, these families are living on 149,614 farms of which 148,157 are less than 10 hectares and 11,370 are less than 5 hectares. 100,000 farmers remain landless, in spite of the active land reform program of the Instituto de Reforma Agraria. A farmer has to have a small amount of capital to benefit from the available loans. The loan requirements which must be met are simply out of reach of most small farmers.

In the first year of its activity (20 September 1961 to 30 December 1962), the National Development Bank directed most of its aid to the major agricultural producers. Credits were given to sugar mills, sugar plantations, tobacco, cotton and rice growers, and to the agricultural cooperatives (Table 12.12).

Land reform is a laudable program, but the simple distribution of land will not improve an agricultural situation complicated by social and economic problems. Land certainly is a part of the whole problem, but it is not the primary problem. The more immediate necessities relate to the development of measures which will help the small farmer, guaranteeing him at least a decent living for himself and his family, and for his community. It is necessary to establish an enlarged system of credit for the development of the potential resources of the land. Nowhere else in the world has it been possible to augment agricultural production without long-term, low-interest loans; such would be even less probable in Paraguay with its low per capita income. Land reform will continue to fail so long as the government fails to provide adequate financial assistance to the small farmer. The success of agrarian reform will be dependent upon improvements in four things: ownership of land, credit, education for farmers, and marketing of farm products.

It is necessary to increase production in general and

agricultural production in particular in order to raise the standard of living in Paraguay. Only through economic and social progress can the vicious cycle of hunger-poverty-economic stagnation be broken. The improvement of nutrition is of course dependent upon an increase in food production, especially in those areas of the nation that are known to be nutritionally deficient. However, this increase in food production must be done in such a way that the soils do not become exhausted. Also, the clearing of forests to convert the land to agricultural production must be done with caution and with due consideration for the role of forests in the protection of the soil and their influence upon climate.

Any increase in the production of foods must be sufficient to accommodate population increases as well as to elevate substandard nutritional levels. For example, if the dietary regimen of 1980 is to be superior to that of the present, then milk consumption will have to increase by 81% and cereal grain consumption by 78% (FAO 1962a). By contrast, it is projected that the same end may be achieved in Europe by only a small increase in in consumption in these categories (milk, 45%; cereals, 22%).

Several factors enter into any attempt to increase food production: land tenancy, technical assistance, credit, crop and seed selection, availability and use of natural and synthetic fertilizers, and protection of crops from diseases and phytophagous insects. About 100 different crop varieties are good, and others leave much to be desired. Very few new varieties have been tested in Paraguay, and even when new varieties are proved suitable, the Paraguayan farmer tends to stick with the familiar varieties unless he has compelling reasons to change. Plant diseases and insect plagues cause enormous losses to crops, but very little money and effort has been spent in teaching farmers how to minimize these losses. The import tax of 51.5% on insecticides and seeds makes these important items unavailable to the small farmer. A progressive farming program is not likely to be undertaken by the landless, the indigent, or the unemployed; farming for both personal and national good requires a man who is competent by education and experience, one who has available to him the necessary technical and financial assistance.

MEAT PRODUCTION

Per capita consumption of meat appears to be decreasing as the population of Paraguay increases. A distinct increase in cattle production is required to meet this situation. Several essential factors enter into any such increase: breed improvement, pasture improvement, management of herd size within the limits of available pasture, and protection of cattle from diseases. Much more emphasis should be placed on poultry production.

The number of small ranch owners diminished during the period 1951–1957 (Table 12.13). These smaller operators owned 27.7% of the cattle in 1951 and 19.9% in 1957. Although the larger operators have taken over a larger share of the business, production remained essentially constant during the period recorded in Table 12.14. The percentage of private ownership in the ranching sector is much more satisfactory than in the other agricultural sectors: Of the 12,125,316 hectares occupied by cattle in 1954, 10,027,880 were in private ownership. Even though cattle production serves as a major source of revenue for the nation, production is not nearly as great as it could be if modern ranch management principles were practiced.

PARTICIPATION IN AGRICULTURE

The 1950 census listed 30% of the population as economically active; 54.6% of these were engaged in farming, ranching, and lumbering. This figure is much higher than the comparable statistic (20%) for North America (Figs. 12.1, 12.2, 12.3), yet North America accounts for 30% of world production in these categories. This indicates that modern techniques of farm production have not yet reached Paraguay in sufficient quantity. Since Paraguay is essentially dependent on its farming-ranching-lumbering complex for economic viability, then it would seem logical to devote the greatest available national resources to the development of this complex. One of the by-products will be the economic liberation of the peasantry.

Food Production

CATTLE PRODUCTION

600,000 head is the estimated average annual harvest of cattle; this figure has remained steady over the 20 years covered by Table 12.15. This harvest is drawn from a herd of about 5.5 to 6 million head. Cattle are raised for beef only; milk production is very incidental, and even the fattening of the beef cattle is rarely undertaken. The meat is not graded in any way. COPACAR has a monopoly on the beef supply to the local market in the metropolitan Asunción region.

It is only very rarely that an attempt is made to improve pasture quality; burning, however, is widely practiced throughout Paraguayan cattle country. The cattle are dependent upon natural sources of water, most usually rain water pools. Many cows die during seasons of prolonged drought. Even under normal conditions mortality is high, about 30% during the first year of life. Those cows that do reach a suitable age for market are generally underweight. Information on the meat packing industry in general and on the COPACAR in particular is given in Tables 12.16 and 12.17.

FARM PRODUCTION

Most of the people of Paraguay are engaged in farming, but their knowledge and tools are rudimentary. Farm production has in general been stationary during the 20 years covered by Table 12.18. Coffee, sugar cane, and wheat production have all increased, but decreases have occurred in other crops. Prices on the international market dropped by about 40% from 1955 to 1960; this has of course affected farm production in a negative way. Table 12.19 shows that farm production in 1958 reached the level of 1863. Farm products are exported in a crude

and unrefined or unprocessed form and therefore command lower prices on the market. Imports on the other hand are mainly manufactured items, the prices of which have increased more than 100% in recent years. This situation is not conducive to increased farm production, at least not to the level required just to meet the increasing population. The population increased 30% during the period 1952–1962, but farm production increased only 21% (Table 12.20), and the amount of new land brought under cultivation only 9%.

The per capita income revealed by the Yaguarón investigation was $54.32; the same figure for farming populations was $75 in 1950 and $76 in 1960. For the population in general during the same decade, the per capita income was about $100, which places Paraguay among the lowest income groups in relation to the other American states. Farming and ranching are the principal contributors to the gross internal product, but the amount of that contribution has decreased (Table 12.12): 44.5% in 1950, 41% in 1958, 37% in 1961. The share contributed by farming decreased from 28% in 1952 to 19.3% in 1961. The ranching share has held steady at about 16% since 1954.

The gross internal product has appeared to increase in recent years (Table 12.22), but when the inflation of the guaraní is taken into account, it can be shown that the gross internal product is actually declining (Table 12.23).

RECOMMENDATIONS FOR INCREASING
FOOD PRODUCTION

To increase the production of foods of plant origin, it will be necessary to increase the amount of land under cultivation, to employ fertilizers, to prevent erosion of cleared land, to select crop varieties on the basis of yield, resistance to pests and diseases, and tolerance of climatic conditions, to employ chemical and biological measures to control plant pests and diseases, to utilize modern management techniques such as crop rotation, soil enrichment by legumes and manures, irrigation, etc., and to emphasize and facilitate the mechanization of farming.

To increase the production of foods of animal origin, it will be necessary to utilize selective breeding to develop animals specially adapted to the climate of Paraguay, to employ modern techniques of feeding (supplements, antibiotics), housing, and pasture improvement, to encourage cooperative community programs of animal production, and to stimulate interest in better methods of animal husbandry and human nutrition through community and school agricultural clubs and projects.

Some Causes of Lethargic Productivity

LAND TENANCY

One of the primary factors associated with unnecessarily low agricultural production and low living standards of rural people is the fact that nearly 50% of the farmers work land they do not own. As squatters, they cultivate only a small plot for their own subsistence; little effort is spent on perennial crops or on techniques to improve either production or the fertility of the soil.

The Agrarian Reform Institute has distributed farms to more than 20,000 families, but 100,000 farmers are still landless. Land-owning farmers are outnumbered by landless farmers by 1 to 5. To correct this situation, about 15,000 farms should be distributed each year. Land available for distribution through ARI amounts to about 4 million hectares. This represents less than 10% of the total available agricultural land and about 25% of eastern Paraguay.

LACK OF TECHNICAL ASSISTANCE

Even some of those few farmers who have financial resources cannot take advantage of modern methods and machinery for lack of technical training. Progress in agriculture and, consequently, improvement in nutrition, are dependent on the 4 factors of tenancy, credit, education, and market. Illiteracy is still considerable: 34% of the economically active population are still imprisoned in the invisible jail of illiteracy, with scant prospects of building a better life for themselves or their communities. When meat is lacking from the farmer's diet, as is often the case, ignorance prevents the farmer from properly compensating for this deficiency by substituting foods that are available to him.

At least a primary school education for every farmer would be a major step in the right direction; but many farmers will require vocational education in agriculture, conservation, farm management, and marketing. The task of providing this specialized education rests with the Agriculture Extension Service. This service was started by STICA. Ten communities (San Lorenzo, Carapeguá, Eusebio Ayala, Encarnación, Villarrica, Concepción, Horqueta, Coronel Oviedo, San Ignacio, and Caazapá) now have two extension agents each, and 4 communities are also served by a lady home economics specialist. Five additional agencies were scheduled to be established by 1963.

The agricultural extension agent must, of course, have a thorough knowledge of the rural environment. Much of this knowledge must come from studies at the experiment stations. Greater financial support must be given to the existing experiment stations, and additional ones must be established. To do this, the Ministry of Agriculture and Ranching must receive a larger share of the annual national budget—that share was 2.1% in 1962 (Table 12.24).

LACK OF CREDIT ASSISTANCE

Credit for the small farmer is scarce in Paraguay. Private banks do not loan to farmers, and only occasionally loan to cattlemen. Business and commercial interests do get loans, especially short-term, high-yield, low-risk loans. The absence of a source of readily available credit means that the farmer must get along without modern equipment. There were, for example, 82,000 iron plows and 33,500 wooden plows in Paraguay in 1956. The low annual income of the farmer does not suffice for adequate housing or a respectable standard of living, let alone for modern equipment and supplies.

Low quality farm products bring low prices; efforts to improve are frustrated by adherence to traditional techniques of production, worn-out land, insect pests, and oppression by loan sharks and other opportunists in a position to take advantage of the farmer. The area of land cultivation declined by 20% during the period 1942–1962. In 1942 each farmer cultivated about 2 hectares; the amount was 0.6 hectares in 1961 (220,000 hectares were available to some 450,000 working farmers).

Like other developing countries, Paraguay must rely on its own human and natural resources, and these must be more effectively utilized. But foreign financial and technical assistance must be brought in to help speed up the process of modernization of agricultural production and to raise the now intolerably low standard of living. During the period 1952–1962, the developed nations invested only 0.4% of their combined gross national products in the form of assistance to the developing countries. This small amount falls short of either meeting the needs of the developing countries or straining the capabilities of the developed nations.

An FAO (1962a) report states that aid to the developing countries amounted to about 3.6 billion dollars a year. The report called for an increase to 5 or 6 billion dollars a year, which would represent only 0.5 to 0.75% of the gross national products of the industrialized nations. A contribution of this magnitude would permit each recipient nation to increase its gross national product by about 2% annually. It is possible, however, that the developing nations may be able to effectively utilize aid even in the amount of 1% of the gross national products of the industrialized countries since the capacity to efficiently utilize foreign assistance often increases in proportion to the amount of aid granted.

Also, it should be pointed out that foreign aid is distributed unequally among the recipient nations. Several other countries besides Paraguay have received a disproportionately small share of foreign assistance. Some much needed development programs have been initiated in Paraguay in spite of this.

One of the great hindrances to economic progress in the developing nations is the instability of the prices of export commodities. Tariff barriers in potential market nations also limit the quantity of exports. In spite of the fact that very little effort has been put into increasing the volume of exports from the developing nations, the value of the exports is about 8 times greater than the value of the international aid which they receive. Davee (1958) has commented on this to the effect that the transition from a developing to a developed nation will be delayed so long as insufficient internal investment, delayed diversification of production, token industrialization, and ineffective agrarian reform are tolerated.

NATIONAL COMMERCIAL POLICIES

Some idea of how commercial policy affects the economy, especially the food production economy, of Paraguay can be had by reviewing data supplied by the Banco Central del Paraguay.

Exports. Lumber and forest products and products of the farm and ranch form the basis of the export economy (Table 12.25). This table demonstrates the unfortunate fact that the diminishing volume of farm and forest products is being compensated for by an increase in meat exports. This trend not only weakens the economy but also further decreases the already small amount of meat consumed by the people.

The sale of export products represents the main source of revenue from private property in Paraguay (Tables 12.26, 12.27). Since the national economy is essentially an "export economy," it is profoundly affected by fluctuations of export commodity prices in the world market. Although the average tonnage of exports increased during the period 1957–1961 over the period 1952–1956, the dollar value decreased. There is a distinct difference in the nature of exported and imported products. The exports are largely in rough, crude or raw form: unsawn logs, unprocessed yerba mate, unspun or unwoven cotton, salted hides, and crude vegetable oils and tannin—all of which bring much lower prices than more completely processed items. By contrast, the imports are products of advanced manufacturing technology—whisky, wine, cigarettes, automobiles, canned foods, textiles, electrical appliances, etc.—all of which, for a developing country, are very expensive.

Until 1958, Argentina was the major recipient of Paraguayan exports. Since that time Argentina and the United States have about equally shared Paraguayan exports. Argentina's share of the export trade is shown in Table 12.28. Unsawn logs and crude yerba mate together accounted for 86.6% and 83.9% of the total value of exports in 1960 and 1962, respectively.

Imports. The major import item, comprising one-fifth of the total value of imports, is food (Tables 12.19, 12.30). Wheat, imported in the form of grain and flour, accounted for 75% of the value of food imports in 1956–1960, 67% in 1961, and 75% in 1962. Other important food imports are milk products, including dried milk, fruits and vegetables, both natural and canned, and confections. It seems paradoxical that a country so often described as an agricultural paradise would have to spend one-fifth of its import budget on food—food that can and should be produced at home.

One of the reasons that agricultural production has fallen far short of its potential may be seen in the statistics on farm implement importation: 2% of the total value of imports in 1956–1960, 1.2% in 1961, and 0.95% in 1962.

Sources of imported items are listed in Table 12.31. Since Argentina has traditionally been the obligatory outlet for many Paraguayan products and the source of many imported items, its roles in the economy of Paraguay in general (Table 12.32) and as a supplier of food (Table 12.33) are very important.

Taxes and duties on exports and imports. The tax structure of Paraguay is arranged in such a way that the producer has to accept low prices for his exports (Table 12.34) but pay high prices for his imports (Table 12.35).

This makes it very difficult for the farmer or rancher to acquire sufficient profits to finance modernization of his operation.

Insufficient governmental support of agriculture. Only 2% of the national budget was designated for the forestry-farming-ranching complex in 1961, in spite of the fact that this complex supplied 40% of the national income (Table 12.24).

Food Distribution

An increase in agricultural production is necessary to provide the population with adequate nutrition. Complementary to this is the necessity of improving the distributional system throughout the country. For example, in the major cattle-producing regions—Misiones and Presidente Hayes—the supply of animal protein in the diet is often greater than necessary for good health. But, for lack of an adequate distributional system, this excess protein does not reach those sections of the country where the diet is distinctly deficient in proteins of animal origin. Several of the factors entering into the complex problem of improving the distribution of foodstuffs will be considered below.

NATIONAL INCOME

The quality and quantity of foods consumed depends on fluctuations of the national income and its distribution among the various sectors of the population. Some foods—meat, milk, eggs, fruit, for example—are more expensive than others because it costs more to produce them. When the income of an individual is raised, he tends to consume more of these relatively expensive but very nutritious foods, while consuming less of the roots and tubers which are so common in the Paraguayan diet. Improvement of the economic situation generally brings about an improvement of the diet. The average annual income per capita in Paraguay was about $100 in the decade 1950–1960, which places Paraguay among the poorest of the developing nations. The rural population in general exists under economic conditions distinctly below the national average.

The situation in Paraguay can only be contrasted with that in the industrialized nations. Average annual per capita incomes were $2,100 in the United States, $1,500 in Canada, $800 in northwestern Europe, and $250 in Japan. The average for Latin America was $150. These inequalities between the developing nations and the industrialized countries are increasing rather than decreasing. The per capita income of the developing countries has increased on the average of 1% annually from 1950 to 1959. That figure for Paraguay was even less than 1% (Table 12.36), indicating a pace of economic progress scarcely adequate to cause any dramatic improvement in the socio-economic status of the people. By contrast, the average annual per capita income increased by $225 in the United States and by $200 in the European Common Market countries during the period 1950–1957.

The low level of personal income and the exaggerated inequality of its distribution in the various segments of the population actually hold back the economic progress of the industrialized nations: the developing nations constitute the greatest potential market for the products of the industrialized countries, but the purchasing power of the developing nations is inadequate.

A considerable portion of the people of Paraguay suffer hunger throughout the year, but it is especially common during the winter. A much larger portion, which includes many children, lack those nutriments necessary for the preservation of health and the full development of the body. Although the available foods could be more effectively used to provide better nutrition, the basic cause of undernutrition and malnutrition is poverty. The vicious circle of hunger, poverty, and unproductivity can only be broken by accelerating economic development and improving the quality and quantity of food products.

Food Prices

Seasonal shortages of certain food items and inadequacies of food distribution cause food prices to rise. Dietary habits are, of course, influenced by food prices and by personal income. Several factors which bear upon food prices are considered below.

BUYING POWER OF MONEY

Paraguayan currency, during the greater part of its existence, has been characterized by devaluation and instability. The monetary policy which permitted marked inflation to occur was terminated in August 1957. In the first five years of its operation, this new policy stopped the inflationary spiral and stabilized the guaraní in relation to the American dollar. A stable currency usually reflects a flourishing and balanced economy, but this is not the case in Paraguay. The stable guaraní is the result of extraordinary popular sacrifice, but the results have all been negative: sluggish production, unemployment, internal devaluation of currency, desertion of the peasant, and widespread discouragement. The people accepted this sacrifice because the promised rewards were great: stabilized currency should attract private foreign investment and international monetary assistance. But during the first five years of this new policy, private investments have not materialized save for some very small loans for public investment. In keeping with the advice of international economic organizations, the Banco Nacional de Fomento was created and charged with the task of moving the economy and stimulating production. The resources of this new bank had to be derived entirely from within Paraguay. It seems unlikely that simply placing restrictions on the circulating currency, an idea of foreign origin, would really strengthen the economy. The fact is that the only way to do this, while imparting impetus to economic and social development, is to increase production. Some indication of the purchasing power of Paraguayan agriculture is given in Figure 12.4.

NATURE AND VOLUME OF PRODUCTION

Prices are affected by supply: generally, the greater the supply, the lower the prices. In Paraguay crop and cattle production provide both food and income; the volume of food, however, is very small. The supply of vegetables is inadequate and seasonal. There is no way to preserve vegetables. Fruit production has fallen off in recent years. Paraguay used to supply the entire La Plata Region with fruits, but it now imports fruits in large volume. The production of sweet potatoes and manioc is stationary, and the supply of Irish potatoes is inadequate. Wheat, either whole grain or milled, represents about 60–74% of the total value of imported foods. Wheat production in Paraguay has greatly increased in recent years.

Cattle production is sufficient to supply either the home market or the export market, but not both. Hunting is done to secure pelts, and the quantity of meat secured thereby is negligible. Fishing is done by people who live near the rivers. The commercial fishery is much smaller than it could be. Yerba mate, a uniquely Paraguayan product, is gathered and processed today in the same manner as four centuries ago and volume of production has remained stationary during the past three decades. Yerba mate production was 22 tons in 1927, an annual average of 20 tons from 1928 to 1938, 18 tons (average) from 1938 to 1948, 11 tons (average) from 1949 to 1958, and 14 tons (average) from 1959 to 1962 (González 1962). Production of sugar and vegetable oils is insufficient to meet domestic needs; the processing plants are modern and well-equipped but production is far below capacity.

The legume harvest is inadequate. Soybean production especially should be encouraged. Soybeans do well in the soils and climate of Paraguay. The high protein content of the bean is much needed in those areas where proteins of animal origin are deficient. Two companies extract soybean oil for the domestic market. One company makes animal feed from the "cake" that is left after the extraction process; the other company exports the solid residue to Europe. The export price of this highly nutritive "cake" (45 gram% protein, 5 gram% fats) is very low. It is paradoxical that a highly nutritious food is exported at a low price so that foods of comparatively low nutrient value (Irish potatoes, wheat flour) can be imported at a high price. The Ministry of Industry and Commerce has investigated the potential for use of the soybean "cake" as human food.

TRANSPORTATION

The availability of adequate transportation affects both production and price of food products, especially perishable foods. The lack of the means for transporting products is one of the main causes for the persistence of subsistance agriculture in many parts of Paraguay. Being rich in the resource of manual labor, Paraguay could effectively use this resource in the maintenance of existing roads and the construction of new ones. The high-wheeled ox carts presently in use can in time make an unpaved road impassable for an ordinary truck. The installation of rubber tires on ox carts would prevent this damage and permit the hauling of a much heavier load.

Perishable foods require special care and handling

during transport if they are to arrive in marketable condition. At present great losses of such products are incurred because of improper handling and transport. Some effort must be made to acquire the necessary equipment for handling and transport of perishable produce and for the training of workers in this specialized area of transportation.

Transportation System

The government has given much emphasis in recent years to improving the highway system. The main highways—Asunción to Encarnación, Asunción to Puerto Presidente Stroessner, Concepción to Pedro Juan Caballero—have been or are being paved. Farm-to-market roads are being constructed. The Trans-Chaco Highway, a dry-weather dirt road, has been completed and provides an outlet to Asunción for the products of the Mennonite colonies of the Chaco.

There is rail service between Asunción and Buenos Aires via a ferry connection across the Alto Paraná River at Encarnación. Both the road bed and the rolling stock are ancient and in very poor condition. There are no boxcars equipped to handle perishable products. Rail service, now a federal operation, is both slow and expensive.

The federal merchant fleet has increased in recent years in both number of ships and tonnage of capacity (Table 12.37). With the exception of a few small wooden boats, all of the ships were purchased from foreign sources. Two shipping companies provide weekly service to Asunción from the United States and Europe. Only a comparatively small amount of freight is handled over the smaller interior rivers. This amount could be greatly increased by the acquisition of suitable ships.

The national and international airlines have previously concentrated on providing passenger service, but in recent years the amount of air freight has greatly increased. There are three national airlines and one international line in Paraguay: Línea Aérea de Transporte Nacional or LATN, and Transporte Aéreo Militar or TAM are passenger lines; Aerocarga is a freight line; Líneas Aéreas Paraguayas S.A. or LAPSA provides international freight and passenger connections to Brazil and Argentina.

Transport of foods in the interior of Paraguay. Food transport by rail, road, or river is accomplished in vehicles ranging from primitive to modern, but all lack the specialized accessories associated with modern food transport. There are no regulations relating to the transport, storage, packaging, or marketing of foods.

Transport of Milk. Metal milk cans are carried on trucks and rail cars and on the backs of donkeys and people. The law requiring pasteurization of milk was passed long ago, but it is still ignored.

Fruits, vegetables and root crops. These are transported in bulk, without special care, in ox carts and trucks; small amounts are carried by donkey and people.

Meats. Meat for consumption in the metropolitan area of the capital is transported under ice or mechanical refrigeration in trucks. In the interior, dressed beef is carried by horse cart. The small quantity of fish for market is carried in baskets by people.

Transport to foreign markets. Food products for export are packed and shipped in accordance with the sanitary requirements of the country of destination. River transport usually costs less than rail or truck freight. More freight leaves via the rivers than by any other route. The new bridges across the Alto Paraná and Apa rivers have opened markets in Brazil.

Storage and Marketing of Foods

STORAGE AND PRESERVATION OF FOOD ON THE FARM

Perishable foods have to be marketed immediately; there are no facilities for preserving perishable foods on the farm. The farms also lack storage facilities for more durable products such as grains. These, too, have to be put on the market immediately upon harvest. This lack of storage space prevents the farmer from taking advantage of higher prices during periods of scarcity, from engaging in the production of poultry or other feedlot animals, or from providing for the nutrition of his family during the off season.

STORAGE AND PRESERVATION OF FOOD IN THE CITY

There is only one public cold storage facility in the entire country, and its services are priced beyond the reach of the farmer. Most perishable foods, then, must be marketed immediately upon arrival in the city. There are limited facilities for the storage of grains and root crops; 57.5% of the total storage capacity is not being used (Table 12.38).

MARKETING OF FOODS

The process of marketing is a vital part of the campaign to improve the general nutrition of the country: marketing gets the food from the producer to the consumer. The products of the truck farms pass through a series of middlemen before they reach the consumer. Each one of these numerous transactions increases the price of the product and subjects the product to contamination as a result of unsanitary practices. In recent years several private markets have appeared which, for a premium price, offer food for sale under sanitary and modern conditions.

MARKETING OF MEAT

Enough meat is produced to adequately supply the internal demand; however, much of the available supply is exported in the form of canned meat, with the result that the domestic demand is never fully satisfied. Decree-Law 2810 of 6 March 1944 created COPACAR—Corporación Paraguaya de Carnes—which, besides canning meat for export, has the franchise for the sale of dressed beef to the butcher shops in Asunción and surrounding communities.

MARKETING IN RURAL AREAS

Contact between producers and consumers is generally direct: farmers sell directly to consumers, either door-to-door or in market places. Middlemen are not required in this system. The system does, however, tend to hold the people in a state of poverty. The farmers can sell only to local consumers, therefore the farmers produce only the kinds and quantities of crops necessary for their own needs and those of the local market. Their land may be capable of greater production in both quantity and variety, but if there is no market, there is no incentive. Both the consumers and the farmers are forced to settle for a monotonous dietary regimen.

Cash crops—cotton, tobacco, sugar cane—are traded for clothing and other necessaries and used to pay debts. Only the surplus foods are sold. The farm-to-market road system is bringing the products of the rural areas to the larger centers of consumption. This has a generally good effect on the farmer's standard of living, but there is at least one negative aspect of it: the farmer trades eggs, poultry and cheeses—items of high nutritional value—for white sugar, vermicelli, polished rice, candy and other items of lesser dietary value.

Recommendations for Improving Marketing

BETTER TRANSPORT
Equipment for handling perishable produce, especially refrigerated trucks, is required; expansion of the farm-to-market road system; regulation of food packing, handling, and transport.

WAREHOUSES
Storage facilities for perishable meats, fruits, and vegetables, and for grains and root crops need to be expanded and fitted with the necessary accessories.

PRODUCT CLASSIFICATION
Food products for sale should be graded, sorted, labelled and sold in units of equal quality so that the consumer can select the level of quality desired and then get what he pays for.

MARKETS
Construction of modern marketing facilities and their sanitary operation.

ECONOMICS
The farmer needs easier access to credit in order to support greater production and favorable marketing of his products.

COMPETITION
Monopolies should be restricted and competitive marketing encouraged.

COÖPERATIVES
Farmers' cooperatives should be established.

It is obvious that the national government must play an active role in all of the above.

The Food Industry
The food industry of Paraguay is in an early and weak stage: most of its products enter the domestic market. Its progress has been inhibited by a lack of technical and financial resources and an uncertain market (Centurión 1962). According to the 1955 industrial census, there were 2,732 industrial concerns in Paraguay; 27.7% of these dealt with food products.

COTTAGE INDUSTRY
The food production industry has changed very little from colonial days. Now, as then, it is largely a cottage industry involved in the production of cheeses, lard, manioc flour, meat stew, baked goods, candies and soft drinks.

FACTORIES
In addition to the cottage industries, there are factories for the refining of sugar, canning of meat, production of wheat flour, and the milling of rice. The output of these factories is insufficient to meet domestic demands; the deficit has to be made up by imports. All of these food-processing plants have suffered from lack of capital and technical assistance. Some plants are capable of increasing production, but lack the necessary capital (Table 12.39).

Table 12.40 indicates that the production of canned meats, sugar, and baked goods increased during the period 1945–1962, but quantities of other products either remained stable or declined.

The establishment of additional food processing plants for farm crops could benefit both the farmers and the consumers. Preserved foods can be sold throughout the year, are easily stored, and are imperishable; seasonal surpluses of fruits and vegetables can be marketed rather than lost. Preserved foods are generally easier to transport and usually occupy much less space than the raw product. Pathogens are eliminated during the preservation process.

FREE TRADE
The creation of the Latin American Free Trade Association has opened the door to a potential market of 160 million people. Fruits and vegetables, canned meat, milk products, and edible oils are especially suited to this new market. Credit, technical assistance, and a progressive governmental policy will be required to help the producers and processors to benefit from this new opportunity.

FIVE-YEAR PLAN
A plan for the improvement of agriculture was initiated in 1963. This plan embodied several recommendations: land tenure—distribution of 1,000 titles of ownership each year; taxes—reduction or abolishment of taxes on items essential for increasing production, especially seeds, fertilizers, pesticides, hardware and implements, and breeding stock; export duties—reduction or elimination of duties on certain exported agricultural products; price

controls—elimination of price controls and return to an economic system based on supply and demand; protection of the farmer—benefits of tax and duty reduction will be directed to the farmer, not to the middlemen; federal spending on agriculture—at least 4% of the national budget will go for improvement of agriculture; tax evasion—closure of tax loopholes and more efficient collection of taxes; luxury tax—imposition of higher taxes on luxury imports; technical assistance—utilization of foreign technicians; credit—loans for increasing production ($20 million), buying modern farm equipment ($12.5 million), improving storage facilities and marketing practices ($5 million); farm-to-market roads—construction and maintenance; and campaigns against diseases of plants and animals.

Production was projected to increase by 10% a year, or 50% by the end of the five years, using 1958–1960 as a base. It was estimated that about 15% of this increase would be nullified by a 15% increase in the population; this would leave 35% available for export. Meat production was gauged at a slower pace—4% annually or 20% during the five years—than agricultural production. A 50% increase in forestry production was also projected for the five-year plan. The value of all exports in 1968 was 56% greater than the 1958–60 average.

The Availability of Foods

GENERAL CONSIDERATIONS

The "National Food Balance Sheets" indicate the quantity of various foods available to each person. From these figures it is possible to calculate average values—total calories consumed, amount of protein, amount of animal protein, amounts of carbohydrates and fats, etc. When these average values fall below the recommended levels, then that diet is considered inadequate in respect to the deficient value. However, the food balance sheets do not indicate what sector of the population (geographic region, socio-economic group, occupation, etc.) happens to be suffering malnutrition.

The Department of Nutrition of the Ministry of Public Health and Social Welfare is responsible for preparing the food balance sheets. Some of the data on availability of foods discussed below were made available to me by Dr. Tamara de Vega, Director of the Department. The accompanying tables provide basic information on human nutrition in Paraguay: caloric requirements (Table 12.41), dietary essentials (Tables 12.42, 12.43), availability of foods (Table 12.44), and caloric content of foods (Table 12.45).

These data indicate that the requirements for calories and essential nutrients are amply met, with the exception of vitamin A, calcium, and riboflavin. However, as mentioned above, the data do not reveal which sectors of the population have dietary deficiencies; and the values obtained from groups of high availability mask those of low availability.

AVAILABILITY OF MILK

The food balance sheets show that each Paraguayan has available to him 218.95 grams of milk each day. A study by the Department of Nutrition, conducted from 1959 to 1961, showed that the consumption of milk per person in the interior amounts to 101.90 grams daily compared to 243.89 grams in Asunción. Moreover, 35.6% of the people of the interior, and 28.13% of the entire population of the country do not have milk available to them. Milk, of course, is very important in human nutrition, especially the nutrition of children. It is therefore appropriate to determine just what the milk requirement is for the people of Paraguay. Using data supplied by the National Institute of Nutrition (Buenos Aires 1961), the minimum milk requirements for Paraguay are as follows: 0–4 years—600 ml/day; 5–9 years—700 ml/day; 10–15 years—800 ml/day; 15+ years—500 ml/day; pregnant or lactating—1,000 ml/day. The estimated population of Paraguay in 1961 was 1,803,000. This population was age-grouped as follows: 0–4 years—16.4%; 5–9 years—14.8%; 10–15 years—12.6%; 15+ years—56.2%. On the basis of these data the milk requirement was calculated, as shown in Table 12.46.

From the figures in Table 12.46, the national daily requirement is 0.5838 liters x 1,803,000 people or 1,052,591 liters. To this figure must be added the extra requirement of gravid and lactating women. The number of births during the year 1961 also gives the approximate number of pregnant women (the error introduced by abortions cannot be estimated; but, since the abortions usually occur before the fourth month of pregnancy, the milk requirement has not greatly increased over that of a non-pregnant woman). There were some 64,800 births (or pregnant women), thus, 64,800 x 0.5 liters = 32,400. An estimate of the number of lactating women can be derived from the number of living children less than one year of age; that number was approximately 63,105. Therefore, 63,105 x 0.5 liters = 32,552 liters. In summary, we have the requirement of the non-Indian population—1,052,591 liters; extra requirement of the pregnant population—32,500 liters; extra requirement of the lactating population—32,552 liters; total—1,117,543; daily requirement per person—0.62 liters.

The Boletín Estadístico (Banco Central del Paraguay) reports that milk production for the year 1961 was 129.2 million liters. This means that each day 353,972 liters were available to the total population of 1,803,000, or 0.1986 liters per person. Thus the amount of milk available falls far short of the amount actually needed (31.6% of the calculated minimum requirement). It is extraordinary that this could happen in a country where cows outnumber people 3 to 1. This deficiency has at least two causes, both of which are amenable to correction: poor quality of the native breeds of milk cows—this can be corrected by bringing in specimens of breeds with proven production records in the Paraguayan climate; poor feeding of milk cows—this can be corrected by supplementing the feed with bone meal and the solid residues left after the extraction of soybean, peanut, and cottonseed oils, materials that now are largely exported.

AVAILABILITY OF MEAT

The food balance sheet shows that each Paraguayan has available to him 121.17 grams of meat each day. Some 600,000 head of beef cattle are marketed each year: live weight averages 325 kg, dressed, 165 kg. Figures on meat consumption are given in Table 12.47. These data show that the Armed Forces, with 10% of the population of the capital, consume 50% of the beef cattle. The metropolitan population of the capital consumes 1.5 times as many head of beef as the rest of the people of the country.

A reveiw of meat consumption over several years (Table 12.48) shows that the amount of meat available to the population of the capital and the interior regions has been decreasing, while the amount destined for the military population and for the meat-canning industry (largely an export industry) has been increasing. If cattle production does not increase, and if there is continued increase in the amount of beef for canning, then it can be expected that the supply of meat for the general population will continue to be inadequate, especially in view of the 3% annual increase in the population. It will be especially difficult for the small farmer to secure a balanced diet for himself and his family, one, because he cannot afford the more nutritious (and expensive) foods, and two, because he has no idea what a balanced diet is.

There is great disparity in the use of the more expensive foods such as meat, milk, and eggs. For the price of 100 grams of eggs, the farmer can get 1,000 grams of corn, 3,000 grams of mandioca, or 300 grams of hardtack, sugar, bread, or vermicelli. For the price of a liter of milk the farmer can buy 7 or 8 kg of mandioca, 1 kg of sugar, 2.75 kg of corn, or 1.25 kg of hardtack.

The citrus fruits are seasonal in availability; abundant in season, scarce at other times, and there is no means of preservation which would carry over these fruits into the scarce season. Cereal grains are subject to considerable losses before reaching the market (an estimated 35% of the corn is lost, for example). These losses can be attributed to deficiencies in handling, transport and storage; the effects of these losses on availability and prices are obvious.

Food Use and Dietary Customs

FOOD USE

Dietary surveys of representative groups of the population provide detailed information concerning the uses of foods. Such a survey requires the consideration of biologic, ecologic, economic, and cultural factors. Concerning biologic factors, it is necessary to determine the nutrient values of the foods, the quantities and kinds of foods available throughout the year, and their adequacy in meeting the nutritional requirements of the population.

Ecological factors to be considered are the geographic location of the population, the climate, the biotic environment, the kind of housing, and other features of the living conditions of the people. On the economic side, there must be considered the costs of the various kinds of foods in relation to the food budget, and the relation of the food budget to income. Also studied are cultural factors such as practices relating to food production, selection, and preparation.

The dietary survey, therefore, goes far beyond simply recording quantities of food, as is done in preparing the food balance sheet. The survey gets at the basic causes of malnutrition, and concerns itself with all the associated economic, cultural, ecological and biologic factors.

FOOD SURVEYS

The first food survey was done in 1940–1944 under the direction of Emma Reh, nutrition specialist of the Institute of Interamerican Affairs. Two areas were chosen for study: a rural village (Piribebuy, in the province of Cordillera), and a metropolitan barrio (Barrio Obrero in Asunción). An additional but smaller study was done in the rural village of Caapucú in the prairie province of Paraguarí, a cattle-ranching region. Calculations were based on nutritional norms supplied by the United States and Argentina. Some of the food and water analyses were done in the United States.

For results of the Reh survey see Table 12.49.

ANTHROPOMETRIC RESULTS

Average height and weight in the various age groups turned out to be well below "normal." The cause of this departure from "normal" could be nutritional or genetic; the actual cause has not been determined, but a genetic cause would have much less serious implications than a nutritional cause (Table 12.50).

CALORIES

The Piribebuy group averaged 3,200 calories per person per day; the Asunción group, 2,800 calories. In the rural group 7% of the families consumed less than 2,400 calories per person per day. In the urban group 10% had less than 2,400, and 70% had less than 3,000 calories. In general terms, the rural and urban groups had the same categorical sources of calories: 14% from proteins, 30% from fats, and 50% from carbohydrates. In Piribebuy mandioca was the principal carbohydrate source, and this food alone contributed 30% of the total caloric intake. The urban group got most of their carbohydrates from wheat.

PROTEINS

The recommended minimum protein intake was 70 grams per person per day. Both the rural and the urban groups exceeded this minimum, with 93 grams and 88 grams, respectively. However, 20% of the rural families ingested less than the recommended minimum, but in no case was the intake less than 54 grams.

CALCIUM

The recommended calcium intake was 0.80 grams per person per day. Neither the rural (with 0.36 grams) nor the urban (with 0.29 grams) groups met this standard. About 50% of the rural families and 80% of the urban families took in less than 0.34 grams.

IRON

Iron is abundant in the Paraguayan diet: intake was 2.5 times the recommended minimum at Piribebuy, and 0.66 times the minimum in Barrio Obrero. The main sources of iron were meat and mandioca. The latter becomes enriched with iron when it is cooked in an iron pot. Tests of the comparative iron content of cowpeas grown in the United States (7.0 mg%) and in Paraguay (4.4 mg%) cause some doubt to be cast upon the assertion that the Paraguayan diet is rich in iron. However, hemoglobin tests on the members of 26 Piribebuy families showed a large proportion of non-anemic individuals.

IODINE

The prevalence of goiter in Paraguay is indicative of the scarcity of iodine. Iodized salt was introduced into general use in 1958, specifically to correct this problem.

FLUORINE

The fluorine content of well water is adequate, but water supplies derived from surface waters are deficient in fluorine. The Asunción water system has been fluoridated since 1959.

VITAMIN A

In the era of this alimentary survey, mangoes were abundant and cheap in the capital and were widely used. The vitamin A intake of the urban group was about 7,000 IU, easily exceeding the recommended minimum of 5,000 IU. The climate of Piribebuy does not favor so much the abundance of mangoes. This is reflected in the average vitamin A intake of 4,000 IU; 60% of the rural families had diets deficient in vitamin A. The population in general derives a small amount of vitamin A from yerba mate.

THIAMIN

In the rural areas, 60% of the families had diets deficient in thiamin; 90% in the urban areas. The recommended minimum was 1,800 micrograms, but the rural group at Piribebuy averaged only 1,300 micrograms per person per day.

RIBOFLAVIN

In both the rural and urban populations the diet was deficient in riboflavin. The amount consumed came to only about 50% of the recommended minimum. It is possible that the habitual use of yerba mate provides small amounts of thiamin and riboflavin.

ASCORBIC ACID

More than 50% of the Barrio Obrero families exceeded the recommended minimum of 75 milligrams per person per day, thanks to the abundance of mangoes. 90% of the Piribebuy families had intakes less than the recommended allowance.

Factors Affecting Dietary Adequacy

ECONOMIC STATUS

In Table 12.51, dietary adequacy is related to economic status and occupation. The highest income families were deficient only in calcium, riboflavin, and ascorbic acid; all the other families were deficient in every category except proteins and iron. The food of the highest income group cost more than double that of the lowest income group. The diet of farm families was generally better, except for vitamin A and riboflavin. Data on the cost of living are given in Table 12.52.

PLACE OF RESIDENCE

The cost of food per person was about 20% greater in the villages than in the rural areas. In terms of meeting the recommended minimum dietary allowances, however, the village diet was superior to the rural diet, except for iron. The preponderance of mandioca in the rural diet explained the greater quantity of iron. Other comparisons between rural and urban families are given in Table 12.53.

HEAD OF HOUSEHOLD

The cost of food per person was about 30% greater in those households headed by men than in those headed by women. The more expensive diet was generally better than the less expensive, except for vitamin A intake, which is accounted for by the fact that the families headed by women were generally poorer and had to make do with the cheaper internal organs, especially the liver, of beef cattle.

SEASON

Food intake is greatest in December-January, when the harvests begin. The intake of the various essential nutrients, especially vitamin A, is also greatest during this period.

Reh's (1946) Recommendations

"The improvement of the Paraguayan diet does not require the introduction of new and unknown foods. All that is necessary is to increase the consumption of certain well-known foods; but this solution immediately creates a problem both economic and educational. The most serious deficiencies—insufficient intake of calcium and some of the vitamins—can best be remedied by increased consumption of milk, leafy and other kinds of vegetables, and fruits."

MILK

There are as many milk cows in Piribebuy as there are families. These cows are pasture fed and produce about 0.1 liters per person per day. The means for increasing milk production have already been discussed.

GREENS AND OTHER VEGETABLES

The required local varieties of vegetables are already available; production of these needs to be extended throughout the year, which is possible in Paraguay, and consumption needs to be increased.

FRUITS

There are many varieties of fruits in Paraguay, but all of

them require improvement in quality and quantity. The orange season could be prolonged by the introduction of early- and late-bearing varieties. Other nutritious fruits are available when oranges are not.

CALCIUM
Calcium is derived from milk and milk products and from green vegetables. Increased consumption of these foods is the only practical way to improve the diet with respect to calcium.

EDUCATION
The public must be taught what constitutes a wholesome diet and how to select the most nutritious foods with the money at their disposal.

PERSONAL OBSERVATIONS
The reader may wonder why I have described in detail a study done 28 years ago. There are several reasons. It was the first bone fide food survey in Paraguay; the results can be compared with more recent surveys; and the diet of the people of Piribebuy has diminished in quality since that time. When that survey was conducted, it was the habit of the school children to carry lunches consisting of a mixture of peanuts and parched corn. Nowadays, if a lunch is carried at all, it consists of a couple of hardtack biscuits.

In the epoch of the Reh survey, Paraguay annually produced some 14,000 tons of peanuts, most of which went into the domestic food market. In 1962 peanut production amounted to about 9,000 tons, a figure typical of annual production during the preceding decade. Most of the current crop goes for the extraction (at a rate of about 25%) of edible oils for export. One cannot help but wonder about the effects of the diminished consumption of this wholesome food, and its substitution in the diet by less nutritious foods.

The opening of farm-to-market roads is normally considered a distinct economic advantage for the farmer. It may, however, work to the disadvantage of the peasant farmer. Thanks to the new roads, he sells his food crops immediately upon harvest, when the price is lowest; later these same foods are available to him only at much higher prices.

National Food Survey of 1959–1961
A representative sample of the population was statistically selected on the basis of the 1950 census. The survey included 10 communities, one in Asunción and nine in the interior. Ranching, farming, industrial, commercial, and mixed communities were included. Food consumption was recorded for seven consecutive days, as was the weight and height of the consumer. Customs regarding weaning were noted. The survey included 462 families: 124 in Asunción (648 persons) and 328 in the interior (1,922 persons). 30% of the families were resampled during a six-month period in order to include seasonal variation in the study. Information was collected about cultural habits relating to foods, income,

tenancy, ownership, housing, weaning, hygiene, etc. Some of the Asunción respondents did not volunteer information about income.

OBJECTIVES OF SURVEY:
To determine by means of standardized FAO techniques the characteristics of food consumption, to define measures to improve diet, and to compare intake of essential nutrients in Paraguay with international standards (supplied by the Instituto de Nutrición de América Central y Panamá, and adjusted to local climatic conditions), and to determine the cost of foods.

DAILY PER CAPITA CONSUMPTION OF FOODS
   (Table 12.54)
The diet of families residing in the capital was diversified. The diet of the interior villages was dominated by roots and tubers (90% mandioca), except in Fuerte Olimpo, and deficient consumption of vegetables, eggs, fish, and milk (Fuerte Olimpo was again exceptional with regard to milk consumption—it is located in a region of ranches and had the highest per capita intake of milk).

ADEQUATENESS OF DIET
   (Table 12.55, Figures 12.5, 12.6, 12.7)
For calcium and riboflavin, the percentage of adequateness seems related to economic status, while vitamin A deficiency affects all economic levels. It is suggested that besides the economic determinants (which, according to the preceding statements, do not appear to be applicable across the board) the level of education, especially as it applies to an understanding of what constitutes adequate diet, is an important determinant of dietary adequacy.

ORIGIN OF CALORIES AND NUTRIENTS (Table 12.56)
For the interior population, root crops, especially mandioca, dominate the diet and provide 30% of the total calories, 33% of the calcium, 70% of the vitamin C, 26% of the thiamin, and significant amounts of the other essential nutrients. For the Asunción population, cereals supplied most of the calories and thiamin, fruits most of the vitamin C, and milk most of the calcium.

PROTEIN OF ANIMAL ORIGIN (Table 12.57)
Meat is scarce in the diet of the interior population, except for the villages of Horqueta (Concepción), Fuerte Olimpo, and General Delgado (Presidente Hayes).

MILK AND CHEESE (Table 12.58)
Milk consumption is very low in the interior, and this fact accounts for the general deficiency of calcium. Very little cheese is eaten; mostly cheese is used as a condiment with traditional Paraguayan dishes (*sopa paraguaya, chipá, mbeyú,* and generally on all foods made with corn or manioc flour).

ORIGIN AND COST OF FOODS (Table 12.59)
Generally, people buy most of their food rather than raising it on their own premises. Upper class families

produce 60–70% of their own food on their own property. On the average there was little change noted in production or prices at the time of the resurvey. In several villages, however, per capita weekly prices did change significantly: Rosario (San Pedro), +32%; Horqueta, +5; Asunción, +11%; Fuerte Olimpo, –30%.

SEASONAL VARIATION IN FOOD CONSUMPTION
   (Tables 12.59, 12.60)
Season does not appear to have any pronounced effect on the quantity of foods consumed or on the adequateness of the diet.

SUMMARY OF FOOD CONSUMPTION FACTS
Diversified diet in the capital; monotonous diet in the interior, with mandioca and corn predominating. Deficient consumption of milk, fruits, eggs, fish, and green vegetables (the latter used mainly as condiments with other foods). Diet deficient in vitamin A, calcium, and riboflavin, but adequate in the other essential nutrients. The importance of education in the role of good nutrition is indicated by across the board deficiencies in all socio-economic groups. Cultural practices have an effect: liver and other visceral organs are considered foods of the poor, with the result that the poor get more vitamin A than the wealthier people. In spite of the fact that the wealthier classes often spent 2.5 times more money on food than did the poor, the diet of the rich was not markedly more adequate in terms of essential nutrients. The wealthy people of the interior produce a large proportion of their food on their own premises; the poor on the contrary produce very little of their own food. There do not appear to be significant seasonal variations in either quantity of food consumed or adequateness of the diet. The influence of cultural, economic and educational factors in the national diet will be considered later.

EVALUATION AND CONCLUSIONS
The objectives of this recent national food survey were achieved, and the data will be useful in planning the social and economic development of Paraguay. It should be borne in mind, however, that there are several circumstances that made the national diet look better than it actually is. The frame of reference for the survey was the dietary standard supplied by FAO. Certainly a more accurate picture of dietary adequacy could be obtained if the standard values had been obtained from analyses of Paraguayan foods. In any program of national dietary improvement it is important to utilize local food resources. In order to have on record for use in future surveys the nutrient values of Paraguayan foods, the Ministry of Health and Social Welfare has established a laboratory of bromatology. This laboratory is now in the process of analysing Paraguayan foods, beginning with mandioca, the dominant food in rural Paraguay. Analyses of raw mandioca, reported above, have been completed. The effects of cooking, not only on mandioca but on all local foods, will be studied. Mandioca, for example, loses about 55% of its ascorbic acid during cooking, but, when boiled in an iron pot, becomes enriched with iron.

Paraguayans ingest enormous quantities of yerba mate. This food does not figure in the FAO tables of food values. Certainly yerba mate contributes vitamins and minerals to the diet. The analysis of yerba mate is one of the important future jobs of the laboratory of bromatology.

Implicit in the term wholesome diet is the necessity of a correct balance of nutrients—the ratio of carbohydrates to proteins, thiamin to calories, riboflavin to proteins, calcium to phosphorus, etc. Such relations cannot be determined until the composition of the local foods is known.

In making determinations of adequacy of the various nutrients during the survey, it was assumed that the sample population was healthy, that is, not suffering from any acute disease. Yet the fact that a large proportion of the Paraguayan population suffers from nematode infestations probably means that the recommended minimum allowances are inadequate. Certainly the nutrient requirements of a parasitized person are different, and probably higher, than a non-parasitized person. Thus the high iron intake discovered during the survey may in fact be a deficient iron supply for a parasitized person.

The final deficiency of the food survey has to do with the averaging of values obtained from each of the survey samples. This of course masks the notably deficient values, making the national diet look much better than it actually is for certain groups within the sampled population. It is very important not to average the data from the capital with those of the interior—dietary habits are markedly different in the two areas.

Effects of Economics on the National Diet
INCOME AND NUTRITION
Economic factors exert a distinct influence on the kinds, quality, and quantity of foods consumed. Low income often prevents the acquisition of foods of adequate quality and quantity. To determine the role of income in influencing the adequacy of the diet, it is necessary to calculate how much an adequate diet costs and compare this figure with available family income (Scrimshaw 1949). No one can spend all his income for food; a realistic income has to cover food costs as well as the other necessities of life. Malnutrition regularly accompanies low wages and affects both the wage-earner and his family. The most nutritious foods—milk, meat, eggs, etc.—are also the most expensive foods and as such they are generally unavailable to low-income families.

Low income is the major cause of malnutrition in Paraguay. A general increase in buying power is urgently required to correct this situation. An increase in the buying power would require a major overhaul of the economic structure of Paraguay. To achieve some perspective on the economic situation in Paraguay, the relationship of cost of living to wages will be examined. This study will be based upon a "worker," as recommended by the International Labor Organization. In Paraguay the situation of the rural worker is quite different from that of the urban worker; the latter will be discussed here.

The minimum wage is officially set by the Labor Department; this minimum wage, however, applied only to unskilled labor. The income of the worker plus any money earned by other members of his family constitutes the family income. A Department of Nutrition study showed that "family income" averages about 20% greater than the income of the unskilled worker alone. It is the family income of course that has to be compared with the cost of living.

Table 12.61 indicates that the discrepancy between wages and cost of living has tended to decrease in recent years: in 1952 wages covered 38.7% of the cost of living, in 1961, 77.8%. It would appear that wages never quite catch up to the cost of living. Every time wages are fixed at a new higher level, prices go up accordingly, but wages nevertheless remain fixed for a certain period of time. This chronic discrepancy doubtless has its effects upon the quality of the diet.

It is appropriate here to note just what necessities of life can be acquired with the laborer's income (Table 12.61). Income barely covered the costs of food, housing, clothing, light, and fuel in 1955. By 1961 most of the worker's needs were covered by his income. Another study (Table 12.63) indicates that the income of the average worker finally exceeded cost of living in May 1961. These studies, however, deal only with steadily employed persons. There are, of course, unemployed persons whose buying power is essentially nil, and those workers whose jobs are interrupted for one reason or another.

Improvement of the nutritional state of the laborers of Paraguay is dependent upon the solution of economic problems. Costs of food, housing, and illness regularly consume 75% of the worker's income, a fact that is often overlooked in planning for the improvement of the public health.

Effects of Educational, Social, and Cultural Factors on Diet

Just how much or how little people understand about the nature of a wholesome diet is reflected in their food habits. Of course, the quality of diet generally improves when economic advantages permit an improvement in the standard of living. Ignorance of human nutrition, however, cuts across all economic levels, as was demonstrated by the national survey of food consumption. Therefore, any improvement of the nutritional situation depends not only upon greater buying power, but also upon education of the people as to what constitutes good nutrition. More than just pointing out what to eat, it is necessary to impart a knowledge of the various categories of essential foods, how to produce them, and where to acquire them.

It is not enough, as is often heard, to simply tell the farmers to eat less mandioca. Where else would they get the calories and nutrients supplied by this important food? To tell them to eat less mandioca would be sensible only if one could suggest a substitute crop with similar low cost-high yield characteristics. Certainly the farmers cannot afford to buy enough of the more expensive foods to provide them with the nutrients they normally get from mandioca. Public education on nutritional matters must cover all aspects of the subject: production, selection on the basis of both price and nutritive value, and preparation of foods in the home in such a way that essential nutrients are conserved.

FOOD FOLKLORE

In human society the diet has acquired a significance that goes beyond the simple nutrition of the body (INCAP 1960); certain foods have social significance that has nothing to do with their nutritive value—white bread is preferred to dark, highly polished rice to less polished, mandioca flour over mandioca meal. Cultural factors, therefore, have to be dealt with in any program of dietetic education, but no overnight changes in tradition need be expected.

Some of the most common beliefs in the food folklore of Paraguay are listed below (González Torres 1958). Some people avoid intrinsically beneficial foods (Paraguayan stew, pork, kidney beans) because they are considered "heavy" or "indigestible." "Hot" foods (fats and oils) must be avoided by people with fevers. Meat and milk should be avoided during bouts of diarrhea. "Cold" foods (fruits and vegetables) are preferred during illness. Fruits, however, are incompatible with milk and alcoholic beverages (nevertheless, *clericó* is a popular refreshment consisting of chopped fruit in semisweet wine).

Another common belief is that citrus fruits should be avoided during menstruation. Some pregnant women eat less from the sixth month on so that the baby will not grow so large and labor will be easier; others believe that eating eggs causes "dry labor" and eating liver causes dark complexioned children. Persian limes cause jaundice, and fruits with small seeds (e.g. grapes) or fibrous seeds (mangoes) cause appendicitis. Citrus fruits cause coughing so they are avoided by persons ill with colds or the grippe.

Some foods (honey, eggs) have aphrodisiac qualities. Some people believe that green vegetables do not possess any food value, and others believe they are good only for *gringos* or for animals. Many kinds of medicinal herbs are relied upon in times of illness. Visceral organs of cattle are considered food for the poor (although in the Capital the price of these is rather high because of the market for them among foreigners). Rural people always prefer corn to kidney beans, the latter being a socially inferior food.

Mothers generally feed their newly-weaned children gruels of semolina, rice, and various flours (these foods tend to cause diarrhea, but this of course is not the intention of the mothers). A child with diarrhea is deprived of milk, meat and eggs (which normally form only a small part of the diet anyway) because it is believed that these foods promote diarrhea.

Cultural factors affect not only the consumption of foods but also their production, distribution, and marketing. Mandioca is raised year-round, but other crops are governed by a pervasive tradition that the farming year begins on St. John's Day (24 June) throughout the country. The result is that the same crops come into season at the same time throughout Paraguay, in spite of the fact that the climate would permit considerable variation in planting dates. Farmers traditionally sell their entire harvest. For a time they may have money to buy the foods they need, but later on there may be a scarcity of both the farmer's money and the storekeeper's stocks. In either case the diet is affected, especially that of the children (including the unborn).

Triministerial Alimentation and Nutrition Education Program

A UNICEF newsletter (1960) pointed out that in order to break the vicious circle of poverty-ignorance-malnutrition, the problem will have to be attacked on several fronts at the same time. To meet this challenge, the Triministerial Program was organized, with technical assistance and supplies provided by several United Nations organizations—WHO, FAO, UNICEF. The message of good nutrition would be spread throughout the country by the Ministry of Agriculture and Cattle-raising through its extension agents, by the Ministry of Education and Worship through the public school teachers, and by the Ministry of Public Health and Social Welfare through its network of health centers.

The program was begun in the First Health Region; plans were laid to extend the program to other regions in subsequent years. The First Health Region had at that time a population of about 750,000 (40% of the national population). The Second Health Region was brought into the program in 1962–63. The combined population of both regions was 1,075,000 (60% of the national total). The provinces included were Central, Paraguarí, Cordillera, Guairá, Caazapá, and parts of San Pedro, Alto Paraná, and Presidente Hayes. There were 89 towns directly affected by the program. The total numbers of schools in the project regions were 140 upper primary, 90 middle primary, and 660 lower primary. A table of organization was established to assure coordination of the program at all levels.

ACTION IN SCHOOLS

The principles of good nutrition were integrated into the curricula of the schools, and modern teaching techniques were put into practice. School lunches were supplemented with milk and with produce from the school garden. Each school was given one-half hectare for a garden. Proper horticultural techniques were taught to and carried out by the pupils, under the direction of the teachers and an agronomist. Another one-half hectare was devoted to an orchard, also cared for by the students. Since deforestation has been widespread in these regions, a tree nursery was organized at each school, and the products used in reforestation programs. Each school also had one-half hectare for a poultry operation. Chicks were supplied by regional hatcheries. An environmental

sanitation project was instituted at each school to demonstrate sanitary water supply and waste disposal systems suitable for rural areas. Future farmers clubs were organized to foster a spirit of cooperation in community service. Future homemakers clubs were organized for girls so that they could learn the skills of meal planning and preparation, sewing, gardening, etc.

ACTION IN HEALTH CENTERS

The technical personnel of the health centers, especially the nurses and nurses aides (FAO 1962), were trained to counsel mothers on how to provide a wholesome diet for themselves and their families, and how to deal with special dietary programs (diet during pregnancy and lactation, diet of infants and children at various ages, diet during illness and convalescence). The health center also supplied skim milk to preschool children, pregnant women and lactating mothers.

ACTION IN COMMUNITIES

Agricultural extension agents and home extension agents of the agriculture department established clubs for farmers, students, and homemakers in the various communities. Home extension agents were concerned with promoting the health and well-being of the families; skills associated with improvements in family life were taught to homemakers. Women's clubs of several kinds were formed according to the interests of the women: improvement of academic skills, home improvement, money management, cottage industry, gardening, cattle production, etc. Communal and family gardens were established, as were orchards and nurseries for forest trees.

ACTION IN TRAINING

The success of the Triministerial Program is largely dependent on the competence of the staff. For this reason great emphasis was placed on training of staff at all levels in nutrition, nutrition education, and other activities related to the program.

The Triministerial Program is a practical means for meeting the challenge of nutritional improvement throughout the country; it is a welcome substitute for the altruistic but inefficient and uncoordinated efforts of individuals and organizations concerned with the problem. The budget for this program in 1962–1963 was Gs 54,757,700.

Present Knowledge of the State of Nutrition

MALNUTRITION AND MORTALITY RATES

No accurate statement can be made regarding the extent of mortality due to malnutrition. Deaths from all causes are under-reported. In 1961, for example, total recorded deaths scarcely reached 50% of the expected deaths. Of the 50% recorded, only 37% were certified by physicians; of this 37% only 10% were attributed to well-defined causes. The remainder were due to causes unknown or poorly defined.

According to the annual report on vital statistics of the Ministry of Public Health and Social Welfare, the infant mortality rate for 1961 was 86.3 per thousand live births in the entire country, 87.6 in Asunción (39.5% neonates, 60.5% postneonates), 86.0 in the interior, 75.9 in the First Health Region, and 90.5 in the Fourth Health Region (the discrepancy between these two regions is doubtless referable to quality of reporting).

In the absence of more precise information, the infant mortality rate and the mortality rate in children aged 1 through 4 are good indices of nutritional status. These two indices for Paraguay are compared with the same figures from the United States:

Age of Child	Paraguay	United States
Less than 1 year	26.0	7.1
From 1 to 4 years	10.0	1.1

The main causes of mortality in less-than-one-year-olds in Paraguay were congenital defects and prematurity, tetanus neonatorum, pneumonia, syphilis, and birth injuries. The main causes of mortality in all children less than five years old were diarrheas, cancer, heart diseases, influenza, pneumonia, accidents, tuberculosis, prematurity, and nutritional disorders. These causes just mentioned accounted for 44% of the total number of deaths. In this 44%, those attributed to nutritional disorders accounted for 2.5 per cent.

Studies conducted elsewhere have shown that there is an inverse relationship between infant and child mortality and any one of four factors—per capita income, consumption of animal protein, potable water, and illiteracy. Good medical care can reduce the infant and child mortality rate only to a certain limit; from that point on any further reduction depends on improvements in the environment and the economic condition of the population (Horowitz 1961). The mortality statistics continue to demonstrate that infectious diseases, especially the diarrheal diseases, are the main causes of death in children, while nutritional disorders play only a small role (2.5%) as a cause of mortality. How can this be an accurate reflection of the true state of affairs when the pediatric wards of every hospital in the country are full of children suffering marasmus and multiple-deficiency syndromes?

The answer lies in the fact that most deaths in Paraguay are not certified by a physician. A government clerk simply notes in the civil register the declaration of death made by a relative or friend of the deceased. The cause of death may or may not be accurate. A study (Scrimshaw 1962) done in Guatemala revealed conditions of mortality reporting which are typical in the developing nations. A survey of four villages showed that 66% of the deaths of children (1–5 years old) that had been officially registered as due to diarrheal or parasitic diseases were actually caused by multiple deficiency syndrome or some other form of malnutrition. One-third of the total deaths were, however, caused by diarrheal diseases. During the nine months of the study, no deaths recorded in the civil registry were attributed to malnutrition. Nevertheless, the observers saw many signs of malnutrition—edema, abnormalities of skin and hair, and other symptoms of multiple deficiencies.

NUTRITION AND MORBIDITY

Reporting of morbidity is not even as good as mortality reporting. Therefore, morbidity figures are of little use in demonstrating the connection between malnutrition and morbidity. The Ministry of Public Health and Social Welfare operates 53 health centers, 3 maternal and child health clinics, 4 first aid posts, and 3 hospitals. The 3 hospitals, the 3 maternal and child health centers, one first aid post, and 6 health centers are located in Asunción, where they serve about 85.3% of the population of the capital. Most of the interior population does not have convenient access to a health facility.

Only two kinds of nutrition-related diseases appear in the vital statistics of Paraguay: goiter and avitaminosis. Goiter, according to these statistics, occurs in 9.8% of the total cases of morbidity, or in 5% of sick children 1 to 6 years old, 14% in sick children 7 to 14, and 80% of sick persons over 15 years of age. Avitaminosis was cited as the cause of morbidity in 4.2% of the sick persons in the Capital and 1.1% in the interior.

The national biostatistical data do not lend much support to the thesis that malnutrition is a significant cause of morbidity in Paraguay. But the frequency of nutritional disorders must be greater and more varied than the statistics indicate. On the one hand the medical and paramedical personnel of the health services are inadequate in both numbers and training to recognize any but a very small proportion of the nutrition-associated diseases. On the other hand there is evidence of widespread occurrence of nutritional diseases and of food customs which tend to lead to nutritional deficiencies: scant consumption of animal proteins and green vegetables, predominance of carbohydrates in the diet, deficiencies of vitamin A, riboflavin and calcium, prevalence of nutritional anemias, numerous malnourished children, underweight school children, and undernourished mothers whose milk fails before it is time for weaning, and a high incidence of dental caries.

The number of malnourished persons increases daily; part of this increase may be due to a greater awareness of and interest in nutritional problems. Numerous clinical and biochemical studies have demonstrated that the severity and duration of infections may be synergized by malnutrition. Any complete public health program must prevent both infection and malnutrition (Scrimshaw 1960). Infection can trigger a nutritional crisis. Severe bacterial infections (tyhpoid, paratyhpoid, tuberculosis) may provoke a critical loss of nitrogen as a result of the destruction of intracellular protein (Peters and Van Slyke 1946). Nitrogen balance may also be seriously affected by chickenpox (Scrimshaw et al. 1960) and yellow fever vaccine (Gandra and Scrimshaw, personal communication).

Illness is often accompanied by loss of appetite and a

consequent decrease in nutriment ingestion. Paraguayan mothers often put their sick children on a diet of semolina or rice broth, unintentionally depriving them of more nutritious foods. The relation between infection and malnutrition is often synergistic: protein deficiency—diminished antibody production; vitamin A, B complex, and C deficiencies—diminished phagocyte production and phagocyte activity; vitamin A deficiency—skin lesions.

SURVEYS OF NUTRITION

The objective of a nutrition survey is to determine the nutritional status of individuals or groups by clinical and biochemical means. Nutrition surveys are often done at the same time as the surveys of food consumption. In 1956 the Department of Nutrition did a nutrition survey of 1,115 subjects in Asunción and several interior towns. Clinical signs of nutritional deficiencies (if any), weight, height, age and sex were noted. The Paraguayan children (Table 12.64) were as tall and heavy at given ages as their Argentinian counterparts (Fig. 12.8). Some nutritional deficiencies and nutrition-associated diseases were observed: vitamin A deficiency—18%; vitamin B complex deficiency—34%; vitamin C deficiency—17%; anemia—7%; goiter—60%.

The survey just described was very superficial in nature and cannot serve as a basis for national policy in nutritional matters. The clinical examinations were cursorily made; a great deal of skill and time is required to recognize signs of deficiency. The absence of such signs, however, does not mean that the subject has no nutritional deficiency. The study did not offer any conclusions about the causes of malnutrition. Biochemical studies were not done at that time because there was no laboratory capability.

The Ministry of Public Health and Social Welfare established a laboratory of nutrition biochemistry in 1962. This laboratory investigated the cause of anemia in Asunción. It was well known that anemia was associated with hookworm infestations, but many non-parasitized persons were also anemic. Two obvious causes of anemia—iron and ascorbic acid deficiencies—were tentatively ruled out by the results of the national food survey. Protein, which is often deficient in the Paraguayan diet, is important in the synthesis of hemoglobin. The possible role of hypoproteinemia as a cause of anemia was therefore investigated.

Protein deficiency often results in a decrease of beta globulin (Lahey *et al.* 1962). Since ferroprotein (siderophilin or transferrin) is a beta globulin, it is possible that protein deficiency would interfere with the synthesis of the hemoglobin molecule. This would then account for the anemia in the non-parasitized population. This hypothesis was tested in a small sample (60 students, 7 to 12 years old) from a school in a lower class suburb of Asunción. All of these children were anemic (Table 12.65). They were divided into three groups and put on a special dietary supplement for 30 days: Group 1, normal diet supplemented with precooked soybean meal; Group 2, normal diet supplemented with ferrous gluconate;

Group 3, normal diet supplemented with soybean meal and ferrous gluconate. Blood studies were done before (Table 12.65) and after (Table 12.66) the 30 days of supplemented diet.

80% of the Group 1 children had a markedly improved blood picture, especially in regard to vitamin A and serum proteins. Only 5 children in Group 2 were less anemic after 30 days on ferrous gluconate. Children in Group 3 had blood values essentially similar to Group 1. Protein deficiency anemias are usually of the normocytic or macrocytic type. When iron deficiency is the cause, the administration of proteins is followed by a gradual change from normocytic to microcytic anemia. Only two cases in the above-mentioned study evolved in this way. These findings lead to the conclusion that either the diet already contains enough iron or that the soybean meal supplies both sufficient iron and sufficient proteins. This was, however, merely a pilot study; a much larger number of subjects will have to be studied before any definitive explanation of the matter can be made.

Three thousand blood specimens, examined during the period 1959 to 1961, showed that low hemoglobin levels occurred more often in women than men, and that certain localities had much lower hemoglobin levels than others (Tables 12.67 and 12.68).

Of all the children admitted to the pediatric ward of one hospital, 54.2% were dystrophic in 1954, 60% in 1955, and 61.5% in 1956 (Table 12.69).

BIOMETRIC STUDIES

Weight and height, when used as the sole criteria, are the least precise indicators of the nutritional state of a population, but height and weight are most useful when used with other criteria. Montalto (1956) collected data on 4,019 neonates (3,657 full term, 362 premature) from 1942 to 1946 (Table 12.70) at the Red Cross Hospital in Asunción. Full-term neonates weighing less than 2,999 grams were considered congenitally weak; 23.3% of the Paraguayan babies were in this category, compared with 18.3% of the Buenos Aires babies. 14.05% of the Paraguayan babies measured less than 48 cm in length, compared with 1.99% of the Buenos Aires babies.

Another study done at the Hospital de Clínicas in Asunción (Table 12.71) showed that 31.88% of the Paraguayan babies weighed less than 2,999 grams, compared with 21.29% of the babies born in Buenos Aires. It is postulated that under-nutrition of the mothers during pregnancy accounts for the relatively lower birth weights of the Paraguayan babies. The patients admitted to the Red Cross Hospital come from all socio-economic levels; the great majority of the Hospital de Clínicas patients are charity cases.

NUTRITION AND SOCIO-ECONOMIC STATUS

Summarized here are the results of a study done in 1958 by Dr. Jesús Riera. Nutritional and socio-economic data were gathered on 1,000 six-year-old children attending the well-child clinic at a health center in Asunción. This health center served an urban population of about

100,000 people, 43% of whom were less than 15 years old, and most of whom belonged to the lower and middle socio-economic classes (Table 12.72). It appears from these data that the nutritional state of the child is largely determined by the social, economic, and cultural situation of the mother. Mother's milk seems to adequately supply the essential nutrients, regardless of the circumstances of the mother. But after weaning, the quality of the child's diet deteriorates. By custom the Paraguayan mother provides her child with a high carbohydrate diet. The small amounts of proteins that chance to enter the child's diet are deliberately deleted whenever the child becomes ill. The resulting food, consisting of 10 parts protein to 260 parts carbohydrates (mother's milk has 10 parts protein to 40 parts carbohydrates), is mildly cathartic and its use when the child is already diarrhetic is particularly unfortunate. The administration to the already sick child of presumably anthelminthic purgatives greatly complicates matters. Beyond the preschool years the child partakes of the usual adult diet and his nutritional state often takes a distinct turn for the better. Although some nutritional deficiencies cut across all socioeconomic levels in Paraguay, it is still generally true that inequality of wealth means inequality of health. As Montalto (1956) aptly pointed out, the smaller a person's wealth, the greater the tribute that must be paid to disease.

Activities of the Department of Nutrition

RESEARCH DIVISION

This division has conducted food consumption surveys and medical-dietary surveys, and has prepared food balance sheets, a weight-height table, and analyses of typical Paraguayan foods, such as mandioca. Data provided by the school health service and other sources have been used to compile a bioanthropological table. The activities of the Goiter Institute also come under this division. Use of iodized salt became obligatory by law in 1958. Three years later the incidence of goiter had decreased from 60% to 37.5% in Asunción and from 60% to 49% in the interior.

The National Survey of Health, Food and Nutrition was carried out nationwide in 1965 and included 7,440 civilian subjects and 1,200 members of the armed forces. Some of the results of this survey are given in Table 12. 73 and in Figure 12.9. Four populations of special interest were surveyed—two Mennonite colonies, one Japanese colony, and one Indian village (Figure 12.10).

APPLIED NUTRITION DIVISION

This division engages in a wide variety of nutrition education programs at all educational levels. The food supplement program is administered by this division.

Concluding Statements

The improvement of the nutritional state of the people of Paraguay involves at least the following steps.

Improvement of Food Supply: increased production, variety, and availability of foods, greater consumption of "protective" foods.

Elevation of Standard of Living: adequate wages, housing, clothing, and other necessaries of life.

Better Use of Foods: the education of the populace as to what is meant by a wholesome diet and how to select and prepare the foods required for good health.

Coöperation with International Agencies: utilization of foreign experts in nutrition and related fields; assignment of Paraguayan scientists to fellowships in nutrition science and related fields; solicitation of educational materials, technical instrumentation, equipment and supplies; organization of national and international courses, conferences and seminars.

Certainly the subject of human nutrition in Paraguay has not been exhausted in these pages, but I have presented, I believe, the fundamental facts and determinant factors required for a basic understanding of the subject.

Literature Cited

Acosta-Solis, M. 1968. Protección y conservación de la Naturaleza en Sudamérica. *In* Fittkau, E. J., J. Illies, H. Klinge, G. H. Schwabe, and H. Sioli (eds.). Biogeography and ecology in South America. Vol. 1. Dr. W. Junk, The Hague. Quoted by permission of the publisher.

Centurión, U. 1962. La industria paraguaya y sus problemas financieros. El Agricultor, May 1962.

Centurión, U. 1963. Organización política de créditos del Banco Nacional de Fomento. El Agricultor, January 1963.

Codas, C. 1962. Reforma agraria. El Agricultor, February 1962.

Davee, R. 1958. El UNICEF y el sentido de su cooperación. Boletín UNICEF 16 (Nov.–Dec.).

FAO, 1961. El hambre y el hombre. *In* El mundo y su alimentación. Estudio básico en nutrición. Food and Agriculture Organization, Rome.

FAO, 1962a. El desarrollo económico mediante productos alimenticios. *In* Campaña mundial contra el hambre. Food and Agriculture Organization, Rome.

FAO, 1962b. La comercialización. Su influencia en la productividad. *In* Campaña mundial contra el hambre. Food and Agriculture Organization, Rome.

FAO, 1962c. La nutrición y el rendimiento en el trabajo. *In* Campaña mundial contra el hambre. Food and Agriculture Organization, Rome.

FAO, 1962d. La educación y la capacitación en el sector de la nutrición. *In* Campaña mundial contra el hambre. Food and Agriculture Organization, Rome.

Fretz, J. W. 1962. Immigrant group settlements in Paraguay. Bethel College, North Newton, Kansas.

González Torres, D. M. 1958. Tres problemas nacionales: El bocio endémico, la leishmaniasis, y la alimentación y nutrición. Asunción, Paraguay.

González, L. M. 1962. Decadencia de nuestra producción yerbatera. El Agricultor, February 1962.

Horowitz, A. 1961. Boletín de UNICEF 23.

INCAP, 1960. Nutrición en salud pública. Una política nacional para mejorar la nutrición de madres y niños. División de Educación Nutricional, Instituto de Nutrición de Centro América y Panamá.

Lahey, M. E., M. Behar, F. Viteri, and N. S. Scrimshaw. 1962. Valores de cobre, hierro y capacidad de fijación del hierro en el suero de niños con sindrome pluricarencial de la infancia. Publ. Cientif. INCAP 4: 138–147.

Mashbitz, Y. G. 1967. Population growth and the food problem in Latin America. *In* Proceedings of the World Population Conference, Belgrade, 30 August–10 September 1965. Vol. 3. Selected papers and summaries, projections, measurement of population trends. United Nations, New York.

Mengüal, L. no date. Análisis técnico de la situación socio-agronómica del país. Asunción, Paraguay.

Mengüal, L. 1962. Perspectivas agro-económicas del Paraguay. Meridiano no. 2, Asunción, Paraguay.

Montalto, F. A. 1956. Aspectos fundamentales del problema de la nutrición en el Paraguay. Impresora Oeste, Buenos Aires.

Montalto, F. A. 1962. La situación alimentaria de la población ante el problema del desarrollo económico-social del país. Emasa, Asunción.

Mora, J. A. 1959. From a speech presented at the Simposio sobre Nutrición del Niño y la Familia, Quito, Ecuador, February 1959.

Paz, L. A. 1959. La extensión y cooperación agrícola en la producción de alimentos. Instituto Interamericano de Ciencias Agrícolas, Cali, Colombia.

Peters, J. P., and D. D. Van Slyke. 1946. Quantitative clinical chemistry. Vol. 1. Interpretations. 2nd ed. Williams and Wilkins, Baltimore.

Reh, E. 1946. Rural life in Paraguay. Institute of Interamerican Studies, Washington, D. C.

Rothman, B. 1959. Conocimientos básicos para el planeamiento de la política alimentaria. Instituto Interamericano del Niño, Quito, Ecuador.

Scrimshaw, N. S. 1949. Estudio sobre los problemas de la nutrición en la América Latina. Bol. Oficina Sanitaria Panamericana 28 (12): 1201–1214.

Scrimshaw, N. S. 1960. Reported in Food and Nutrition News.

Scrimshaw, N. S. 1962. La nutrición y metas de la salud en el mundo. Publ. Cient. INCAP 59: 9–14.

Scrimshaw, N. S., D. Wilson, and R. Bressani. 1960. Infection and kwashiorkor. J. Trop. Ped. 6: 37–43.

Service, E. R., and H. S. Service. 1954. Tobatí: Paraguayan town. University of Chicago Press, Chicago.

Stewart, N. R. 1967. Japanese colonization in eastern Paraguay. National Academy of Sciences, National Research Council, Washington, D. C.

UNICEF, 1960. Reported in UNICEF Newsletter no. 20.

Warren, C. A. 1946. Paraguay. Emancipación económica americana. Ceibo, Montevideo.

Author's address: Dr. Pabla Duarte de Storni
                  Instituto de Patología Regional
                  Universidad Nacional del Nordeste
                  Resistencia, Chaco
                  Argentina

Table 12.1. Land Use in Paraguay, 1942–1957

	1942	%	1954	%	1957	%
Agriculture	1,549,786	3.8	1,670,000	4.1	1,675,000	4.1
Grazing land	16,125,414	39.6	16,100,000	39.6	16,100,000	39.6
Forests	22,000,000	54.1	21,905,000	53.9	21,899,000	53.9
Other	1,000,000	2.5	1,000,200	2.4	1,001,200	2.4
Total	**40,675,200**	**100.0**	**40,675,200**	**100.0**	**40,675,200**	**100.0**

Source: STICA, Ministry of Agriculture, Paraguay. Figures in hectares (one hectare = 2.471 acres).

Table 12.2. Agricultural Land Use in Paraguay, 1942–1957

	1942	%	1954	%	1957	%
Crop land	333,980	21.6	365,000	22.0	383,000	22.9
Fallow land	132,353	8.5	152,000	9.1	148,600	8.9
Pasture	677,767	43.7	705,000	42.2	700,000	41.8
Woodland	360,723	23.3	400,000	24.0	392,600	23.4
Farmyard	15,509	1.0	30,000	1.7	31,000	1.8
Other	29,454	1.9	18,000	1.0	20,000	1.2
Total	**1,549,786**	**100.0**	**1,670,000**	**100.0**	**1,675,200**	**100.0**

Source: STICA, Ministry of Agriculture, Paraguay. Figures in hectares (one hectare = 2.471 acres).

Table 12.3. Distribution of Private Rural Properties in Paraguay, 1945*

Location	Number of Landowners	%	Size of Holdings (hectares)	%
Large estates of more than 100,000 hectares				
Paraguay Oriental	11	0.01	4,970,000	33.9
Chaco	14	1.1	7,500,000	52.5
Entire country	*25*	*1.04*	*12,470,000*	*43.0*
Estates of 100 to 2,000 hectares				
Paraguay Oriental	1,119	1.0	9,094,000	62.0
Chaco	327	2.6	5,445,000	38.1
Entire country	*1,526*	*1.4*	*14,539,000*	*50.2*
Small farms of less than 100 hectares				
Paraguay Oriental	109,970	98.9	608.000	4.1
Chaco	926	73.1	1,332,000	9.3
Entire country	*110,896*	*98.7*	*1,940,000*	*6.7*
Totals				
Paraguay Oriental	111,100	98.9	14,672,000	50.7
Chaco	1,267	1.1	14,277,000	49.3
Entire country	**112,367**	**100.0**	**28,949,000**	**100.0**

Source: Montalto 1956 and Warren 1946. One hectare = 2.471 acres.
*Properties in the 2,000 to 100,000 class are not considered in this table.

Table 12.4. Land Occupancy in Paraguay (1956)

Type	Number	%
Squatters	65,863	44.0
Owners	48,650	32.5
Tenants	10,761	7.2
Others	24,350	16.3
Total	**149,624**	**100.0**

Table 12.5. Land Occupancy According to Size of Farm

Size of Farm (hectares)	Number of Farms	%	Total Area (hectares)	%	Owners (number)	%
1–7.49	63,200	66.9	228,269.7	14.7	377,042	64.2
7.5–19.9	22,481	23.8	253,632.8	16.4	139,528	25.8
20.0–99.9	7,448	7.8	244,616.2	15.8	45,537	8.4
100.0–999.9	1,215	1.3	276,314.9	17.8	7,544	1.4
1000+	154	0.2	546,952.9	35.3	1,172	0.2
Totals	**94,498**	**100.0**	**1,549,785.5**	**100.0**	**540,973**	**100.0**

One hectare = 2.471 acres.
Source: Censo Agropecuario, Ministerio de Agricultura y Ganadería, 1956.

Table 12.6. Statistics on Farm Income

Type of Income	High Income Farms		Low Income Farms	
	Total Income	Income per Hectare	Total Income	Income per Hectare
Net Production	₲ 67,100	₲ 16,800	₲ 19,700	₲ 3,700
Effective family income	39,700	8,800	9,500	1,700
Return on capital	20,900	2,900	-12,900	-4,100
Laborers' wages	52,800	13,700	9,900	1,700
Farmers' wages	18,700	3,700	-12,900	-4,700
Cash profit	7,300	-50	-21,800	-6,100
Percentage return on investment	18.8%		-44.0%	

Table 12.7. Factors Affecting Income from Agriculture

Factors	High Income Farms		Low Income Farms	
	Total Income	Income per Hectare	Total Income	Income per Hectare
Capital investment	₲ 102,500	₲ 24,000	₲ 92,200	₲ 16,500
Gross income	₲ 77,400	₲ 19,300	₲ 23,800	₲ 5,000
Working days	328.3		247.7	
Production (tons per hectare)				
Peanuts	1.20		0.88	
Corn	1.09		0.86	
Mandioca	10.64		8.24	
Cotton	0.80		0.77	
Sweet potatoes	7.05		5.89	
Cowpeas	0.46		0.43	
Work efficiency				
Number of men working	1.97		1.68	
Number of workers available	2.21		1.80	
Man-days worked	137.36		107.47	
Gross income/work days	₲ 302.		₲ 182.	

Table 12.8. Rural Living Conditions

House Construction Materials						Facilities			
Walls	%	Roof	%	Floor	%	Number of Rooms	%	Water Source	%
Adobe	50	Thatch	77	Dirt	77	One	78	Well	39
Brick	30	Tile	22	Brick	33	Two	15	Spring	25
Stick	18	Metal	1			Three	5	Stream	4
Board	2					Four	1	None	22

Table 12.9. Rural Living Conditions in 1943–44 and 1950

Description of House	Study by Reh (1943–44)	Census of 1950
Walls of mud and sticks	63.0%	67.0%
Thatched roof	78.4	72.0
Dirt floor	80.7	73.0
One room only	65.0	62.0

Table 12.10. Statistics on Income from Certain Crops

Crop	Cropland per Farm (hectares)	Production (tons per hectare)	Capital Investment per Hectare	% of Total Capital Investment	Work Days per Hectare	Net Profit per Hectare
Cotton	0.30	0.75	₲ 12.79	12.6	68	₲ 5.99
Mandioca	1.00	9.83	9.83	30.7	51	4.73
Peanuts	0.90	1.41	9.84	28.7	72	2.64
Corn	0.89	1.06	5.31	15.2	30	2.31

Table 12.11. Bank Loans to Agriculture

Year	Amount (in millions of guaranís
1957	299.7
1958	223.5
1959	205.2
1960	110.5

Table 12.12. Loans Granted by the National Development Bank
(20 December 1961 to 30 December 1962)

Type of Recipient	Amount	%
Forestry	₲ 184,530,000	28.9
Manufacturing	168,103,000	26.4
Farming and dairying	139,276,000	21.8
Business	75,664,000	11.9
Ranching	70,279,000	11.0
Total	637,852,000	100.0

Source: Centurión 1963.

Table 12.13. Numbers of Cattle Ranchers in Relation to the Size of Their Herds

Size of Herd	1951 Number	1951 %	1952 Number	1952 %	1953 Number	1953 %	1954 Number	1954 %	1956 Number	1956 %	1957 Number	1957 %
1–250	39,206	95.9	41,535	96.5	37,379	96.1	34,988	94.8	30,205	94.4	28.835	94.5
251–5,000	1,549	3.8	1,387	3.2	1,436	3.7	1,800	4.9	1,642	5.2	1,552	5.1
5,000+	120	0.3	113	0.3	108	0.2	122	0.3	131	0.4	130	0.4
Total	40,875	100.0	43,035	100.0	38,923	100.0	36,910	100.0	31,978	100.0	30,521	100.0

Source: Statistical Manual of Paraguay, 1951–1957 (no data for 1955).

Table 12.14. Number of Cattle in Relation to the Size of Herd
(in thousands)

Size of Herd	1951 Number	1951 %	1952 Number	1952 %	1953 Number	1953 %	1954 Number	1954 %	1956 Number	1956 %	1957 Number	1957 %
1–250	1,253.2	27.7	1,240.5	30.0	1,198.7	28.8	944.6	21.8	808.7	19.7	784.1	19.9
251–5,000	1,258.0	35.2	1,400.4	33.9	1,453.8	34.9	1,703.2	39.3	1,604.4	39.2	1,498.6	38.2
5,000+	1,446.1	37.1	1,491.3	36.1	1,510.9	36.3	1,688.3	38.9	1,682.3	41.1	1,646.6	41.9
Total	3,957.3	100.0	4,132.2	100.0	4,162.4	100.0	4,366.1	100.0	4,095.4	100.0	3,929.3	100.0

Source: Statistical Manual of Paraguay, 1951–1957, and STICA (no data for 1955).

Table 12.15. Cattle Production
(in thousands of head)

Years	Number	% Produced in Eastern Paraguay	% Produced in Western Paraguay
1941–45	3,750	61	39
1954–58	3,703	60	40
1959	3,666	54	46
1960	3,689	54	46
1961	4,695	53	47
1963	5,622	56	44

Source: Central Bank of Paraguay.

Table 12.16. Cattle Processed for Domestic and Industrial Use in Paraguay, 1951–1957

Year	Domestic Consumption		Meat-Packing Industry		Totals	
	Number of Head	Live Weight (tons)	Number of Head	Live Weight (tons)	Number of Head	Live Weight (tons)
1951	407,386	146,099	22,380	8,045	429,766	154,144
1952	406,635	139,597	29,285	9,844	435,920	149,441
1953	535,238	193,169	12,251	4,365	547,489	197,534
1954	490,468	170,436	26,907	9,868	517,375	180,304
1955	435,760	154,710	64,730	22,313	500,490	177,023
1956	432,193	151,976	74,723	26,192	506,916	178,168
1957	436,067	148,686	84,637	26,345	520,704	178,030

Source: Department of Economic Studies, Central Bank of Paraguay, and STICA.

Table 12.17. Cattle Processed by COPACAR, Paraguay, 1951–1957

Year	Number of Head	Live Weight	Dressed Weight	Yield (%)
1951	123,663	45,440	21,769	48.2
1952	126,436	45,375	21,413	47.2
1953	134,205	48,348	—	—
1954	127,120	44,076	21,235	48.2
1955	125,054	42,789	20,532	48.0
1956	111,386	38,361	18,879	49.2
1957	97,465	32,993	16,224	49.2

Source: Department of Economic Studies, Central Bank of Paraguay, and STICA.

Table 12.18. Agricultural Production in Paraguay
(thousands of tons)

Product	1941–45*	1955–59*	1960–63*	1964
Alfalfa	7.7	15.4	19.0	19.6
Cotton	29.2	33.4	25.5	32.8
Cowpeas	16.8	18.0	17.5	23.6
Rice	12.0	19.2	16.0	20.0
Sweet potatoes	73.5	74.1	72.0	86.2
Coffee	0.1	0.4	0.5	–
Onions	3.2	6.8	8.8	13.6
Sugar cane	275.7	461.7	656.9	964.1
Corn	103.4	121.1	124.0	206.0
Peanuts	10.9	9.9	8.8	19.2
Potatoes	1.3	3.3	4.0	6.4
Mandioca	729.4	972.6	992.4	1,448.8
Tobacco	6.9	6.5	14.5	9.3
Wheat	1.8	7.2	8.4	8.6

*Annual average for the period.
Source: Central Bank of Paraguay and STICA.

Table 12.19. Historical Review
of Agricultural Production in Paragauy

Year	Metric Tons	Year	Metric Tons
1863	1,807,996	1956	1,615,325
1943	1,389,200	1957	1,752,840
1947	1,470,481	1958	1,848,400
1950	1,487,290	1959	1,875,600
1952	1,629,793	1960	1,900,200
1953	1,606,960	1961	1,926,000
1954	1,569,000	1962	1,994,400
1955	1,530,500		

Source: L. Mengüal.

Table 12.20. Agricultural Production during the Decade 1952–1962

Year	Tons	Hectares
1952	1,642,700	295,700
1953	1,619,300	262,800
1954	1,569,000	257,500
1955	1,530,500	271,600
1956	1,630,500	268,400
1957	1,783,500	302,000
1958	1,869,500	322,200
1959	1,897,700	329,700
1960	1,900,200	314,200
1961	1,929,000	292,000
1962	1,984,400	310,800

Source: Banco Central del Paraguay, Departamento de Estudios Económicos,
Boletín No. 61, Junio de 1963.

Table 12.21. Contribution of Farming, Forestry, and Ranching to the National Economy of Paraguay

Year	Gross Internal Product Gs.	Farming		Ranching, Poultry Production, Bee-Keeping		Forestry		Total %
		Gs.	%	Gs.	%	Gs.	%	
1950	13,678,000	2,603,000	19.0	3,122,000	22.8	302,000	2.6	44.3
1951	14,900,000	3,828,000	25.7	2,723,000	18.2	267,000	1.7	45.6
1952	11,874,000	3,342,000	28.1	1,681,000	14.1	104,000	0.8	43.0
1953	14,330,000	4,091,000	28.5	2,203,000	15.3	165,000	1.1	44.9
1954	15,455,000	3,991,000	25.8	2,486,000	16.0	267,000	1.7	43.5
1955	16,704,000	4,610,000	27.6	2,708,000	16.2	260,000	1.5	45.3
1956	15,762,000	4,048,000	25.6	2,570,000	16.3	356,000	2.2	44.1
1957	16,434,000	3,809,000	23.1	2,743,000	16.6	356,000	2.1	41.8
1958	16,921,000	3,737,000	22.0	2,793,000	16.4	440,000	2.6	41.0
1959	15,116,000	3,086,000	20.4	2,566,000	16.7	223,000	1.5	38.6
1960	15,231,000	3,144,000	20.6	2,581,000	16.2	259,000	1.7	38.9
1961	15,623,000	3,019,000	19.3	2,578,000	16.5	288,000	1.8	37.6

Source: Departamento de Estudios Económicos, Banco Central del Paraguay, 1962.

Table 12.22. National Income from Various Sources in Paraguay
(figures in millions of guaranís, unless otherwise indicated)

Sources of Income and Other Information	1956	1957	1958	1959	1960	1961
Agriculture	4,048	4,438	4,686	4,787	5,206	5,554
Ranching	2,570	3,195	3,508	3,982	4,274	4,743
Forestry	356	415	552	346	429	531
Hunting, fishing	121	130	139	153	175	200
Manufacturing	2,006	2,698	3,011	3,313	3,505	4,022
Construction	126	151	193	181	188	235
Subtotal	9,227	11,027	12,089	12,762	13,777	15,285
Electricity	81	101	134	173	290	309
Communications, Transport	278	314	357	380	414	519
Subtotal	359	415	491	553	704	828
Commerce	2,485	3,041	3,482	3,619	3,993	4,828
Financial institutions	145	265	318	347	382	415
Public administration and defense	640	1,058	1,227	1,585	1,327	1,784
Non-profit activities	104	127	148	178	204	225
Miscellaneous services	861	904	934	1,284	1,434	1,681
Housing	1,941	2,309	2,530	3,141	3,402	3,810
Subtotal	6,176	7,704	8,639	10,144	10,742	12,633
Gross internal product	15,762	19,146	21,219	23,459	25,223	28,746
Disbursements to foreign concerns	68	213	169	157	188	233
Gross national product	15,694	18,933	21,050	23,304	25,035	28,513
Reserve for depreciation	392	473	459	606	626	713
Net national product	15,302	18,460	20,501	22,698	24,409	27,800
Indirect taxes	1,025	1,237	1,374	1,515	1,635	1,853
National income	14,121	17,223	19,127	21,183	22,774	25,947
Direct taxes	156	188	208	230	248	283
Available national income	13,395	17,035	18,919	20,953	22,526	25,664
Available national income expressed in millions of U.S. dollars	104	156	171	173	185	210
Per capita income in U.S. $	96	96	103	102	106	107.7
Population in thousands	1,613	1,650	1,688	1,727	1,766	1,807

Table 12.22. (Continued)

Sources of Income and Other Information	1956	1957	1958	1959	1960	1961
Per capita gross national product in Gs.	9,790	11,475	12,470	13,494	14,176	15,779
Economically active population, in thousands	488	499	500	521	534	546
Gross national product per capita of economically active population	32,160	37,942	41,275	44,729	46,882	52,222
Gross internal product index (1956 = 100)	100	104.2	107.3	95.9	86.6	99.1
Weighted general index of workers' wages (1938 = 100)	6,399	7,563	9,685	11,164	12,356	15,005
Weighted general index of cost of living (1938 = 100)	9,182	10,545	10,939	11,881	12,994	14,730
Weighted general index of major prices (1938 = 100)	7,410	8,640	9,186	11,290	12,277	13,797
Rate of exchange: $1.00 = Gs.	92.33	109.08	110.29	120.24	121.41	123.58
Exports F.O.B. in millions of U.S. dollars	37	33	34	31	27	31
Value of exports per capita in U.S. dollars	23	20	20	18	15	17
Imports F.O.B. in millions of U.S. dollars	25	27	32	26	32	35
Value of imports per capita in U.S. dollars	15	16	19	15	18	19

Source: Banco Central del Paraguay, Dirección de Estadística y Censos, and STICA.

Table 12.23. National Income from Various Sources in Paraguay Adjusted to 1950 Prices
(figures in millions of guaranís, unless otherwise indicated)

Sources of Income and Other Information	1956	1957	1958	1959	1960	1961
Agriculture	404.8	399.4	374.9	335.2	312.4	277.7
Ranching	257.0	287.5	280.6	278.7	256.4	237.2
Forestry	35.6	37.4	44.2	24.2	25.7	26.5
Hunting, fishing	12.1	11.7	11.1	10.7	10.5	10.0
Manufacturing	200.6	242.8	240.9	231.9	210.3	201.1
Construction	12.6	13.6	15.4	12.7	11.3	11.7
Subtotal	922.7	992.4	967.1	893.4	826.6	764.2
Electricity	8.1	9.1	10.1	12.1	17.4	15.5
Communications and transport	27.8	28.3	28.5	26.6	24.8	25.9
Subtotal	35.9	37.4	39.2	38.7	42.2	41.4
Commerce	248.5	273.7	278.5	253.3	239.6	236.4
Financial institutions	14.5	23.9	25.4	24.3	22.9	20.2
Public administration and defense	64.0	95.2	98.2	111.0	79.6	89.2
Non-profit activities	10.4	11.4	11.8	12.5	12.2	11.2
Miscellaneous services	86.1	81.4	74.7	89.9	86.1	84.1
Housing	194.1	207.8	202.4	219.1	204.1	190.5
Subtotal	617.6	693.4	691.1	710.1	644.5	631.6
Gross internal product	1,576.2	1,723.2	1,697.5	1,642.3	1,513.4	1,437.3
Disbursements to foreign concerns	6.8	19.2	13.5	11.0	11.3	11.6
Gross national product	1,569.4	1,704.0	1,634.0	1,631.3	1,502.1	1,425.7
Reserve for depreciation	39.2	42.6	43.9	42.4	37.6	35.7
Net national product	1,530.2	1,661.4	1,604.1	1,588.9	1,464.5	1,390.8
Indirect taxes	102.5	111.3	109.9	106.1	98.1	92.6
National income	1,427.7	1,550.1	1,530.3	1,482.8	1,366.4	1,297.4
Direct taxes	15.6	16.9	16.7	16.1	14.9	14.2
Available national income	1,412.1	1,533.2	1,513.5	1,466.7	1,351.5	1,283.2
Available national income expressed in millions of U.S. dollars	15.3	14.0	13.6	12.2	11.1	10.4
Per capita income in U.S. dollars	9.5	8.5	8.0	7.1	6.3	5.7
Population of Paraguay in thousands	1,613	1,650	1,688	1,727	1.766	1,807

Table 12.23. (Continued)

Source of Income and Other Information	1956	1957	1958	1959	1960	1961
Per capita gross national product in Gs.	973	1,033	998	945	851	789
Economically active population, in thousands	488	499	510	521	534	546
Gross national product per capita of economically active population	3,216	3,415	3,302	3,131	2,813	2,611
Exports F.O.B. in millions of U.S. $	3.85	2.87	2.92	2.45	2.11	2.38
Value of exports per capita in U.S. $	2.39	1.74	1.72	1.42	1.17	1.31
Imports F.O.B. in millions of U.S. $	2.60	2.35	2.75	2.05	2.50	2.69
Value of imports per capita in U.S. $	1.50	1.41	1.63	1.18	1.40	1.46
Factor of devaluation of the guaraní	0.104	0.087	0.086	0.079	0.078	0.077

Sources: Banco Central del Paraguay, Dirección de Estadística y Censos, and STICA.

Table 12.24. Federal Budget, Paraguay, 1961–1962

Expenditures of Government Department and Offices	1961		1962	
	Millions of Gs.	%	Millions of Gs.	%
Office of the President	18.3	0.64	20.8	0.6
Ministry of the Interior	289.4	10.3	348.0	10.1
Ministry of Foreign Affairs	116.3	4.1	129.4	3.7
Ministry of Finance	103.6	3.7	118.9	3.5
Ministry of Education and Worship	461.5	16.5	545.6	15.96
Ministry of Agriculture and Animal Industry	70.9	2.5	74.0	2.1
Ministry of Public Works	56.0	2.0	66.8	2.0
Ministry of National Defense	640.3	22.8	737.3	21.6
Ministry of Public Health and Social Welfare	142.0	5.1	163.3	4.8
Ministry of Justice and Labor	22.1	0.8	26.7	0.8
Ministry of Industry and Commerce	10.0	0.4	10.9	0.3
Minister Without Portfolio	1.6	0.06	1.5	0.04
Public Debt	361.0	12.9	510.7	15.0
Judiciary	51.3	1.8	62.0	1.8
House of Representatives	20.6	0.7	23.6	0.7
Other Obligations	440.5	15.7	582.1	17.0
Total	2,805.4	100.00	3,421.6	100.00

Table 12.25. Principal Exports, Paraguay, 1952–1962

Export Category	% of Volume			% of Dollar Value		
	Average 1952–56	Average 1957–61	1962	Average 1952–56	Average 1957–61	1962
Timber	70	10	9	32	22	7
Quebracho extract	11	57	58	15	11	19
Cotton	4	2	2	19	8	7
Meat products	2	5	5	7	24	22
Other	13	26	26	27	35	45

Table 12.26. Income and Disbursements from Holdings, Paraguay, 1952-1962
(in thousands of U.S. dollars)

Income and Disbursements	Average 1952-56	Average 1957-61	1962
Total income	49,179	49,902	49,222
Exports	33,244	37,126	40,847
Income from other sources	15,935	12,776	8,375
Total disbursements	51,117	53,142	51,902
Imports	53,155	36,421	35,766
Other necessities	17,962	16,721	16,136

Source: Banco Central del Paraguay.

Table 12.27. Major Export Commodities, Paraguay

Commodity	Thousands of Tons			Thousands of Dollars		
	Average 1952-56	Average 1957-61	1962	Average 1952-56	Average 1957-61	1962
Yerba mate	2.5	8.6	6.5	822	1,514	902
Sugar	0.2	5.1	0.3	146	420	45
Quebracho extract	29.5	30.4	30.6	5,379	3,432	2,530
Furs and hides	7.7	9.5	7.3	1,837	2,273	1,687
Fruit	2.8	5.6	5.6	403	274	309
Tobacco	3.3	3.9	11.9	1,313	1,083	3,091
Timber	191.3	175.6	202.2	10,939	6,935	6,660
Essential oils	0.23	0.27	0.31	1,201	1,021	1,078
Meat products	5.3	16.8	16.9	2,649	7,474	7,474
Vegetable oils	3.9	6.0	8.2	1,877	1,708	2,334
Cotton fiber	12.3	5.9	6.9	6,539	2,441	2,469
Other	11.1	39.3	49.8	1,034	2,578	4,870
Totals	**270.13**	**306.97**	**346.51**	**34.141**	**31,153**	**33,602**

Source: Banco Central del Paraguay.

Table 12.28. Argentina as a Market for Paraguayan Exports

Year	Thousands of Dollars			Thousands of Tons		
	Total Exports	Exports to Argentina	% of Total	Total Exports	Exports to Argentina	% of Total
1958	34,102.4	13,219.0	38.7	341.6	223.6	65.4
1959	31,195.0	6,439.8	20.6	236.2	100.1	42.4
1960	26,978.2	7,651.3	28.3	299.4	159.0	53.1
1961	30,676.8	8,720.0	28.0	341.3	199.0	58.3
1962	33,467,0	9,609.0	28.7	350.4	200.3	57.1

Source: Banco Central del Paraguay.

Table 12.29. Major Imports by Volume, Paraguay
(in thousands of tons)

Commodity	Average 1957–60	1961	1962
Food	96.8	104.2	115.7
Tobacco and beverages	0.8	0.9	1.1
Fuel oils and lubricants	91.6	119.2	122.9
Paper and paper products	2.6	3.4	3.2
Chemicals and drugs	3.0	3.3	3.2
Cars, trucks and accessories	5.6	3.2	4.2
Textiles	2.5	3.1	3.6
Farm equipment, accessories	0.7	0.5	0.4
Iron and iron tools	8.7	7.9	7.6
Metals and metal products	2.7	2.7	2.6
Machines and motors	3.0	2.8	3.5
Other	11.6	12.3	19.2
Total	**229.6**	**263.7**	**287.2**

Source: Banco Central del Paraguay.

Table 12.30. Major Imports by Value, Paraguay
(in thousands of U.S. dollars)

Commodity	Average 1956–60	1961	1962
Foods	6,528	7,058	7,130
Tobacco and beverages	232	346	382
Fuel oils and lubricants	3,120	3,494	3,436
Paper and paper products	690	931	818
Chemicals and drugs	1,330	1,498	1,626
Cars, trucks and accessories	4,503	3,910	5,050
Textiles	2,854	2,695	3,096
Farm equipment, accessories	606	384	326
Iron and iron tools	1,960	1,575	1,633
Metals and metal products	1,153	1,126	982
Machines and motors	4,383	3,882	5,457
Other	2,715	3,631	4,227
Total	**30,074**	**30,531**	**34,263**

Source: Banco Central del Paraguay.

Table 12.31. Major Sources of Imported Commodities in 1961, Paraguay

Category	Sources	% Total Value of Category from Each Source Indicated
Foods	Argentina	71.5
Tobacco and beverages	England	49.4
Fuel oils and lubricants	Netherlands Antilles	63.3
Paper and paper products	Sweden	39.0
Chemicals and drugs	Argentina, Germany, United States	74.3
Cars, trucks, and accessories	Japan, Spain, Germany, United States	87.2
Textiles and clothing	Japan, England, United States, Spain, Argentina	67.2
Farm implements and accessories	Germany, United States, Spain	70.4
Iron and iron tools	Argentina, Germany, Belgium	76.0
Metals and metal products	England, Germany, Argentina	73.8
Machinery and motors	Germany, United States, England	63.0

Source: Banco Central del Paraguay.

Table 12.32. Argentina as a Source of Paraguayan Imports

	Thousands of U.S. Dollars			Thousands of Tons		
Year	Total Imports	Imports from Argentina	% of Total	Total Imports	Imports from Argentina	% of Total
1958	32,592	7,188	22.0	222.9	92.3	41.4
1959	26,194	7,417	28.3	227.2	102.3	45.0
1960	32,463	7,480	23.9	244.9	100.4	40.9
1961	34,734	8,337	24.0	273.9	108.1	39.0
1962	34,263	5,032	14.7	237.3	50.4	21.2

Source: Banco Central del Paraguay.

Table 12.33. Argentina as a Source of Food for Paraguay

	Thousands of Dollars				Thousands of Tons			
Year	Total Food Imports	Foods Imported from Argentina	% Total Imported Foods	% of All Imports from Argentina	Total Food Imports	Foods Imported from Argentina	% Total Imported Foods	% of All Imports from Argentina
1958	5,993	5,126	86.4	71.3	94.1	87.2	92.6	94.3
1959	6,135	5,447	88.8	73.4	98.5	94.3	95.7	92.1
1960	5,981	5,281	88.3	70.0	96.6	91.1	94.3	90.7
1961	7,059	5,969	84.4	71.5	104.2	96.0	92.1	88.7

Source: Banco Central del Paraguay.

Table 12.34. Selected Examples of Duties on Paraguayan Exports, February 1962

Commodity	Unit	Minimum Price in U.S. $*	Duty 1962 (%)	Duty Value in U.S. $	Duty in 1965 (%)
Petit-grain	Metric ton	4,000	10.1	404.00	7.5
Tung oil	Metric ton	311	9.1	28.30	7.5
Cotton	Metric ton	300	10.1	40.40	7.5
Tobacco	Metric ton	270	10.1	27.27	7.5
Yerba mate	Metric ton	160	9.1	14.56	5.0
Hides	Metric ton	267	10.1	26.97	7.5
Logs	Cubic meter	45	9.1	4.09	5.0
Canned meat	Case of 100	925	8.1	74.93	2.5
Canned grapefruit	Case of 100	120	1.6	1.92	–
Canned pineapple	Case of 100	120	1.6	1.92	–

*Set on 19 July 1960 by Banco Central del Paraguay.
Source: Banco Central del Paraguay and STICA.

Table 12.35. Examples of Import Duties, February 1962

Commodity	Unit	Price c.i.f. Asunción in U.S. $	Duty %	Duty Value ($)
Tractors	Each	5,000	43.5	2,175.00
Harvester	Each	8,000	43.5	3,480.00
Disc plow	Each	800	43.5	348.00
Colter plow	Each	18	43.5	7.83
Insecticide	100 kg	250	58.5	128.75
Fertilizer	100 kg	15	44.5	6.68
Seeds	100 kg	500	51.5	257.50

Source: Banco Central del Paraguay, and STICA.

Table 12.36. Income per Capita, Paraguay

Year	Income per Capita	Year	Income per Capita	Year	Income per Capita	Year	Income per Capita	Year	Income per Capita
1950	$ 94	1955	$ 99	1960	$205	1965	$224	1970	$240
1951	101	1956	96	1961	211	1966	220	1971	243
1952	98	1957	96	1962	217	1967	228		
1953	93	1958	103	1963	214	1968	231		
1954	96	1959	102	1964	217	1969	233		

Source: Banco Central del Paraguay.

Table 12.37. Freight-Carrying Capacity of the Federal Merchant Fleet, 1963

Type of Ship	Number	Usable Cargo Capacity in tons	Cargo Capacity in tons	Registered Gross Weight in tons	Registered Net Weight in tons
Freighter	3	850.45	1,080	573.72	328.00
Freighter	6	1,000.00	2,000	1,086.61	626.95
Freighter	3	1,000.00	2,000	1,126.21	728.58
Tanker	1	850.45	1,000	573.72	328.00
Tanker	1	—	1,900	1,173.73	588.95
Tanker	1	—	1,900	1,121.89	627.71
Refrigerated freighter	1	300.00	500	—	800.00
Cattle boat	1	700.00	500 (head)	1,278.85	394.33
Tugboat	1	—	—	13.43	—
Tugboat	2	—	—	105.00	—
Barge	5	500.00	1,296	517.55	479.77
Barge	1	236.00	500	—	—

Source: Flota Mercante del Estado, Asunción.

Table 12.38. Food Storage Silos in Paraguay

	Type		Unit Capacity (tons)	Total Capacity (tons)	Comments
	Above Ground	Under- ground			
Asunción	1	—	1,500	1,500	Usable
Paraguarí	1	—	1,500	1,500	Usable
Villarrica	1	—	1,500	1,500	Incomplete, disrepair
Encarnación	1	—	1,500	1,500	Incomplete
Itá	—	2	433		
	—	2	500	1,866	Has dryers; minor repairs required
San Lorenzo	—	2	433		
			500	1,866	Has dryers; minor repairs required
Carapeguá	—	2	433	866	Usable
Piribebuy	—	2	160	320	Usable
Eusebio Ayala	—	2	160	320	Usable
San Ignacio	—	2	160	320	Usable
Villa San Pedro	—	1	160		
	—	1	433	593	Usable
Carmen del Paraná	—	2	433	866	Usable
Caazapá	—	2	433	866	Leaks
Acahay	—	2	433	866	Needs repairs
Caraguatay	—	1	150	150	Many leaks
Coronel Oviedo	—	1	150	150	Many leaks
Total	4	26		15,049	

Source: Banco Nacional de Fomento, Asunción.

Table 12.39. Capacity and Utilization of the Food Industry in Paraguay

Type of Operation	Number of Plants	Number of Working Days per Year	Annual Capacity in tons	Annual Production in tons	Percent Utilization
Cotton gins	14	300	286,500	18,000	6.3
Sugar refineries	8	150	600,000	310,000	51.7
Extraction of edible oils	3	300	10,000	5,000	50.0
Extraction of industrial vegetable oils	4	300	28,829	8,798	30.5

Table 12.40. Production by the Food Industry of Paraguay

Type of Industry	1945–1950 (average in tons)	1952–1956 (average in tons)	1957–1961 (average in tons)	1962 (tons)
Meat industry				
Canned meat	9,206	3,265	10,634	—
Tongue paté	62	23	78	—
Pecho paté	188	64	172	—
Meat extract	71	44	381	—
Meat broth concentrate	636	294	554	—
Matambre	—	79	30	—
Meat and bone meal	—	919	943	—
Cracklings	—	251	75	—
Milling industry				
Rice	4,747	11,200	11,960	11,400
Corn	1,486	900	960	1,000
Wheat	—	53,200	—	—
Sugar refining industry				
Sugar	15,253	16,580	30,480	32,800
Oil extraction industry				
Cottonseed oil	2,213	2,180	1,340	1,200
Peanut oil	522	360	840	1,000
Palm oil	—	840	1,300	1,900
Other processed foods				
Bread	5,467	11,840	14,980	14,900
Hardtack	11,256	22,500	30,080	30,200
Crackers	169	160	340	500
Vermicelli	2,183	8,980	12,000	11,800
Masas and confections	266	300	620	700
Lard	2,762	2,800	3,100	3,300
Suet	1,436	1,351	1,845	—
Caramels	596	660	680	700
Manioc flour	119	100	100	100
Farina	96	100	180	200
Chocolate	—	14	18	20
Coffee	407	200	580	700
Yerba mate	17,825	13,000	15,480	14,300

Source: Banco Central del Paraguay.

Table 12.41. Age and Caloric Requirements, Paraguay

Age	Population by Age Groups According to 1962 Census					Caloric Requirement			Caloric Requirement at Annual Mean 23°C			Total Caloric Value		
	No. of Males	% Males	Both Sexes	No. of Females	% Females	For Males	For Both Sexes	For Females	For Males	For Both Sexes	For Females	For Males	For Both Sexes	For Females
1			63,591(3.5%)				1,120			1,120			4,020	
1-3			176,238(9.7%)				1,300			1,212			11,756	
4-6			165,337(9.1%)				1,700			1,585			14,423.5	
7-9			159,886(8.8%)				2,100			1,958			17,230.4	
10-12	72,675	4.0		65,408	3.6		2,500			2,331			17,230.4	
13-15	65,408	3.6		59,957	3.3	3,100		2,600	2,891		2,425	10,407.6		8,002.5
16-19	67,225	3.7		70,859	3.9	3,396		2,232	3,167		2,081	11,717.9		8,116.9
20-29	139,900	7.7		152,619	8.4	3,019		2,146	2,815		2,003	21,675.5		16,825.2
30-39	98,112	5.4		107,179	5.9	2,928		2,082	2,730		1,943	14,742.0		11,463.7
40-49	65,408	3.6		76,309	4.2	2,838		2,017	2,646		1,883	9,525.6		7,908.6
50-59	47,239	2.6		52,690	2.9	2,596		1,846	2,421		1,721	6,294.6		4,990.9
60-69	32,704	1.8		34,521	1.9	2,385		1,695	2,224		1,581	4,003.2		3,003.9
70+	19.986	1.1		23,620	1.3	2,083		1,481	1,942		1,381	2,136.2	2,077.55	1,795.3

Sources: Ministerio de Salud Pública, Ministerio de Hacienda, and FAO.

Table 12.42. Some Essential Nutrient Requirements for Paraguayans

Category	Proteins grams	Calcium grams	Iron milligrams	Riboflavin milligrams	Vitamin C milligrams	Vitamin A milligrams
Male, 25 years old	60	0.5	10	1.2	50	1.3
Female, 25 years old	50	0.5	10	1.2	45	1.3
Female, pregnant	75	1.2	14	1.8	65	1.6
Female, lactating	80	1.2	14	2.0	95	2.1
Child, age 1–3 years	40	0.5	7	1.0	25	0.4
age 4–6	50	0.5	8	1.2	35	0.6
age 7–9	60	0.5	10	1.5	40	0.8
age 10–12	70	0.7	12	1.8	50	1.0
Male, age 13–15	85	0.6	15	2.1	60	1.1
Female, age 13–15	80	0.6	15	2.0	50	1.1
Male, age 16–20	85	0.6	13	2.1	65	1.3
Female, age 16–20	70	0.6	13	1.8	50	1.3

Source: Ministerio de Salud Pública y Bienestar Social.

Table 12.43. Requirements for Thiamin and Niacin According to Age and Sex, Paraguay
(in milligrams)

Age	Thiamin			Niacin		
	For Males	Both Sexes	For Females	For Males	Both Sexes	For Females
1		0.6			6	
1–3		0.7			7	
4–6		0.8			8	
7–9		1.0			10	
10–12		1.2			12	
13–15	1.5		1.3	15		13
16–19	1.6		1.1	16		11
20–29	1.5		1.1	15		11
30–39	1.4		1.0	14		10
40–49	1.4		1.0	14		10
50–59	1.3		0.9	13		9
60–69	1.2		0.8	12		8
70+	1.0		0.7	10		7

Source: Ministerio de Salud Pública y Bienestar Social.

Table 12.44. Provisional National Food Balance Sheet for 1961 Based on a Population of 1,816,890 in Paraguay*

Kinds of Foods	Production in tons	Imports in tons	Exports in tons	Tons Available	Tons of Animal Feed	Seeds in tons	Tons Manufactured	Losses in tons	Gross tons	% Extracted	Net Metric Tons/Year	Net kg/ Capital/Year	Net Grams/ Capital/Day
Cereals													
Wheat flour	—	3,927	—	3,927	—	—	—	—	3,927	—	3,927	2.161	5.92
Wheat	9,000	73,767	—	82,767	—	1,200	—	—	81,567	72	58,728	32.323	88.56
Corn	110,000	—	10,398	99,602	24,900	916	—	19,920	53,866	95	51,173	28.165	77.16
Rice	16,000	—	20	15,980	—	277	—	1,598	14,105	67	9,450	5.201	14.25
Root crops													
Mandioca	994,000	—	—	994,000	248,500	—	20,000	99,400	626,100	—	626,100	344.599	944.10
Sweet potatoes	72,000	—	—	72,000	3,600	—	—	7,200	61,200	—	61,200	33.628	92.13
Potatoes	4,000	3,920	—	7,920	—	396	—	396	7,128	—	7,128	3.923	10.74
Sugars													
Refined	28,756	—	3,300	25,456	—	—	—	—	25,456	—	25,456	14.013	38.39
Confectioner's	—	78	—	78	—	—	—	—	78	—	78	0.043	0.12
Corn syrup	8,724	—	—	8,724	—	—	—	—	8,724	—	8,724	4.802	13.15
Honey	106	—	—	106	—	—	—	—	106	—	106	0.058	0.16
Legumes													
Peanuts	9,000	—	—	9,000	—	240	2,700	—	6,060	—	6,060	3.335	9.14
Cowpeas	16,800	—	—	16,800	—	220	—	1,680	14,900	—	14,900	8.201	22.47
Peas	2,100	223	—	4,423	—	210	—	210	4,003	—	4,003	2.203	6.04
Vegetables													
Onions	7,800	1,048	—	8,848	—	—	—	531	8,317	—	8,317	4.578	12.54
Others	21,797	—	—	21,797	—	—	—	2,180	19,617	—	19,617	10.797	29.58

Fruits												
Oranges	119,365	—	5,641†	254,781†	—	—	13,021†	241,760†	—	241,760†	133.062	364.55
Grapefruit	7,102	—	—	—	—	—	—	—	—	—		
Tangerines	7,705	—	—	—	—	—	—	—	—	—		
Lemons	1,500	—	—	—	—	—	—	—	—	—		
Pineapples	5,200	—	—	—	—	—	—	—	—	—		
Bananas	120,000	—	—	—	—	—	—	—	—	—		
Others	1,845	534	—	2,379	—	—	119	2,260	—	2,260	1.244	3.41
Meats												121.17
Beef	54,083	—	—	54,093	—	—	—	54,083	—	54,083	29.767	81.55
Pork	5,408	—	—	5,408	—	—	—	5,408	—	5,408	2.977	8.15
Poultry	11,500	—	—	11,500	—	—	—	11,500	—	11,500	6.329	17.34
Fish	1,453	—	—	1,453	—	—	—	1,453	—	1,453	0.799	0.22
Others	9,223	—	—	—	—	—	—	9,223	—	9,223	5.076	13.91
Eggs (units, not tons)	19,900,000	—	—	—	—	—	—	995	—	995	0.548	1.50
Milk												225.42
Milk	129,200	2,000	—	145,200	—	—	—	145,200	—	145,200	79.916	218.95
Cheese	3,500	90	—	4,290	—	—	—	4,290	—	4,290	2.361	6.47
Fats												
Suet, lard	5,190	—	—	5,190	—	—	—	5,190	—	5,190	2.856	7.83
Butter	85	—	—	85	—	—	—	85	—	85	0.047	0.13
Oils	3,200	—	—	—	—	—	—	—	—	—	—	—

*Foods donated through charitable and international organizations are not included.

†Total for oranges, grapefruit, tangerines, lemons, pineapples, and bananas.

Source: Ministerios de Hacienda, Agricultura y Ganadería, and Salud Pública.

Table 12.45. Provisional National Balance Sheet of Essential Nutrients, Paraguay, 1961

Kinds of Foods	Net/Capita (grams)	Calories*	Proteins (grams)	Calcium (milligrams)	Iron (milligrams)	Vitamin A (micrograms)	Thiamin (milligrams)	Riboflavin (milligrams)	Niacin (milligrams)	Vitamin C (milligrams)
Cereals										
Wheat	94.41	344	10.3	15.11	0.94	0	0.12	0.04	1.04	0
Corn	77.26	275	7.34	13.13	1.78	348	0.35	0.08	1.55	0
Rice	14.25	51	0.95	0.14	0.13	0	0.01	0.004	0.23	0
Total	**185.92**	**670**								
Root Crops										
Mandioca	943.83	1,069	8.49	235.95	4.72	0	0.38	0.19	3.78	255
Sweet potatoes	92.05	89	1.01	25.77	0.74	387	0.07	0.04	0.46	17
Potatoes	10.74	9	0.21	0.86	0.08	–	0.001	0.003	0.15	1
Total	**1,046.62**	**1,167**								
Sugars										
Granulated	50.16	194	–	–	–	–	–	–	–	–
Molasses	13.28	36	–	4.38	0.28	–	0.008	0.008	0.02	–
Total	**63.44**	**230**								
Legumes										
Peanuts	9.04	35	1.65	0.33	0.12	2	0.08	0.01	1.44	0
Cowpeas	28.50	97	6.67	21.66	1.62	11	0.26	0.05	0.54	0.6
Total	**37.54**	**132**								
Vegetables										
Onions	12.55	5	0.16	3.77	0.06	0.63	0.04	0.05	0.03	1
Others	29.60	7	0.41	15.10	0.33	5.62	0.02	0.02	0.15	9
Total	**42.15**	**12**								
Fruits										
Citrus, pineapple, bananas	364.5	131	2.18	69.08	1.09	284	0.14	0.07	0.68	90
Others	4.68	2	0.03	0.66	0.02	12	0.001	0.002	0.02	1
Total	**369.18**	**133**								
Meat										
Beef	106.78	175	16.23	9.61	1.92	21	0.05	0.15	3.42	–
Other	13.92	20	2.30	2.64	1.27	484	0.02	0.16	0.67	1
Total	**120.69**	**195**								
Eggs	147	2	0.18	0.74	0.04	15	0.001	0.004	0.001	0
Milk										
Milk	218.90	131	7.22	24.5	0.22	262	0.07	0.35	0.22	2.2
Cheese	6.47	9	0.97	5.31	0.02	18	0.001	0.02	0.006	0
Total	**224.37**	**140**								
Fats										
Butter	7.84	64	–	–	–	–	–	–	–	–
	0.13	1								
Oils	7.42	66	–	–	–	–	–	–	–	–
Total	**15.39**	**131**								

*Available calories per person per day = 2,812.   Source: Department of Nutrition, Ministry of Public Health and Social Welfare.

Table 12.46. Milk Requirements, Paraguay, 1961

Age	% of Population	Milk Requirement ml Daily	Total Liters*
5	16.4	600	9.84
5–9	14.8	700	10.36
10–14	12.6	800	10.08
15+	56.2	500	28.10
Total			58.38

*For each 100 consumers.   Source: Codas 1962.

Table 12.47. Availability of Meat, Paraguay, 1961

Category of Consumer	Number of Consumers	Number of Cattle	Live Weight	Dressed Weight	Amount Available per Capita per Year (kilograms)	per Day (grams)
Asunción	300,000	100,000	32,500	16,500	55.00	150.68
Armed forces	30,000	50,000	16,250	8,250	275.00	753.00
Interior Paraguay	1,400,000	300,000	97,500	49,500	35.35	96.85
Industry	—	150,000	48,750	24,750		
Totals		600,000	195,000	99,000		

Source: Codas 1962.

Table 12.48. Utilization of Cattle in Paraguay, 1953–1961
(figures represent numbers of head of cattle)

Year	Asunción	Interior	Private	Military	Packing Plant	Subtotal	Industry	Grand Total
1953	134,205	370,524	5,078	25,431	—	535,238	12,251	547,489
1954	127,120	325,088	6,519	31,592	149	490,468	26,907	517,375
1955	125,054	255,000	17,659	38,047	—	435,760	64,730	500,490
1956	111,386	262,978	12,820	43,568	1,441	432,193	74,723	496,923
1957	97,465	274,298	16,325	45,857	2,122	436,067	84,637	520,704
1958	68,175	306,393	9,221	49,309	—	421,474	178,633	611,731
1959	94,953	273,746	2,849	49,926	—	421,474	196,204	617,678
1960	79,881	127,435	2,068	45,486	—	391,747	148,070	539,817
1961	43,885	252,445	1,341	43,911	—	341,582	184,953	489,652

Table 12.49. Dietary Adequacy in Rural and Urban Paraguay, 1943–44

Descriptive Data	Recommended Allowance	Rural Piribebuy	Urban Barrio Obrero
Number of families surveyed		56	10
Number of persons per family		6.02	4.50
Cost (Gs) of food per week		2.24	2.66
Essential nutrients (per capita per day)			
Number of calories	3,000.00	3,179.00	2,796.00
Total protein (grams)	70.00	93.00	88.00
Calcium (grams)	0.80	0.36	0.29
Phosphorus (grams)	1.32	1.24	1.11
Iron (grams)	0.012	0.032	0.022
Vitamin A (IU)	5,000.00	4,386.00	7,405.00
Thiamin (micrograms)	1,800.00	1,550.00	1,258.00
Riboflavin (micrograms)	2,700.00	1,469.00	1,258.00
Ascorbic acid (milligrams)	75.00	33.00	181.00
Sources of calories			
Proteins (%)		13.00	14.00
Fats (%)		30.00	29.00
Carbohydrates (%)		57.00	57.00
Sources of protein			
Animal (%)		51.00	58.00
Plant (%)		49.00	42.00
Sources of calcium			
Animal (%)		54.00	48.00
Plant (%)		46.00	52.00

Source: Reh 1946.

Table 12.50. Average Height and Weight of Subjects Included in Nutrition Studies
in 1943–1944 and in 1965

	Males				Females			
	Weight (kg)		Height (cm)		Weight (kg)		Height (cm)	
Age	1943–44	1965	1943–44	1965	1943–44	1965	1943–44	1965
1	8.2	7.0	–	72	8.7	8.5	72	70
2	12.1	10.0	86	79	10.7	10.0	81	79
3	14.1	10.5	87	88	13.6	12.5	91	87
4	18.3	10.8	95	95	14.8	14.2	96	94
5	19.8	15.2	105	104	15.5	16.0	101	102
6	17.3	15.6	106	107	20.9	17.0	106	108
7	21.0	15.9	116	115	21.0	19.2	112	112
8	24.0	20.4	115	118	23.2	22.0	119	118
9	25.8	20.9	121	122	24.2	24.5	121	123
10	27.8	25.0	128	128	27.6	27.6	127	129
11	30.1	28.5	126	130	31.8	31.2	131	134
12	34.3	35.0	136	136	40.5	34.0	140	139
13	36.4	35.5	141	141	39.8	38.4	144	145
14	43.9	40.3	158	146	41.8	44.1	149	148
15	44.0	45.2	154	151	52.4	48.0	157	151
16	53.7	50.2	161	157	49.1	51.7	154	154
17	47.9	50.9	159	162	48.1	52.5	153	155
18	65.3	55.7	166	164	54.4	52.6	158	156
19	59.0	60.2	161	165	49.6	53.5	154	156

Source: Reh 1946, and National Food Survey of 1965.

Table 12.51. Dietary Adequacy Related to Socio-Economic Circumstances in Paraguay,
1943–1944 and 1965

PIRIBEBUY, PARAGUAY, 1943–1944 (REH 1946)

Descriptive Data	Recommended Allowance	Socio-Economic Status			Occupation	
		Upper	Middle	Lower	Farmer	Non-farmer
Number of families surveyed		13	29	14	37	19
Number of persons per family		6.67	6.47	4.47	6.60	4.88
Cost (Gs) of food per person per week		3.20	2.16	1.50	2.24	2.23
Essential nutrients per capita per day						
Calories	3,000	3,763	3,148	2,701	3,727	3,085
Proteins (grams)	70	118	90	74	94	90
Calcium (grams)	0.80	0.51	0.38	0.18	0.38	0.34
Phosphorus (grams)	1.32	1.58	1.24	0.92	1.32	1.15
Vitamin A (IU)	5,000	6,710	3,634	3,709	3,852	5,425
Iron (grams)	0.012	0.033	0.033	0.032	0.35	0.027
Thiamin (micrograms)	1,800	1,825	1,510	1,378	1,605	1,444
Riboflavin (micrograms)	2,700	1,916	1,342	1,317	1,410	1,684
Ascorbic acid (milligrams)	75	53	33	15	33	33
Sources of Calories (%)						
Proteins		14	13	13	13	14
Fats		33	30	28	31	29
Carbohydrates		59	57	59	56	57
Sources of proteins (%)						
Animal		60	51	44	52	49
Plant		40	49	56	48	51
Sources of calcium (%)						
Animal		71	60	27	57	49
Plant		29	40	73	43	51

PARAGUAY, 1965, NATIONAL FOOD SURVEY (RECALL METHOD)

Descriptive Data	Socio-Economic Status			
	Upper	Middle	Lower	All
Number of families	58	46	165	269
Number of consumers	320	306	1,081	1,707
Essential nutrients per capita per day				
Calories	2,566	2,183	2,340	2,354
Proteins (grams)	79	65	58	63
Fats (grams)	65	52	52	54
Carbohydrates (grams)	419	370	424	413
Calcium (grams)	0.599	0.443	0.511	0.516
Phosphorus (grams)	1.140	0.909	1.025	1.026
Vitamin A (micrograms)	1,720	698	571	810
Iron (micrograms)	0.019	0.016	0.020	0.019
Thiamin (micrograms)	1,270	1,090	1,500	1,390
Riboflavin (micrograms)	1,660	1,210	1,180	1,280
Niacin (milligrams)	17	14	16	16
Ascorbic acid (milligrams)	265	271	423	366
Sources of protein				
Animal (%)	56	56	43	51
Source of fat				
Animal (%)	57	59	60	59

Table 12.52. Cost of Living in Piribebuy, Paraguay, in 1944
Based on a Survey of 11 Families

	Cost (Gs)		
Expenses for	per Family per Year	per Person per Year	% of Total Expenses
Food	547	109	54
Clothes and shoes	171	34	17
Housing	52	10	5
Household items	43	9	4
Household utensils	25	5	3
Medical services	76	15	8
Personal expenses	78	16	8
Garden expenses	12	2	1
Totals	**1,004**	**200**	**100**

Source: Reh 1946.

Table 12.53. Cost and Quantity of Foods Used by Rural and Urban Families in Paraguay,
1943–44

	Weekly Amounts per Family			
	Piribebuy		Barrio Obrero	
Food Items	Amount (kg)	Cost (Gs)	Amount (kg)	Cost (Gs)
Milk and milk products	27.95	1.80	19.85	0.76
Eggs	0.88	0.46	0.23	0.26
Meat and meat products	9.22	3.02	9.04	2.51
Fresh vegetables	2.87	0.71	2.39	1.03
Fruits	2.18	0.20	11.00	1.20
Root crops	32.80	1.39	3.52	0.37
Dried vegetables	1.80	0.36	0.54	0.14
Grain crops	9.37	2.72	8.39	2.81
Sweets	1.94	0.72	2.26	0.73
Fats and oils	1.43	1.19	0.69	0.61
Yerba mate, tea, coffee and condiments	1.89	0.73	1.80	0.82
Totals		**13.30**		**11.24**

Source: Reh 1946.

Table 12.54. Daily per Capita Consumption of Foods at Selected Localities in Paraguay, 1959–1961
(in grams)

Localities	Cereals			Root Crops			Sugars		Fruits and Vegetables			Meat	Eggs	Milk and Products	Fats and Oils
	Corn	Wheat	Rice	Manioc	Manioc Products	Others	Granu-lated	Cane Juice	Legumes	Fruits	Vegetables				
Yaguarón	55.56	56.52	26.34	777.61	52.53	197.39	16.24	9.34	42.93	91.85	31.12	167.61	6.21	47.90	22.48
Itacurubí	93.17	20.01	9.42	1,152.09	15.21	11.96	17.60	12.61	18.24	41.89	28.08	165.04	14.74	47.54	27.89
Cardozo	36.78	77.13	13.42	950.33	4.52	30.01	30.89	33.33	6.01	38.03	49.80	178.94	10.87	81.40	17.07
Acahay	75.36	53.21	8.87	508.44	1.93	41.82	20.70	3.90	23.02	106.11	52.08	105.32	5.32	78.41	10.88
Rosario	34.67	106.61	16.89	672.31	6.11	29.59	27.06	7.53	17.17	313.33	42.01	191.34	7.12	30.59	20.44
Horqueta	36.49	88.88	23.26	839.99	3.01	9.37	20.54	8.40	23.50	282.92	18.81	192.33	11.09	96.35	38.80
General Delgado	176.16	47.27	21.67	551.22	43.17	0.93	18.89	2.76	21.24	81.17	43.66	167.25	25.61	110.34	30.81
Pedro Juan Caballero	11.19	194.32	68.96	152.25	16.52	28.21	52.11	—	17.14	26.80	68.43	126.28	6.78	117.89	29.63
Fuerte Olimpo	16.96	209.17	34.25	33.45	12.92	33.03	1.82	0.79	7.35	66.59	22.03	208.03	8.72	330.74	21.71
Interior average	59.60	94.79	24.79	626.41	17.32	42.48	22.87	8.74	19.62	16.52	39.56	166.90	10.71	105.08	24.41
Asunción	23.02	356.78	33.37	141.32	74.75	0.40	98.12	3.33	12.84	242.52	90.25	251.67	12.15	244.40	38.50
National average	55.94	120.99	25.64	577.90	23.07	38.27	30.40	8.20	18.94	129.12	44.63	175.58	10.85	140.11	25.88

Source: Department of Nutrition, Ministry of Public Health and Social Welfare, Asunción.

Table 12.55. Dietary Adequacy (Expressed as a Percentage of the Recommended Allowance)
According to Socio-Economic Status and Place of Residence, Paraguay, 1959–1961
(Number of Families Surveyed Shown in Parentheses)

Essential Nutrients	Lower Class			Middle Class			Upper Class			General Averages		
	Interior (241)	Asunción (60)	Average (301)	Interior (74)	Asunción (47)	Average (121)	Interior (13)	Asunción (27)	Average (40)	Interior (328)	Asunción (134)	Average (462)
Calories	101	103	102	108	139	120	120	135	130	103	122	109
Proteins	106	129	111	125	172	144	169	190	184	113	157	126
Calcium	75	85	77	101	123	110	103	162	143	82	114	92
Iron	131	124	130	149	162	154	155	156	156	137	144	139
Vitamin A	54	56	55	37	78	53	48	76	67	48	68	54
Thiamin	122	92	116	132	125	129	128	124	125	123	110	119
Riboflavin	71	86	74	83	132	102	92	138	123	75	113	86
Niacin	188	209	192	212	320	255	239	279	266	197	262	216
Vitamin C	530	285	481	540	352	467	523	322	387	522	316	462

Source: Department of Nutrition, Ministry of Public Health and Social Welfare, Asunción.

Table 12.56. Sources of Calories and Essential Nutrients (Expressed as Percentages) in Asunción (Averaged Data) and the Interior of Paraguay (Averaged Data from Five Localities) in 1959–1961

Essential Nutrients	Place	Cereals	Root Crops	Sugar	Legumes	Vegetables	Fruits	Meat	Eggs	Milk	Fats	Miscellaneous
Calories	Asunción	39.62	7.92	14.81	1.65	1.36	4.96	10.16	0.73	6.77	11.99	0.03
	Interior	30.07	30.69	8.75	2.83	1.98	2.45	9.60	0.78	4.50	9.69	0.86
Proteins	Asunción	28.34	2.51	0.09	2.74	1.87	2.00	49.74	1.45	11.02	0.13	0.01
	Interior	24.92	10.20	0.33	5.91	1.90	1.59	44.16	2.01	9.06	0.60	0.02
Fats	Asunción	4.38	0.61	0.78	1.74	0.40	9.25	12.36	2.40	14.39	53.63	0.06
	Interior	7.47	3.40	0.04	4.00	0.29	1.09	16.75	2.72	12.35	51.95	–
Calcium	Asunción	12.29	7.85	0.71	1.92	5.25	5.67	6.33	0.97	57.12	0.07	1.81
	Interior	6.59	33.09	1.24	3.60	3.25	6.83	5.59	1.26	36.09	0.01	2.39
Iron	Asunción	24.13	9.86	1.97	4.27	6.73	6.50	36.20	2.20	2.09	–	6.05
	Interior	20.15	23.72	2.89	7.17	3.29	3.30	29.45	2.06	2.26	–	6.90
Vitamin A	Asunción	1.59	0.48	0.10	0.39	18.92	8.62	50.49	3.62	12.90	2.83	0.06
	Interior	9.52	2.29	0.05	0.99	9.82	15.20	40.75	7.22	13.49	–	–
Thiamin	Asunción	38.64	12.36	0.67	6.50	6.70	11.94	11.30	1.18	10.65	0.02	0.03
	Interior	35.49	26.10	0.99	8.51	3.98	6.92	10.44	1.13	5.92	–	–
Riboflavin	Asunción	14.06	3.63	0.26	1.17	3.38	8.55	34.24	2.36	32.33	–	0.02
	Interior	13.20	13.46	0.54	2.41	2.44	3.76	36.97	3.16	23.90	–	–
Niacin	Asunción	18.94	6.21	0.35	1.65	2.09	5.03	64.45	0.06	1.18	0.01	–
	Interior	18.08	15.71	0.11	3.54	1.76	1.59	58.23	0.09	0.82	–	–
Vitamin C	Asunción	0.06	38.11	0.28	0.42	14.79	42.39	1.42	–	2.03	–	–
	Interior	0.01	70.71	0.14	0.55	6.05	19.51	1.31	–	1.81	–	–

Source: Department of Nutrition, Ministry of Public Health and Social Welfare, Asunción.

Table 12.57. Consumption of Proteins of Animal Origin, Paraguay, 1959-1961

Towns or Regions	Number of Persons Surveyed	Grams per Capita per Day
Yaguarón	191	28.9
Itacurubí	279	34.3
Félix Pérez Cardozo (Yhaty)	221	34.5
Acahay	274	34.1
Rosario	176	29.9
Horqueta	201	66.0
General Delgado	153	52.8
Pedro Juan Caballero	192	28.2
Fuerte Olimpo	235	56.8
Interior total	1,922	
Interior average		28.2
Asunción	648	58.4
National total	2,570	
National average		44.0

Source: Departamento de Nutrición, Ministerio de Salud Pública y Bienestar Social, Asunción.

Table 12.58. Consumption of Milk and Cheese, Paraguay, 1959-1961

Town or Region	Number of Families Surveyed	Families Not Using Milk during 7 Days of Food Survey		Per Capita Consumption of Milk per Day (grams)	Per Capita Consumption of Cheese per Day (grams)
		Number	Percent		
Yaguarón				44.79	2.73
Itacurubí				43.87	1.86
Félix Pérez Cardozo (= Yhaty)				77.01	4.39
Acahay				70.24	8.17
Rosario				29.13	1.55
Horqueta				92.77	2.46
General Delgado				101.38	9.14
Pedro Juan Caballero				116.61	0.79
Fuerte Olimpo				327.43	2.67
Interior total	328	117	35.7		
Interior average				101.81	3.74
Asunción	134	13	9.7	243.89	0.38
National total	**462**	**130**	**28.1**	**137.63**	**2.90**

Source: Department of Nutrition, Ministry of Public Health and Social Welfare, Asunción.

Table 12.59. Sources of Foods and Weekly Cost, Paraguay, 1959–1961

Town or Region	Date of First Survey	Date of Second Survey	Number of Families Surveyed	Percent Produced by Familiy	Percent Purchased by Family	Percent from Other Sources	Weekly per Capita Cost
Yaguarón	Jul 59		30	26	71	3	Gs 81
		Jan 60	11	20	77	3	85
Itacurubí	Aug 59		42	40	55	5	87
		Mar 60	14	48	46	6	90
Félix Pérez Cardozo	Oct 59		36	30	65	5	104
		Jul 60	12	35	65	–	99
Acahay	Mar 60		48	42	52	6	92
		Oct 60	14	38	57	5	79
Rosario	May 60		32	21	75	4	99
		Nov 60	12	15	85	–	131
Horqueta	Jun 60		36	28	67	5	106
		Nov 60	12	30	69	1	117
General Delgado	Sep 60		32	46	49	5	104
		Mar 61	14	42	58	–	120
Pedro Juan Caballero	Dec 60		36	10	90	–	202
		Jun 61	12	14	96	–	195
Fuerte Olimpo	Apr 61		36	17	83	–	195
		Oct 61	12	7	87	6	125
Interior total	59–61		328				
		60–61	113				
Interior average	59–61			29	65	6	119
		60–61		28	70	2	116
Asunción	Mar 61		132	2	98	–	295
		Nov 61	40	4	95	1	332
National total	59–61		462				
		60–61	153				
National average	59–61			15	82	3	207
		60–61		16	83	1	224

Source: Department of Nutrition, Ministry of Public Health and Social Welfare.

Table 12.60. Dietary Adequacy (Expressed as a Percentage of the Recommended Allowance)
Related to Socio-Economic Status in the Interior of Paraguay, 1959–1961

Essential Nutrients	Lower Class		Middle Class		Upper Class		General Average	
	First Survey	Second Survey	First Survey	Second Survey	First Survey	Second Survey*	First Survey	Second Survey
Calories	101	105	108	116	120	110	103	113
Proteins	106	113	125	129	169	222	113	115
Calcium	75	73	101	127	103	120	82	79
Iron	131	135	149	133	155	154	137	132
Vitamin A	54	50	37	50	48	29	48	53
Thiamin	122	146	132	191	128	145	123	135
Riboflavin	71	78	83	100	92	110	75	83
Niacin	188	176	212	203	239	374	197	185
Vitamin C	530	430	540	509	523	406	522	448

*Represented by one family in the village of Fuerte Olimpo.
Source: Department of Nutrition, Ministry of Public Health and Social Welfare, Asunción.

Table 12.61. Minimum Salary and Real Income in Relation to Cost of Living
for the Worker in Asunción, Paraguay, 1951–1961

Date of Last Adjustment of Minimum Salary in Year Indicated	Minimum Daily Wage, Gs.[1]	Minimum Monthly Wage, Gs.	Estimated Real Income per Month Gs.[2]	Worker's Cost of Living during Year Indicated[3]	Difference between Minimum Salary and Cost of Living = $(e)-(c)$	Adequacy (percent) of Minimum Salary in Relation to Cost of Living = $\frac{(c)}{(e)} \times 100$	Difference between Real Income and Cost of Living = $(e)-(d)$	Adequacy (percent) of Real Income in Relation to Cost of Living = $\frac{(d)}{(e)} \times 100$	Worker's Deficit (percent) in Cost of Living = $\frac{(h)}{(e)} \times 100$
(a)	(b)	(c)	(d)	(e)	(f)	(g)	(h)	(i)	(j)
Jun 51	14.70	367.50	441.00	719.76	352.26	51.0	278.76	61.2	38.8
Jul 52	26.45	661.25	793.50	1,706.58	1,045.33	38.7	913.08	46.5	63.5
Nov 53	39.68	992.00	1,190.40	2,243.00	1,251.00	44.2	1,052.60	53.0	47.0
May 54	55.55	1,388.75	1,666.50	2,854.58	1,465.79	48.8	1,189.08	58.3	41.7
Nov 55	67.30	1,682.50	2,019.00	3,462.10	1,779.60	48.6	1,443.10	58.3	41.7
Feb 56	84.13	2,103.25	2,523.90	4,189.91	2,086.66	50.2	1,666.01	60.1	39.9
Feb 57	100.96	2,524.00	3,028.80	4,659.92	2,135.92	54.2	1,630.82	65.0	35.0
Jul 58	127.05	3,176.00	3,811.20	4,980.58	1,804.58	63.7	1,169.08	76.5	33.5
Jun 59	146.74	3,668.50	4,402.20	5,292.09	1,623.59	69.3	1,623.59	83.2	26.8
Jan 60	161.41	4,035.25	4,842.30	5,519.59	1,484.34	73.1	677.29	87.7	12.3
May 61	193.69	4,842.25	5,810.70	6,214.63	1,372.38	77.9	403.93	93.5	6.5

[1] Set by the Departamento Nacional del Trabajo.   [2] Estimate based on latest salary adjustment during a given year.   [3] Based on data from the Banco Central del Paraguay.

Table 12.62. Estimated Real Income and Cost of Living, Asunción, Paraguay, 1951–1961
(figures in guaranís)

Date	Food	Housing	Light and Fuel	Clothing	Misc. Expenses	Cost of Living	Estimated Real Income*
Jun 51	118.50	85.67	108.17	282.50	124.92	719.76	491.00
Jul 52	353.58	171.33	260.42	659.75	261.50	1,706.58	793.50
May 53	465.83	297.67	282.83	850.57	346.00	2,243.00	1,190.40
May 54	453.83	543.17	327.58	1,033.42	496.58	2,854.58	1,666.50
Nov 55	597.50	650.50	373.02	1,231.42	609.33	3,462.10	2,019.00
Feb 56	702.58	770.83	557.84	1,479.08	679.58	4,189.91	2,523.90
Feb 57	835.50	828.67	561.75	1,613.33	820.67	4,659.92	3,028.80
Jul 58	837.08	828.67	632.42	1,787.08	895.33	4,980.58	3,811.50
Jun 59	953.42	828.67	699.25	1,874.92	935.83	5,292.09	4,402.20
Jan 60	1,140.92	856.50	836.75	1,874.75	810.67	5,519.59	4,842.30
May 61	1,308.75	958.33	856.47	2,141.08	950.00	6,214.63	5,810.70

*Based on latest salary adjustment in year indicated

Table 12.63. Comparison of Indices of Worker's Wages and Cost of Living
in Asunción, Paraguay, 1950–1961

Date of Salary Adjustment[1]	Weighted Indices[2]		Difference between Cost of Living and Worker's Salary	Adequacy (percent) of Minimum Salary in Relation to Cost of Living	Deficiency (percent) of Worker's Salary in Relation to Cost of Living
	Worker's Salary	Cost of Living			
May 1950	Gs 695	Gs 921	−226	75.5	−24.5
Jun 1951	1,048	1,148	−100	91.3	−8.7
Jul 1952	1,048	2,816	−1,768	37.2	−62.8
May 1953	2,753	4,963	−2,210	55.5	−44.5
Sep 1953	3,222	4,715	−1,493	68.3	−31.7
Jun 1954	4,208	5,789	−1,581	72.7	−27.3
Dec 1955	5,124	7,762	−2,638	66.0	−34.0
Feb 1956	6,399	9,182	−2,783	69.0	−31.0
Feb 1957	7,563	10,545	−2,982	71.7	−28.3
Jan 1958	9,685	10,939	−1,254	88.5	−11.5
Jul 1959	11,164	11,881	−717	93.9	−6.1
Jan 1960	12,356	12,994	−638	95.0	−5.0
May 1961	15,005	14,730	+725	101.8	+1.8

[1] The dates of salary fixation are established by the Department of Labor. [2] Indices supplied by the Banco Central del Paraguay.

Table 12.64. Average Height and Weight of 1,115 School Children
in Asunción and Several Towns in the Interior of Paraguay, 1956

	Males		Females	
Age	Height (cm)	Weight (kg)	Height (cm)	Weight (kg)
6	114.6	20.6	114.4	20.4
7	119.4	22.9	117.7	21.7
8	123.2	24.2	122.8	23.7
9	127.4	26.2	128.1	26.5
10	132.7	29.5	132.7	29.3
11	136.5	32.0	141.3	33.6
12	142.8	39.2	144.5	36.2
13	146.9	38.3	149.5	42.8
14	154.5	44.1	152.9	48.4
15	156.5	47.2	154.0	50.1
16	163.4	54.1	154.3	51.6

Source: Department of Nutrition, Ministry of Public Health and Social Welfare, Asunción.

Table 12.65. Averaged Biochemical Data on 60 School Children, Ages 7 to 12,
from a Lower Class Barrio of Asunción, 1960

Test	Result
Total serum proteins	5.2 gram %
Albumin	3.0 gram %
Globulins	3.2 gram %
Serum vitamin A	12.0 microgram %
Serum carotenes	64.2 microgram %
Serum ascorbic acid	0.5 milligram %
Urine ascorbic acid	12.5 milligram %
Erythrocytes	3.6 million/mm^3
Hemoglobin	9.0 gram %
Hematocrit	32.0%
Red cell volume	84.7 cubic microns
Hemoglobin per red cell	23.9 picograms
Hemoglobin concentration per red cell	28.1%

Table 12.66. Changes in Biochemical Factors in 60 School Children
Given Dietary Supplements in Asunción, 1960

Test	Group 1[a]	Group 2[b]	Group 3[c]
Total serum proteins in grams %	6.8	5.4	6.6
Albumin in grams %	3.8	2.9	3.7
Globulins in grams %	3.0	3.5	3.2
Serum vitamin A in micrograms %	18.9	11.8	21.4
Serum carotenes in micrograms %	65.4	65.7	64.3
Serum ascorbic acid in milligrams %	0.61	0.68	0.52
Urine ascorbic acid in milligrams %	15.4	17.4	14.7
Erythrocytes in millions per mm^3	4.1	3.7	4.4
Hemoglobin in grams %	11.6	8.8	11.9
Hematocrit %	39.1	34.5	39.6
Red cell vol. in microns^3	85.2	84.2	85.4
Hemoglobin per red cell in picograms	27.1	24.0	26.8
Hemoglobin concentration per red cell %	29.7	27.9	30.3

[a] Normal diet supplemented with precooked soybean meal. [b] Normal diet supplemented with ferrous gluconate. [c] Normal diet supplemented with soybean meal and ferrous gluconate.

Table 12.67. Variations in Hemoglobin Values
According to Sex (Based on 3,000 Specimens
from Various Parts of Paraguay in 1959-1961)

Averaged Hemoglobin Values in Grams %	% of Females Sampled	% of Males Sampled
4.0–4.5	1.0	–
4.5–5.0	1.2	0.2
5.0–6.5	1.6	1.0
6.5–7.5	4.0	2.7
7.5–8.5	3.5	4.0
9.0–10.0	11.0	5.2
10.0–11.0	52.2	19.4
11.0–12.0	20.0	41.7
12.0–13.0	5.0	24.2
13.0–14.0	0.4	1.0
14.0–15.0	0.1	0.7

Table 12.68. Variations in Hemoglobin Values of Persons
Living and Working in Various Localities
in and near Asunción, Paraguay, 1960

Locality	Averaged Hemoglobin Value in Grams %
Central Public Health Laboratory	12.6*
Fernando de la Mora	11.2
San Lorenzo	11.1
Luque	10.2
Hospital Cruz Roja Paraguaya	11.0
Chacarita	10.3
Lambaré	9.3

*Based on a sample of 72 persons, mostly middle class, who are professional workers or friends and relatives of persons employed at the Central Laboratory.

Table 12.79. Nutritional Status of Pediatric Patients in the Hospital of the
Instituto de Previsión Social, Asunción, Paraguay, 1954-1956

Classification	1954		1955		1956	
	Number	%	Number	%	Number	%
Well nourished	285	45.1	285	41.8	302	37.1
Malnourished	293	48.0	311	46.8	374	46.0
Severely malnourished	49	7.7	72	10.5	127	15.6
Premature or congenitally weak	4	0.6	14	2.0	11	1.4
Totals	631		682		814	

Source: Data supplied by Dr. Ricardo Odriozola.

Table 12.70. Comparative Study of Full-Term Neonates
at Asunción, Paraguay, and Buenos Aires, Argentina, 1942–46

Measurements	Number of Asunción Neonates			Percent	
	Females	Males	Total	Asunción[a]	Buenos Aires[b]
Weight in grams					
Less than 2,500	70	51	121	3.31	c
2,500–2,799	172	115	287	7.85	7.02
2,800–2,999	222	212	434	11.87	11.35
3,000–3,799	1,152	1,246	2,398	65.57	63.89
3,800–4,999	123	293	416	11.37	17.74
5,000+	c	1	1	0.03	c
Total	1,739	1,918	3,657	–	–
Length in cm					
Less than 46	21	24	45	3.34	c
47–48	91	53	144	10.71	1.99
49–51	432	484	916	68.15	86.50
52+	90	149	239	17.78	11.49
Total	634	710	1,344	–	–

[a]Born at the Cruz Roja Paraguaya hospital from 1942–1946. [b]Based on 34,442 neonates born circa 1940.
[c]Indicates no measurements in this category.
Source: Montalto 1956.

Table 12.71. Length and Weight of Neonates Born
at Asunción, Paraguay, and Buenos Aires, Argentina

Measurements	Number of Asunción Neonates			Percent	
	Females	Males	Total	Asunción[a]	Buenos Aires[b]
Weight in grams					
Less than 1,999	98	102	200	3.67	1.81
2,000–2,599	219	191	410	7.51	3.96
2,600–2,799	302	271	573	10.49	6.68
2,800–2,999	296	261	557	10.21	8.84
3,000–3,799	1,390	1,573	2,963	54.29	59.88
3,800–4,999	271	456	727	13.32	c
5,000+	11	17	28	0.51	18.82
Total	2,587	2,871	5,458	–	–
Length in cm					
Less than 46	231	189	420	14.92	4.46
47–48	262	207	469	16.66	14.08
49–51	727	953	1,680	59.68	66.62
52+	93	153	246	8.74	14.82
Total	1,313	1,502	2,815	–	–

[a]Born at Hospital de Clínicas, Asunción, 1944–1955. [b]Based on 10,247 neonates (weight data) and
9,323 neonates (length data) born circa 1940. [c]Indicates no measurements in this category.
Source: Montalto 1956.

Table 12.72. Incidence of Malnutrition among 1,000 Six-Year-Old Children
Associated with Socio-Economic Status and Cultural Circumstances
in Asunción, 1956

| | Incidence of Malnutrition | |
Category	% of Total Number Surveyed	% of Total Non-Nursing
Organized family[a]	39.0	48.0
Disorganized family[b]	46.0	63.0
Economic situation adequate[c]	29.0	35.0
Economic situation deficient[d]	42.0	59.0
Cultural situation adequate[e]	23.0	42.0
Cultural situation deficient[f]	41.4	55.0

[a]Both parents live at home with the child. [b]One or both parents absent from home in which child lives. [c]Income sufficient to provide child with basic necessities. [d]Child deprived of certain basic necessities because of lack of money. [e]Parents with sixth grade or higher level of education. [f]Parents with less than sixth grade education.

Table 12.73. Some Results of Laboratory Tests
during the National Food Survey of 1965

| Type of Test | Group | Nutritional Status (Figures in per cent) | | | |
		Deficient	Low	Acceptable	Elevated
Hemoglobin	Men	14	43	23	20
	Women	3	5	83	9
	Children	9	17	43	31
Serum proteins	All samples	1.0	5.0	22.7	71.3
Serum vitamins	All samples				
Carotenes		0.8	8.6	51.2	39.4
A		0.1	6.4	72.2	21.3
C		0.0	0.4	2.4	97.2
Urinalysis	All samples				
Thiamin		0.7	8.2	25.9	65.2
Riboflavin		10.0	31.9	29.5	28.6
Iodine		78.5	14.8	6.7	0.0

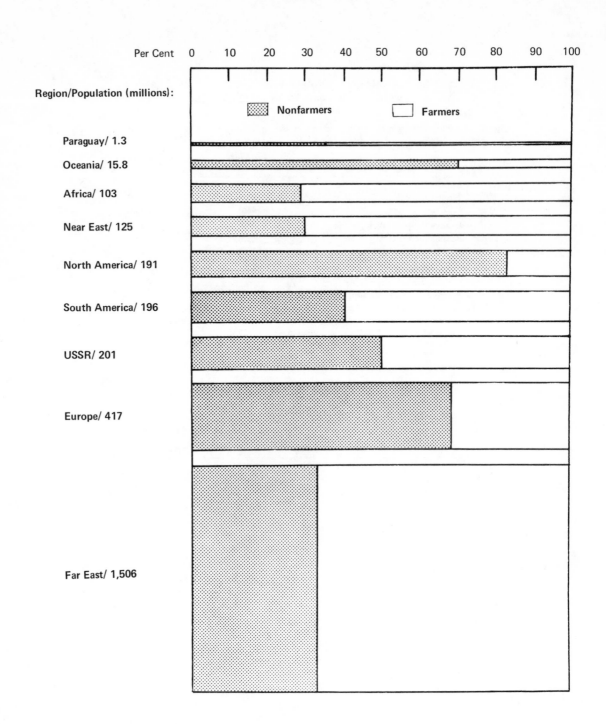

FIG. 12.1. REGIONAL DISTRIBUTION OF POPULATION OF FARMERS AND NONFARMERS, 1958

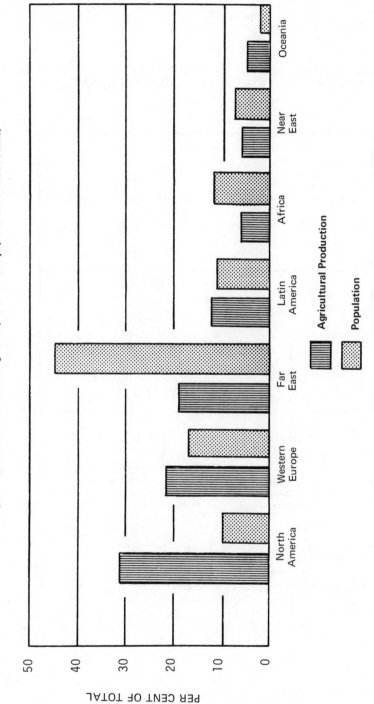

FIG. 12.2. PROPORTIONAL DISTRIBUTION OF POPULATION AND AGRICULTURAL PRODUCTION ACCORDING TO MAJOR WORLD REGIONS

(Averaged 1957–1959 data. Excluding USSR, Eastern Europe, and Communist China)

Agricultural Production

Population

PER CENT OF TOTAL

North America Western Europe Far East Latin America Africa Near East Oceania

Source: Desarrollo Económico Mediante Productos Alimenticios. World Campaign Against Hunger. Basic Study No. 2, FAO, Rome, 1962.

FIG. 12.3. RELATION OF AGRICULTURAL POPULATION AND PRODUCTION TO TOTAL POPULATION AND PRODUCTION IN PARAGUAY
(Average of 1950–1960 data)

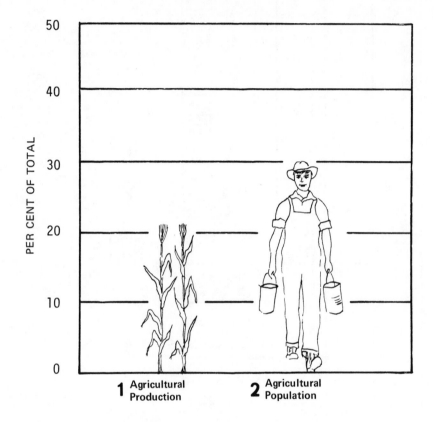

1 Agricultural Production

2 Agricultural Population

Source: (1) Departamento de Estudios Económicos,
             Banco Central del Paraguay
             Agricultural Production in Tons.

       (2) Censo de Población y Vivienda, 1962.
            (30% Increase in Population in Decade 1950–1960).

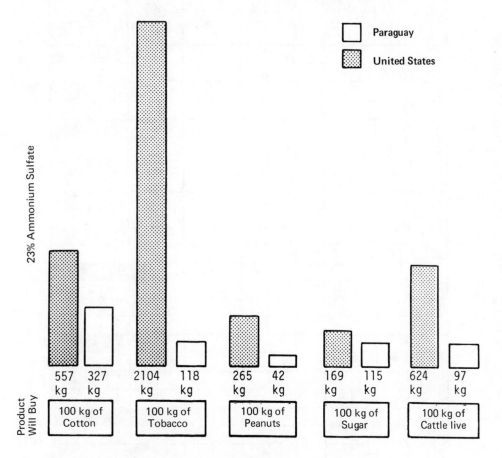

FIG. 12.4. COMPARATIVE PURCHASE POWER OF SEVERAL PRODUCTS
IN PARAGUAY AND THE UNITED STATES
RELATED TO EQUIVALENT VALUE OF 23% AMMONIUM SULFATE

Source: FAO Bol. Men. Econ. Estadíst. Agric., 1960 (May), 1961 (June, October, November);
Ministry of Agriculture and Livestock; and STICA, 1962.

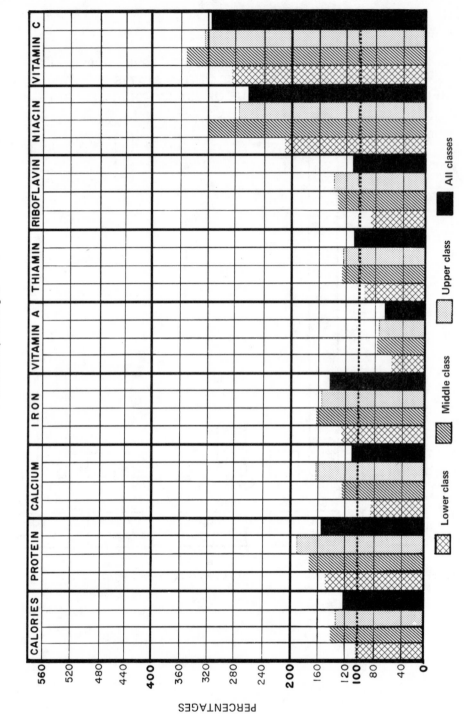

FIG. 12.5. DEGREE OF FULFILLMENT OF MINIMUM DIETARY REQUIREMENTS RELATED TO SOCIO-ECONOMIC STATUS IN ASUNCIÓN, PARAGUAY

(Shown in percentages)

Lower class   Middle class   Upper class   All classes

Source: Department of Nutrition, Ministry of Public Health and Welfare, Asunción, Paraguay, 1961.

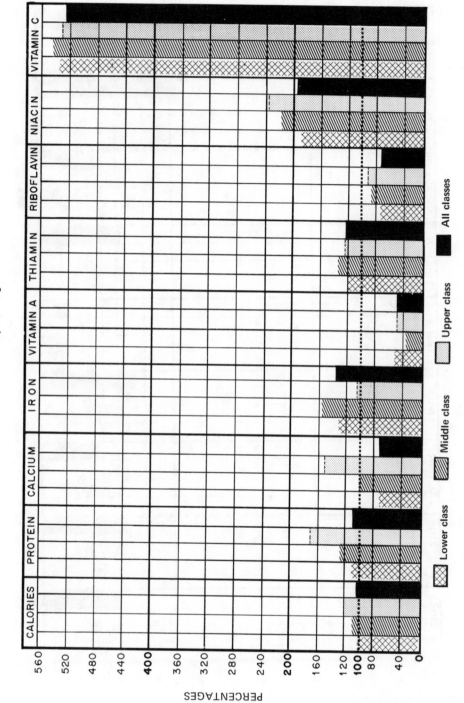

FIG. 12.6. DEGREE OF FULFILLMENT OF MINIMUM DIETARY REQUIREMENTS RELATED TO SOCIO-ECONOMIC STATUS IN ALL PARTS OF PARAGUAY (EXCEPT IN CAPITAL)

(Shown in percentages)

Source: Department of Nutrition, Ministry of Public Health and Social Welfare, Asunción, Paraguay, 1961.

FIG. 12.7. DEGREE OF FULFILLMENT OF MINIMUM DIETARY REQUIREMENTS RELATED TO
SOCIO-ECONOMIC STATUS IN ALL PARTS OF PARAGUAY

(Shown in percentages)

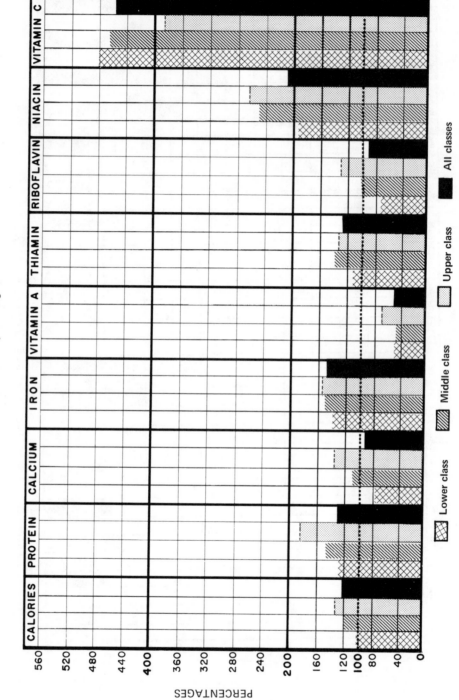

Source: Department of Nutrition, Ministry of Public Health and Welfare,
Asunción, Paraguay, 1961.

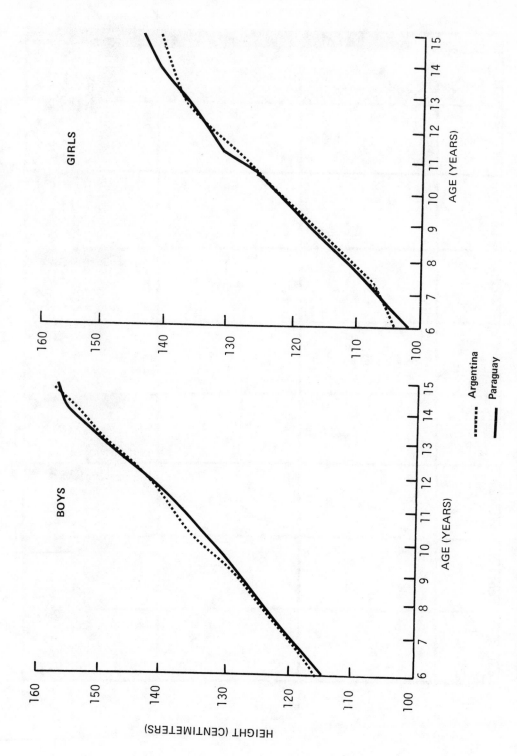

FIG. 12.8. AVERAGE HEIGHT IN RELATION TO AGE AND SEX

Source: Departamento de Nutrición, Ministerio de Salud Pública y Bienestar Social, Asunción, Paraguay.

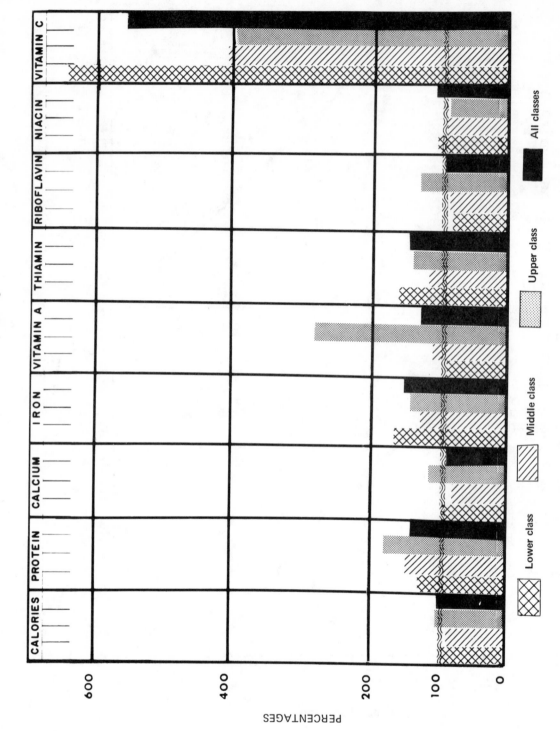

FIG. 12.9. DEGREE OF FULFILLMENT OF MINIMUM DIETARY REQUIREMENTS RELATED TO SOCIO-ECONOMIC CLASS, PARAGUAY, 1965

(Shown in percentages)

Source: Encuesta de Salud, Alimentación, y Nutrición, Ministerio de Salud Pública y Bienestar Social, Asunción, Paraguay.

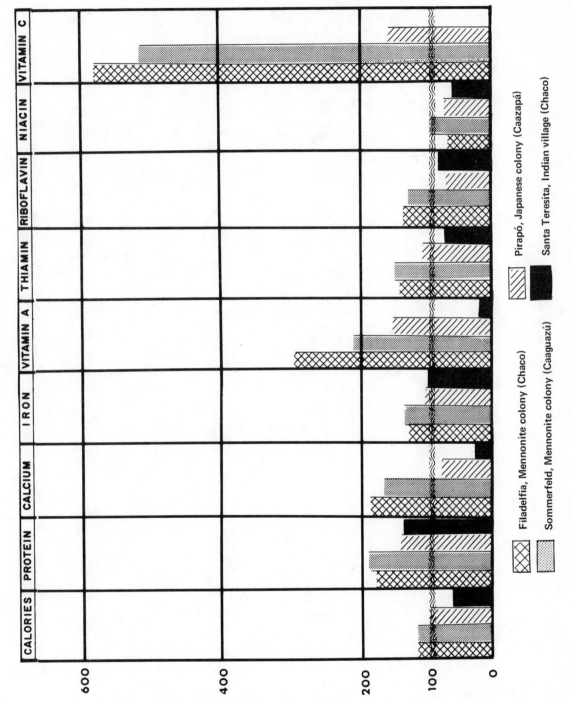

FIG. 12.10. DEGREE OF FULFILLMENT OF MINIMUM DIETARY REQUIREMENTS IN 4 PARAGUAYAN SETTLEMENTS

(Shown in percentages)

Filadelfia, Mennonite colony (Chaco)

Sommerfeld, Mennonite colony (Caaguazú)

Pirapó, Japanese colony (Caazapá)

Santa Teresita, Indian village (Chaco)

Source: Encuesta de Salud, Alimentación, y Nutrición, Ministerio de Salud Pública y Bienestar Social, Asunción, Paraguay.

XIII. Portraits of Paraguay*

J. RICHARD GORHAM

To publish a book with all information quite up-to-date is not an easy matter, when conditions are constantly changing.

Macdonald 1911

Picturesque Paraguay was published 62 years ago. Alexander Macdonald, the author, was an optimist. He believed that, in response to his candid and factual description of Paraguay, immigrants would flock to the country and transform it into the "garden of South America."

Beyond what I read in his book, I know nothing of Alexander Macdonald. His words, however, reveal much about him. He was a practical farmer, a practiced observer of nature, a disciple of free enterprise, gifted with remarkable foresight, but a little too class-conscious to be welcome today in the land which he held in such high regard.

Aside from such innovations as automobiles and paved roads, airplanes and airports, his antique observations are delightfully – or disappointingly – current. The locomotives still burn wood, the oxcarts still creak over rutted trails, and the log rafts still drift down meandering rivers. The hoe still lags behind the weeds, sap still drips from the homemade cane press, and the Guayakí still falls with the crack of "civilized" man's rifle. The siesta still punctuates the day as the guitar does the night. The prairie burns, the tree crashes, the animals retreat, the Indians acculturate, and the leaf-cutting ants harvest the crops.

What all of this means today is that many of Paraguay's natural attractions, which so appealed to Alexander Macdonald, are still largely intact, and hopefully will now attract the serious attention of ecologists. Time is short. Macdonald was 50 years ahead of his time, but he was still right: expanding populations will solve the "problem" of "vacant" lands, and "What has been already done in North America will be done . . . in the South . . ."

Macdonald's descriptive prose was enhanced by 65 well-chosen photographs. In a vain effort to copy his technique, I have embellished this series of 33 photographs with quotations taken directly from *Picturesque Paraguay*. I trust that this combination of Macdonald's narratives and my photographs will serve the objective of intensifying any interest engendered by the preceding collection of essays on the ecology of Paraguay.

In conclusion, the writer makes his "salaam" and goes his way to join the ranks of the great unknown whose descriptive powers have proved unequal to the task allotted to them.

Macdonald 1911

Author's address: Dr. J. Richard Gorham
Department of Biological Sciences
University of Alaska
Fairbanks, Alaska 99701

*Photographs by the author.

"At Tacumbu—on the summit of the ridge at the back of the city—one gets a magnificent view over the reaches and backwaters of the river in all its ramifications both above and below the town, and away over the woods of the Chaco, for leagues and leagues, into the wilderness of the interior. . . The city itself has lost much of its primitive charm during late years in the process of being modernized. Foreigners—mostly in the way of mechanics or small shopkeepers of the Latin races—are now much in evidence, while in the wholesale business, the Spanish, Italians, and Germans take the lead. Why the English should be left out of it is hard to understand. . . In spite of its drawbacks, Asunción is by far the cleanest and nicest town on the river above Buenos Ayres. This is partly owing to its fine natural drainage upon a ridge and the occasional tropical downpours, which remove all impurities in torrents of rain water. At other times the clear air and constant sunshine give disease germs a bad time of it. . . . the capital is very much like any other South American town of its class, with its really pretty gardens hidden away from public view in central courtyards after the old Oriental custom introduced into Spain by the Moors. . . . With a population of only 80,000 pretty well centralized, the wheel traffic is mostly confined to mule trams from the port to some of the suburbs. For some reason, hotel accommodation is about twice as costly as in Buenos Ayres, probably because their expenses in Paraguay are about 50 per cent less. . . . One is struck by the fact that there are no idle people about awaiting the chance of employment; in fact, the very poor as we know them in Buenos Ayres and Europe do not exist in Paraguay. . . . There is a project to lay down electric tramways costing 2,000,000 gold. Where the traffic is to come from in such a compact town of this size to pay for the initial outlay is difficult to see."

Plate 1. Hotel Guaraní, Asunción. Symbol of modern Paraguay.

"An old Spanish author stated, after seeing one Jesuit village, one had seen the lot—that each bore the like similarity to the other, as one drop of water to another drop of water. A fact to be noted by those extreme Socialists or Communists who would merge the individuality of the unit in the slavery of the social commonwealth, sacrificing the inventive and artistic ideas of the many to the stereotyped tyranny of the state. Progress in the individual or community can only come with responsibility. . . Some of the old towns remain to this day, more or less as the Jesuits left them at the time of their expulsion. A central square, with a huge church conspicuous at one end and a nice lawn in the centre as a playground for the children, was the invariable plan of all the old reductions."

Plate 2. Jesuit mission church, San Cosme, Itapua. This building was completed around 1760, just a few years before the Jesuits were expelled from Paraguay. It is still in use as a school and administrative center for the little community of San Cosme.*

*For more descriptive information about the remnants of Jesuit *reducciones,* see Ibáñez Padilla, A., 1971, Vanishing Guaraní treasures, Américas 23(10): 32–35.

"The mission churches were decorated with silver and gold, statuary and paintings equal to the best of those in Madrid or Rome. Celebrated masters in the arts and sciences were brought over from Europe to teach their crafts to such Indians as were needed for skilled workshops. Firearms, cutlery, and even cannons were turned out for their own use and even for sale to the government of the colony. In the course of time the missions became so strong as to practically rule the whole country. . . Under these circumstances the Indian converts now found to their cost that they had escaped one form of slavery only to pass their lives under the most rigorous surveillance of their spiritual advisers. Read, mark, learn, and spiritually digest, you people who would like to improve the human race out of existence under the rule of a Socialistic Commonwealth. . . Most of the old towns are now a mass of ruins, all grown over with tropical forest; a few of the churches and other public buildings, being built of stone, only having resisted the disintegrating element which destroyed the more temporary houses of the common people. . . The arts and professions taught to a few by the Jesuits have mostly been long forgotten with the existence of the teachers."

Plate 3.   Jesuit mission church, San Cosme, Itapua. Detail of one wing of church building. The monolithic columns, the wooden scroll work at the top of each column, the stone font (right center), and the sun dial (far right) all represent the handiwork of the Guaraní Indians under the supervision of the Jesuits. Some of the interior walls still bear evidence of Guaraní artistry, now more than 200 years old.

"Cane-cutting provides an occupation for a large number of peons for several months, during the crushing season. The cane grows up something like the bamboo in appearance, but thicker in proportion, and much shorter. Some varieties do indeed reach a height of twenty feet, but nine or ten is a good average, even on new forest land. The original cutting stools out into ten or a dozen plants, which, once started, grow rapidly, and are fit for crushing at the end of the year. In the process of cutting, the top crown of leaves must be lopped off, and the stem stripped of dead leafage with a machete. The stalks are then carted to the factory, where the juice is extracted by crushing between powerful rollers, and finally crystallized by boiling and various chemical processes."

Plate 4. Sugar cane press, San Cosme, Itapua. This Paraguayan family produces molasses, an enterprise in which the entire family participates. This press is horse-powered, but oxen are more commonly used for this purpose.

"Some of the peasants have their own little patches of cane, which they crush in a homemade wooden mill, which they call a 'Trapiche.' The juice is then boiled down to the state of treacle, and mostly used for the purpose of making 'Cana' or native rum. This business of converting good food into bad liquor is more profitable than wise. However, these people are no worse in these matters than others who should know better."

Plate 5.   Sugar cane press, San Cosme, Itapua. Detail of press, showing the hand-carved cogs and drums. The entire apparatus is hand-hewn from logs taken from the nearby forests.

"The Paraguayan peasant is certainly in some respects wise in his generation. . . . he has compensation in being absolutely unconscious of the pains
and penalties incidental to a more refined and intellectual organization, in
this grossly materialistic age. . . He doesn't care a Spanish 'carramba' for all
the fluctuations of the Exchange; and he is equally ignorant and indifferent
whether gold be at 600 or 6,000. An exceptionally well-informed man may
sometimes be familiar with the name of the President. Usually he has not the
remotest idea who he is, and cares even less; in fact, he is absolutely and
utterly indifferent to politics. . . However, taking all things into consideration,
in striking contrast to the Argentine, with a floating cosmopolitan population, Paraguay, with all its backwardness, thanks to a strong peasantry, forms
a united nation, with undeveloped possibilities for good or ill, which must
leave its mark on the history of the continent."

Plate 6. A five-year-old boy, Curuguaty, Caaguazú. Portrait of a typical Paraguayan child in the interior of Paraguay.

"Many of the daughters of Paraguay—out in the country—lead an ideal life, as far as health is concerned. She usually gets up at daylight . . . and trips away to the nearest market, with a basket of fruit or vegetables upon her head, thinking nothing of carrying her burden several miles on the way to town. . . Arrived in town, she does a pleasant gossip, disposes of her wares, buys a few pounds of meat and groceries—and flits away home with a good appetite for the homely meal which has been prepared by the old grandmother, who was left in charge of the house. Then she goes to the spring to wash her clothing, or, perhaps, to hoe the weeds in the family cultivation patch. A siesta in the middle of the day, and then the pounding of maize in a wooden mortar, for the evening repast. . . Later on the cows are milked, supper partaken of by the simple folk, and away to bed—unless there is a dance at a neighbour's . . ."

Plate 7. Making ñandutí lace, Itauguá, Central. An elderly woman engaged in one of the typical cottage industries of this region of Paraguay. The production of ñandutí lace is a slow and tedious process and requires considerable artistic skill.

"There is a wonderful diversity of type in the ant. We have insectivorous, omnivorous, graminivorous, grass-eating, leaf-eating, and exclusively wood-eating ants. Some live in the ground; others make heaps of loose soil—or leaves—on the surface, while some of their distant cousins bore holes in wood. Certain varieties cement their dwellings with well-worked red clay, which bakes hard in the sun, while yet another makes a roof of thatch. . . The Indians extract a very powerful poison from the red leaf-eater, using it to smear the points of their arrow-heads. It is at first curious to see long troops of these ants, marching along in single file each carrying a leaf over their heads . . . The red leaf-eating ants have a very complex social organization, making tunnels, yards beneath the surface, for a radius of half a mile from the central nest, connected by cross-roads, large air spaces, and numbers of ventilating holes, reaching up to the surface. A squad of leaf-cutters climb up amongst the branches, snipping off the tender shoots and freshest leaves, while the carriers pick them up and carry everything home. They are the most exasperating sinners imaginable."

Plate 8. Cerro Corá, Amambay. A region of mixed grasslands and forests, characterized by many isolated hills. The small mounds are termite nests.

"West of the watershed, the country rapidly drops down toward the Rio Paraguay to an elevation of only a few hundred feet above sea-level. Almost the entire area consists of a wavy succession of round ridges, or 'lomas' as they are called, covered with dense forest, in contrast to the intermediate depressions which are invariably pasture land, often indeed somewhat damp during the rains, but rarely degenerating into positive swamp land. . .

"The long expanses of low scrub are redeemed from monotony by the waving fronds of the lovely coco palm and long vistas of open prairies. A considerable population is evidenced by the numbers of little brown cottages scattered, as it were, broadcast over the whole country side, each with its microscopic cultivation patch of staple foods and tobacco. The camps are still covered with coarse indigenous grasses. . . Proceeding inland, the low woods gradually merge into veritable primaeval forests. At Paraguarí, the high rolling camps, in contrast with distant hill tops, are very attractive. Then for some leagues the almost perpendicular face of a forest-clad ridge gives what is practically a bird's-eye view of tropical wood. . . Most of the houses are hidden away amidst shady orange groves. . . Many of these people possess right to their hand a wealth of nature and beauty which rich people in other lands can only acquire by the expenditure of thousands or even hundreds of thousands of pounds."

Plate 9. A portion of the Cordillera de los Altos near Paraguarí, Paraguarí.

"The clearing of forest land costs by ordinary methods about twenty-five dollars gold per hectarea. . . Marketable timber may be removed, and the balance hauled out for future use as firewood, or for the production of charcoal. A still better method—which comes out a hundred per cent. cheaper in the long run—is to remove a little earth on one side of each tree, cut away a few of the roots thus exposed, and leave the rest to Nature. The first windstorm will blow the whole forest thus treated down on a face, tearing out the remaining roots. . . By either of the methods thus described no firing is required, therefore no destruction of the rich humus necessary for the best development of plant life."

Plate 10.   Near Pedro Juan Caballero, Amambay. Much of this region has been deforested and planted to coffee and other crops. The lone lapacho tree at the right is a remnant of the former forest.

"The higher ground is almost invariably covered with dense forest. Naturally, the growth and decay of roots loosens and blends the primary red soil with a thick layer of vegetable mould, composed of rotten leaves and the trunks of fallen trees. . . The resultant soil is eminently suitable for the production of the plant life of sub-tropical regions, giving satisfactory results for a number of years without cultivation. . . In the course of a few years [after clearing], as the air spaces in the soil, formed by the decayed roots, get filled up and the earth sets down hard, the results of cropping without cultivation become less satisfactory. And in this way has originated the fiction of the soil being impoverished after a few years. . . Such land is really very rich, and, with proper cultivation and rotation of crops, will maintain its productiveness for all time. In some of the old settled districts, where land is scarce, the peasants use a wooden plough—like the natives of India—which merely scratches the ground without turning a furrow. Need we wonder then that the native farm averages something like two acres for each family? and that they eat most of their produce at home? Not much chance of a surplus for trade under such circumstances!"

Plate 11. Near Guairá Falls, Alto Paraná. A temporary shelter in the midst of a new agricultural community carved from virgin forests.

"There are many pleasant drives in the vicinity of Asunción. A few leagues away a colony of European fruit-growers have been successfully established for some years. San Bernadino—a rather nice watering-place on the banks of a pretty lake—is within easy reach by a short railway journey through lovely scenery at Aregua, or Patinoque, from thence by steamer across the lake to the foot of the Cordilleras. . . Socially, things are dull for English people, but they cannot expect to have everything they want—with sunshine and butter-flies thrown in—in the middle of winter, even in Paraguay."

Plate 12. Lake Ypacaraí. A view of Paraguay's largest lake from San Bernadino (de la Cordillera) on the eastern shore of the lake.

"The Rio Paraguay is certainly a beautiful river. The graceful palm, the feathery bamboo, and drooping willow, casting reflections into silvery lagoons, all blend in exquisite harmony to charm the eye. The only thing to disturb our philosophical contemplation of all this beauty is the busy hum and equally energetic action of the ubiquitous mosquito, who, during the summer months, in his own practical way, resents the presence of any sacrilegious intruder in his domains. . . Millions of alligators lie about the banks, ready to take refuge in the water in case of disturbances. . . The quantity of fish must be considerable to support the vast numbers of these creatures. . . The Chaco Indians harpoon the alligator in much the same style as the Arabs of the Soudan. They consider the flesh excellent, and make use of the fat to rub over their bodies in order to keep mosquitoes away. A very effectual process after it becomes a bit rank."

Plate 13. Río Paraguay, Villa Hayes, Presidente Hayes. The ferry in the background is an essential link between the Chaco and eastern Paraguay.

"The forest roads of Paraguay are really long tunnels lined with thick foliage and luxuriant creepers often meeting overhead amidst the branches. Ferns and undergrowth fill up the sides of the path, and only constant traffic prevents the exuberant vegetation of the tropics from claiming its own again. The wild animals are all hidden away in the silence of the forest, and rarely cross a path used by human beings in the daytime. . . In the less frequented spots one sometimes sees deer or pigs crossing the path, or flocks of monkeys scampering amongst the tree tops; the gay-plumaged 'toucan' is also in evidence. . . Bird life is mostly conspicuous by its absence except, perhaps, the woodpecker, leisurely putting in his time as inspector of forests. . . Many coloured butterflies flit about from side to side in their peculiar erratic way. They may be seen in myraids on the damp sand on the banks of creeks, presumably sucking up the moisture in the same manner as domestic bees. It is an easy matter to make beautiful collections."

Plate 14. Forest of Caaguazú. High-wheeled oxcarts carve deep ruts in these forest tracks and make passage of ordinary vehicles very difficult. The improvement of farm-to-market roads, such as this one, is one of the major programs of the Paraguayan government.

"It is a far cry from London or New York, with their motor-cars, electric tramways, and luxurious living, to the woods of Central South America. Yet the Indians of the stone age, hacking out honey with their little flint hatchets, may easily be reached in a few days by steam and rail from Buenos Ayres or Monte Video. . . Once north of Caaguassu the country rapidly improves. We mostly find high rolling camps dotted with 'Iatahy' palms and covered with sweet wholesome grasses. Some of these camps are indeed sandy, and are partly covered with tufts of wiry coarse grasses, as formerly in the unrefined camps of Buenos Ayres. But there is always quite a lot of good pasturage in between. Horses, sheep, and cattle do remarkably well if looked after. . . On the borders of the woods where they slope down to the lower grass lands, for the first fifty yards or so we find an almost impenetrable barrier of vines and undergrowth, owing to the extra sunlight. Once fairly inside, the wood opens out, and in some montes it is even possible to pass on horseback, but usually dwarf trees and vines creeping over fallen branches make this impossible. A carpet of decaying leaves covers the ground everywhere, and, as the sun never penetrates the foliage overhead, ferns abound. Under the banks of forest streams, huge tree-ferns ten or twelve feet high may be found. Many arboreal fruits provide sustenance for the monkeys and other animals.

. . . the forest 'picada' opened out upon a narrow inlet of open prairie. Then a long expanse of grassy camp lands, island 'montes,' and distant woods, spread out on every side as far as the eye could reach. In the midst, a winding strip of low timber outlined the course of the nearest river. These low flats are most exasperating. In the distance, they appear to be perfectly lovely— as indeed they are—to look upon; but the moment one attempts to cross from one point to another, it is mostly a case of floundering amongst a hateful succession of tiny hillocks, clumps of bunch grass, and little clay pot-holes of rain water, alternating now and again—on lands subject to inundation— with perfect jungles of reeds and swamp grass. . . In most cases the intelligent use of plough or scoop would drain these lands at insignificant expense. The trouble is that the rank vegetation frequently obstructs small water-courses, causing them to spread out and get lost, thus forming a swamp or 'estero.' The accumulation of water soon re-forms into a stream once more, which again and again is lost in the plains, until eventually there is a sufficient body of water to force its way past all obstacles.

Plate 15. Island of grassland in Caaguazú forest. Although the Caaguazú forests do occur in great unbroken stretches, the more typical situation is that the forest is punctuated with islands of grassland.

"Most of the peasant proprietors possess a huge high-wheeled bullock-cart and several span of oxen, which they use occasionally for the carting of timber, yerba, or other country produce to the towns in their neighborhood, or for transport by the railway for export to the Argentine. A number of neighbours usually time their journey so as to travel together for their mutual comfort and society. The idea of the enormous wheels is to lift the body of the cart beyond the reach of the frequent mud holes in the undrained roads, as also in crossing the frequent streams, which become swollen into wild torrents after the rains."

Plate 16. Oxen and cart at confluence of Río Jejuí Guazú and Río Curuguaty. These specialized carts are used to transport logs from the forests to the river banks. At that point the logs are bound together as rafts and floated down to the Río Paraguay.

"The history of a log of cedar from the time it has been felled in the wilds of Paraguay, until it is finally transformed into table tops in London or New York, is quite a romance. Half-naked woodsmen cut long 'picadas' to reach their tree, square the sides in the most laborious methods with their clumsy axes in order to make it lighter for the wooden axles of their antediluvian cart, finally conveying it the nearest river by means of bullock teams. At this stage the river man takes charge to gather the scattered logs and form a raft. To pilot his unwieldy craft down the great river is anything but a picnic. Mosquitoes are in their own peculiar domain on the water frontages and, except during the heat of the day, make things lively for the voyager. The raft must be guided by poles around the frequent bends of the stream, and shoals obstruct the navigation of these streams except in flood time. . . [On] the embankment thousands of logs of fine timber lie on the banks and in the water awaiting shipment. The arrangements are worthy of the flint age period, the logs being rolled about from place to place by gangs of barefoot peons."

Plate 17. Río Paraguay near Rosario, San Pedro. Logs awaiting transshipment to Argentine sawmills.

"The eastern portion of the Republic may be considered an extension of the Highlands of Brazil, a region mostly covered with primaeval forest, at all events, to the north of Villa Encarnacion... Owing to the shortness of their courses, and the nature of the country, the tributary streams of the Alto-Parana are not navigable to any extent, being generally small, and obstructed by rapids. There is indeed a certain amount of rafting and barge work on the upper part of the Mondayi. But the lower reaches of this river form a magnificent cataract, much more imposing and beautiful than the far-famed Iguassu, a few leagues away on the other side of the Parana... A few wild Indians, generally simple, harmless creatures, roam the forest, eking out a precarious living by the gathering of wild fruits and the proceeds of the chase... At one time Jesuits had quite a large population in their settlements above Guayra Falls. These people lived prosperously for a considerable time until the raids of Brazilian slave-hunters made the position untenable. The residue were removed by strenuous efforts to Villa Rica, Paraguay... The Parana, taking its rise in the heart of Brazil, has cut out a deep gorge through this district on its course to the sea, taking a leap over the hills on its way that throws the Niagara into insignificance... The Guayra Falls are the Niagara of South America, really of much greater magnitude and volume of water—as may be seen from the following figures: Niagara has a fall of 160 feet; the Guayra runs into 180 feet. In width the former is approximately 1,800 yards, while the latter has a spread of over 4,000 yards... Unfortunately, this marvel of nature... is not as yet readily accessible to tourists. To visit the Falls by land requires a long horseback journey through open prairies, and finally, long forest cuttings in the tangled woods which characterize this region. There is no population, except a few yerba gatherers for a few months in the year, and wild Indians, whom one never sees, hiding away in the darkness of the forests... What the falls may be worth in the future in the way of developing electrical power for a radius of a hundred miles or more around the district it is difficult to imagine or foresee... Indeed, the Falls alone might provide sufficient electrical power for the whole Republic. What has been already done in North America will be done in the future in the South of the continent. If a fraction of the capital, enterprise, and labour which is expended in Alaska were only devoted to the opening up of the 'Sunny South' we should see things begin to move... Some day an enormous population will develop the hidden wealth of this region."

Plate 18. Iguazú Falls, Argentina. Although not located within Paraguayan territory, Iguazú Falls is easily accessible from Asunción. The International Friendship Bridge, which crosses the Río Alto Paraná between Brazil and Paraguay, is located just a few miles from the falls. Iguazú Falls is one of many cataracts that line both sides of the Río Alto Paraná between Encarnación, Itapua, and Guairá Falls.

"Our river proved to be a muddy, rapid flowing stream, with deep perpendicular banks cut out by the rush of water in flood time. After a succession of heavy rains, the waters spread out for half a league on either side. These flat country rivers are anything but lovable. The water is seldom clear and transparent, and myriads of mosquitoes take refuge in the bamboo thickets and fringe of wood usually lining the banks; while all the camps subject to inundation, for at least half the year, are infested by several species of gad-fly. . . The tributaries of the Paraguay and Parana, having short courses, both flood and subside quickly after heavy rains. . . This superfluous water will some day be used for irrigation purposes, which pays even in the well-watered Tropics. . . In times of rain it is necessary to swim one's horses over to the opposite bank. Some of the Montes are of considerable extent, such as the Caaguassu-San Joaquin Monte, which must have an area of much more than a hundred leagues. Unknown animals hide away in its fastness, and the untamed Guajaki Indian wanders from place to place, depending entirely for sustenance upon his bow and arrow and the little stone axe used in Britain thousands of years ago.

The Guajaki is in some respects a hero. Just fancy a naked man and woman stranded in a tropical forest, exposed to the attacks of mosquitoes, ticks, and other insect pests. They have no tools. A blade of tough cane grass serves as a knife. The axe represents the labour of weeks or months, and the bow and arrows, carved out of hard wood, the concrete evidence of unremitting toil and tireless skill of a most fastidious artist. Fire is carried from place to place in a piece of smouldering fungus. Yet they do manage to live, and have put the fear of judgement into the prowling jaguar. Fortunately, pigs, tapir, and deer are numerous, as also a certain amount of wild honey. Yet the seeking of this sweet dainty is often their undoing. If a party of native hunters hear the tapping of the Indian's axe, they sneak up quietly and murder the poor wretch up in the tree with no more compunction than if they were killing a monkey. I asked one of these fellows why they killed these people without provocation. He shrugged his shoulders and replied, 'Quien sabe.' Don't you know that the skin of an Indian is tougher than any other for making hammocks or 'guascas' for carrying yerba leaves? Will not some good souls take the matter up, and see that these wild men of the woods get some protection? It is true the poor beggars sometimes are compelled by hunger to kill a cow or a horse, but for three hundred years every man's hand has been against them. On sight of their fellow man they fly like a wild animal—and with reason—for they are often hunted with dogs for sport. No one knows their language, and their children, who have been taken by Paraguayans, even if they escape after a few years, would be looked upon as spies and killed. I am ashamed to say that one European estanciero up there, now owning several large cattle ranches, who arrived in Paraguay without a cent, has been urging the local authorities to destroy these Indians, threatening to withdraw his interests from the country. Only six short months ago, some estancia peons, guided by two tame Cangwah Indians, made a night raid upon a group of sleeping Guajakis. The first man seen was shot, the rest stampeded in all directions. Two of the children were seized. These screamed pitifully, and the father, a fine bearded man, came back to the rescue brandishing a club. The poor fellow was mercilessly shot. How long shall these things be?"

Plate 19. Near Itaquyry, Alto Paraná. Heavy thundershowers often turn roads into streams, and make the fording of streams hazardous.

"Southern Matto Grosso is noted for its fine grazing lands and superior stock, disproving the theory that cattle will not thrive in the equatorial regions. . . In 1546 seven cows and a bull were imported from Europe, and became the progenitors of all the enormous herds which form the principal wealth of all the River Plate countries to-day. The rate of increase in these virgin pastures may be imagined when it is said that in his time the historian and traveler Azara estimated the number of cattle in the Plate at 18,000,000 head. In modern times these animals have been crossed in the South with the best European breeds, and in the North with a strain of the African Cebu or humped cattle. In Paraguay, Corrientes, and some remote estancias of the Argentine, they remain mostly in their original state. The hides are the best in the world; but the animals are inferior for meat or milking purposes, having been allowed to run practically wild for hundreds of years. Indeed, in the seventeenth and eighteenth centuries, vast herds of cattle and horses roamed the plains to all intents and purposes in a state of nature, the property of any one who cared to make use of them."

Plate 20.   Near Pedro Juan Caballero, Amambay. Near the border between Amambay, Paraguay, and Mato Grosso, Brazil, the forests of Amambay gradually fade away into the enormous prairies of Mato Grosso.

"Some day Paraguay will become the garden of South America. There is hardly a yard of waste land in the whole country, even the 'esteros' or swamps being in almost every case easily drained by plough or scoop. The soil is excellent for rice, sugar cane, or grazing-land. Indeed, for pasturage, if the rough native herbage is destroyed by ploughing, and suitable artificial grasses substituted, the results are wonderful. The growth is continuous. Generally speaking, in the south, centre, and west of the Republic, there is an equal distribution of wood and plain, the contour of the country being a series of wavy undulations—with here and there and isolated outcrop of low hills. . .

Three hundred leagues beyond the city of Buenos Ayres—away up the river—we find the greatest contrast possible to the sheep-walks and wheat-fields of the lower Plate provinces. An undulating country, with high 'lomas' and sweeping plains, gives an alternation of tropical forest and verdant prairie, no less pleasing to the eye and fair to look upon than practically advantageous to the settler, and full of possibilities for a combination of stock-raising and agriculture. An extraordinary landscape, composed of islands of wood, of every shape and form, and lakes of grassy 'campo,' redeems the scenery from the monotony of an otherwise flat country; while here and there a hillside displays a variety of foliage quite unknown beyond the forest regions of South America. At certain seasons of the year, masses of lovely flowers, mostly pink or yellow, framed in blended shades of silver and green, are transformed by the quivering sunlight into a mirage of fairly-land. Myriads of butterflies, flitting in the woods, in a despairing effort to get into harmony with the prevailing hues of the scenery, seem to have exhausted the ingenuity of Nature's artists, in the painting and shading of their wings with all the colours of the rainbow. In such a country the position of man is somewhat disappointing."

Plate 21. Prairies of Caazapá. The grassland is the dominant plant formation, but the islands of forest are always present.

"In other parts of the world great companies have played no mean part in the history of our modern civilization, affording outlet for the enterprise of millions of industrious citizens, and even to the founding of solid Empires. So far, one of the finest fields of all has been strangely neglected. I allude to that enormous area in the heart of South America, watered by the tributaries of the Rios Parana and Paraguay, comprising parts of the Republics of Bolivia, Brazil, Paraguay, and the Argentine. Steamers drawing up to nine feet easily penetrate up to a thousand miles from the estuary of the River Plate, and the water frontage accessible to flat-bottomed river craft runs into at least a hundred thousand miles. Here we find millions of acres of very fine pastoral and agricultural lands, absolutely in a state of nature. . . In this country we find frequently a strange alternation of prairie and forest, comprising all the advantages and none of the disadvantages of similar tracts of open plain or unbroken wood in other parts of the world. But it must be understood that in this climate the growth of grass is continuous, the result being that, with insufficient stocking, the vegetation degenerates into rankness and decay. The only remedy practised is the primitive and destructive process of burning the grass in hot weather. The cattle, too, are the degenerate product of three hundred years of wilful neglect."

Plate 22. Burning prairie near San Juan Bautista, Misiones. Most Paraguayan ranchers are convinced that burning the prairie improves grazing conditions for the cattle.

. . . the Paraguayan Central Railway . . . in combination with the North East Argentine and Entre Rios Railways, are now running a through passenger and freight service to Buenos Ayres, and vice versa. The journey at present occupies three days, but will be shortened to forty-eight hours when the new ferry service is completed on the Alto Parana, about the end of the present year. In the meantime passengers must stop over a night at either Villa Encarnacion or Posadas, from whence, if they so desire, it is an easy matter to pay a flying visit by steamer to the far-famed Iguazu Falls, before resuming their voyage by 'terra firma.' In this manner the overland trip is very much less monotonous than the corresponding voyage by steamer, as one may see from the train the enormous herds of cattle and horses for which Corrientes and Entre Rios are famous, as also the prairies and primaeval forests of Central Paraguay, the rolling downs of Southern Missiones and Northern Corrientes, and the wooded banks of the silvery Uruguay, celebrated as being the Rhine of South America."

Plate 23. The Asunción-Encarnación train at Yuty, Caazapá. Although everything about this railroad is ancient, the roadbed has held up over the years because the ties are made of the virtually indestructible *quebracho* wood, harvested in the Paraguayan Chaco. The ties have long since sunk into the ground, but they continue to resist the attacks of termites and fungi.

"A glance at the map will show the peculiarly advantageous position of Paraguay in the interchange of the varied products of the temperate and tropical zones of South America. . . Yet, so far, the country is entirely in a state of nature. There is neither canal nor irrigation work in the whole area, not a single swamp has been drained, nor a forest cleared for the planting. The number of square miles represented by forest clearings could be pretty well reckoned up upon the fingers of one hand. Not an acre of pasture land has been put under the plough and refined by means of artificial grasses. Half-a-dozen horses and a scoop would reclaim nine-tenths of the lowlands at less cost than the hundredth part of their intrinsic value. At present periodical fires are needed to burn off the surplus vegetation, used by nature to fill up vacant places. . .

"About half the area of the Republic consists of dense forests, distributed as a rule very evenly over the whole country in clumps or patches of wood amongst the grazing lands; in the East and North having a tendency to run into large forests, which sometimes stretch out continuously for hundreds of square miles. In other parts of the world, we frequently find large areas of woodland composed entirely of the same kind of timber. Here, on the contrary, the variety is infinite—to such an extent as to be an actual drawback to the woodcutters, if they are in search of any particular class of wood. The isolated specimens of any given kind are dotted about here and there, often at considerable distance from their fellows. This necessitates no end of road-cutting from tree to tree, to get a quantity of any given sort. On the other hand, the wonderful variety of woods upon any circumscribed area enables people to obtain whatever class of timber they require for special purposes—without traveling any considerable distance for the purpose."

Plate 24.   Locomotive fuel, Caazapá. Wood is a major source of energy for both home and industry, and the great demands for this fuel have led to widespread deforestation. The prairie is burning in the background.

"About a thousand Europeans, including women and children, are settled on the public lands in Paraguay, practically all of whom—having learnt their agricultural methods in the country—are laboriously cultivating a couple of hectareas in native style with the machete and hoe. These people, working by such crude methods, would have starved in any other part of the world. A very few practical agriculturalists, who understood their business, have done well. Others are prospering in commercial pursuits—or in the timber trade; while yet again, some, who have had exceptional opportunities, have made quite a good thing out of cattle. Camps are going up in price. . . No doubt the cattle business . . . all the world over is on the move. Even here in Paraguay— in spite of the prophecies of pessimists—prices have been steadily going up during the past two decades. A wretched criollo novillo—which dresses at 200 kilos when clean—fetches in the market from twenty-five to thirty dollars gold. Fairly decent herds of mixed cattle of the country fetch about twelve dollars gold per head. Dr. Kemmerich, the 'La Fonciere' Company, and others have gone in for stock in a fairly large way—counting their animals up to six figures. This business offers unlimited scope to the man who is intelligent and energetic enough to refine his camps and to improve the type of his breeding animals. Herefords have already been proved to be a success."

Plate 25. Cattle country in the southeastern Chaco. Palms occur both scattered and clumped. Areas of dense scrub forest may be seen in the background.

"The Paraguayan Chaco—on the western side of the Rio Paraguay—is a striking contrast in every way; generally low and swampy on the banks of the river, with extensive lagoons and backwaters, the home of millions of alligators and unknown amphibious creatures, providing in the open places excellent pasturage on the flooded lands, but often requiring the utmost care to prevent the loss of one's whole amount of stock during periodical inundations, which extend for fifty miles inland from the great river. . .

"In such a country, the camps being understocked, the grass grows wild and rank, except during certain periods, after burning the new grass mixed up with old decaying leaves. This neglected pasturage cannot be expected to give the best results. Owing to the unchecked vegetation and proximity of forests, blow-flies are troublesome, and, at certain seasons, the least wound requires an application of tar. In fact, the weekly round-up and doctoring is about the only work done by the people who profess to be stock-breeders. . . Stock-breeding gives good returns, even by these primitive methods."

Plate 26. Inundated chaco near Benjamín Aceval, Presidente Hayes. These areas of wet chaco possess an abundant and varied bird fauna. Jabiru storks *(Jabiru mycteria)*, shown here, are often the most conspicuous inhabitants of the wet chaco.

"The banks of the Chaco are always low, consisting mostly of tangled undergrowth, alternated by open savannahs, thickly dotted with palms, as far as the eye can reach. Nature is everywhere supreme, and there is but seldom any evidence of human existence. The population theories of some philosophers don't count for much here in South America, where millions of acres of the finest land in the world—as yet practically untouched by the hand of man—are still available for settlement. Many of our present evils arise not from over-population, but from the manner in which that population is distributed."

Plate 27.   Fording Río Brazo Norte, Presidente Hayes. Chaco rivers are sluggish and turbid, and are often inhabited by sting rays and pirañas. Bridges, except on the Trans-Chaco Highway, are non-existent, so the traveler has the choice of swimming or chancing the dugout.

"Large areas are covered with Quebracho forests, generally with an impenetrable undergrowth of cactus and euphorbias. Then again most of the plains are dotted, as far as the eye can reach, with lovely palms, known locally as 'Palmares.' The climate is hot and dry, except in the vicinity of the river, where a damp and humid climate characterizes most of the year. Myriads of mosquitoes and sandflies pester the animal life of those riverside districts. A few estancias are established in the vicinity of the river; and the stock do splendidly if looked after and saved from possible inundations. . .

"In Paraguay cattle breeding is under very much the same conditions as in the northern half of Corrientes. The herd must be kept under observation, to obviate loss from the larva of flies being deposited in open wounds. Epidemic diseases are rare, and of milder type than elsewhere—if one excepts the *mal de cadera*, which attacks horses in some districts."

Plate 28. Ranch house, Presidente Hayes. Palm trees play an important role in the life of the rancher of the southeastern Chaco. Palm logs form the frame and walls of his house, and palm leaves the thatch of his roof.

"The natural history of Central South America is less known than that of Central Africa. . . Careful and systematic investigation, continued for a number of years, would no doubt result in the discovery of many creatures which remain still to be classified. Owing to the distinct dividing line between forest and plain, and the peculiar distribution of 'island forests,' there is a tendency for certain species to become localized—for the simple reason that such animals and birds will not venture out from their shelter to cross the open space leading over to the nearest part of an adjoining wood. This fact is well known to all backwoodsmen. When one comes down to the study of reptiles and insects the difficulties are obvious. A life-time might be spent in collecting without exhausting the list of creatures which have a fashion of putting in an appearance just when one fancies he is well posted on the subject. The alternations of wood and prairie and conformation of the country also tend to grade off different varieties, even in the case of the larger animals. . .

"When one considers the sparsity of the population and the enormous areas of dense forest affording a secure retreat for the fauna of the country, the thing is easily comprehensible. As a case in point, the writer passed ten consecutive years in one district, observing in a casual way the forms of animal life commonly in evidence. It might have been expected that in a year or two one could have exhausted the list of creatures making use of that habitat. On the contrary new varieties and species, some even unknown to the natives of the district, were always turning up quite unexpectedly. If this is the case in a thickly populated, old, settled part of the country, what must be expected in the wilderness of forest and backwaters of the great rivers and swamps, where there are no people except a few Indians, and when the naturalist must be extremely enthusiastic to endure the discomforts and physical hardship incidental to years of life spent in such places in the search for rare and shy animals which are seldom seen by man?"

Plate 29. Trans-Chaco Highway, Boquerón. This highway is a dirt road running diagonally across the Chaco from the Río Paraguay to the Bolivian border. The highway has been a great boon to the economic life of the ranching and agricultural communities of the Chaco. The borrow pits paralleling the road produce myriads of mosquitoes, including the anopheline vectors of malaria.

"This view represents the homestead of a German colonist in the land of oranges. Evidently the hardships of the backwoods have not troubled him very much. The sons of the Fatherland may be found scattered all over Paraguay on farms, estancias, or in business. . .

"The drier lands of the interior are subject to drought, and require something to be done in most cases in the way of water conservation. The soil is mixed with a proportion of mineral salts in most places, and unsuitable for cultivation, except in parts which are eminently suited for cotton growing, where the dryness of the climate renders it possible to harvest the crop without constant loss of the almost daily rains in Paraguay, east of the river."

Plate 30. Mennonite farmstead, Filadelfia, Boquerón. Mennonite farmers from Canada, Russia, Germany and other places have created an agricultural oasis in the middle of the Paraguayan Chaco.

"The Gran Chaco, or Great Wilderness, is even yet to a great extent a blank upon the map of South America. Here and there, along the banks of the great river, a few sugar plantations, sandalwood extract mills, and cattle-ranches have been established, but in the interior there are no inhabitants excepting a few tribes of semi-nomadic Indians. In the north, Mr. Barbrooke Grubb, of the South American Missionary Society, settled amongst these people twenty-two years ago, and after an adventurous career, by the exercise of tact and common sense, acquired a very considerable influence over the Lenguas—one of the largest tribes in that part of the Chaco. But in the early days, this pioneer of mission work had a decidedly rough time of it, on one occasion only escaping death by a miracle from the effects of an arrow-wound in the chest. That tragic incident seemed to mark a turning-point in the influence of the white race, and since that period the Indians have proved themselves amenable to the possibilities of civilization, if the frequent extremes of drought or flood only rendered an agricultural life anything like a certainty as the reward of their labour."

Plate 31. Meat day, Fortín Nueva Asunción, Boquerón. Each military outpost, ranch and farm in the Chaco seems to have its complement of acculturated Indians. The Paraguayan Army has assisted Indians for many years by providing them with food and clothing.

". . . in the Chaco . . . large companies are running establishments with their own little railways, and employing thousands of peons, in the Quebracho extract business. . . The Indians are few in number—of more or less nomadic habits, doing a little primitive cultivation at times, and possessing a few horses and sheep. The South American Mission Society have been at work amongst them for many years—without any marked degree of success, although a few have settled down to a quiet life. The seed sown by the missionaries may fructify in time, but the nature of the country makes it difficult to offer inducement to the hunter and nomad to settle down to the monotony of domestic life on land which hardly offers him a subsistence as the reward of his labour. Indirectly the mission people have done a great work in the pacification of wild tribes, who now offer no resistance to people embarking in pastoral or timber-getting industries. In the north, toward the Bolivian border, the country improves very much. But, up to date, little is known of many parts of the Chaco—merely sufficient to generalize. As far as one can see, there is a future for sugar and cotton on parts of the river banks and, possibly, the north; in the centre and west, stock-breeding and the Quebracho business. The railway in course of construction from Formosa to Bolivia will open up part of the region to civilization, as also will the projected canalization of the River Pilcomayo, if realized. People interested in the Chaco might read up Mr. Barbrooke Grubb's *Unknown Land,* a record of twenty years of mission work in Central South America."

Plate 32. *Quebracho* parklands, Boquerón. This region of grassland and scattered *quebracho* trees is located near Fortín Gabino Mendoza in the extreme northwestern section of the Paraguayan Chaco. Except for the activities associated with the Chaco War and oil exploration, this region has rarely been touched by "civilized" man. Moro Indians inhabit this region, and pass freely across the frontier between Bolivia and Paraguay.

"Working homewards we managed to take a short cut—by riding through a tropical forest. Hordes of travelling ants sometimes routed us out at night. Although causing considerable annoyance for the time, these creatures are rather a blessing than otherwise, making a clean sweep of all noxious insects in their path. It is very funny to see them streaking off with their prizes; often two at a time, straddling a long caterpillar and running along like a four-wheeled timber-carriage with a log of timber underneath. . .

"At this time of year the nights are often hot, humid, and sultry, and the atmosphere highly charged with electricity. Mosquitoes and sandflies literally make things hum during the short twilight till the last rays of the setting sun have merged into inky darkness. Then the spirits of the wood begin to flit around, like erratic stars, seeking their final destiny. Has any one ever explained the nature of the light of these fire-beetles, less sparkling, perhaps, but purer and more brilliant than the electric light itself? To say that it is phosphorescent is sheer moonshine. It is quite under control of the will power, being produced or turned off at any time as the insect may desire. The largest variety displays a light in each side of the head, almost as large as a tiny pea, and, when flying, another rather larger in front of the body. Perhaps, more curious still is the appearance of a small nocturnal worm, with a row of varied lights, red, blue, green, and white, on either side, for all the world like the port-holes of a ship, passing by night at sea. . .

"Enough has been said to show the aspiring young naturalist that discoveries of more or less importance will reward the man who makes a careful survey of the area."

Plate 33. Western Chaco (Boquerón). Near the Bolivian border, around Fortín Eugenio Garay, the thorn scrub is nearly continuous. At this point begin the small undulations which eventually grow and become, farther west, the foothills of the Andes of Bolivia. The rhea *(Rhea americana)* may often be seen in this part of the Chaco.

Annotated List of Contributors

Guillermo Tell Bertoni. Professor Bertoni was for many years Professor of Economic Geography at the National University of Asunción, even though he did not possess a university degree. Much of his education was acquired under the tutelage of his celebrated father, Moisés Santiago Bertoni. Like his father, Prof. Bertoni was an intellectual with many and varied interests. Besides geography, he was an avid student of languages, anthropology, history, and natural sciences. His *opus magnum,* a dictionary of the Guaraní language, was nearly complete at the time of his death in 1963. Prof. Bertoni was the editor's principal and most enthusiastic advisor during the planning stages of this book.

Moisés Santiago Bertoni, Dr. Nat. Sci. Dr. Bertoni graduated from the University of Zürich in 1880. He lived in Paraguay from 1882 until his death in 1929. His scientific contributions are discussed in the first chapter of this book.

Ricardo Boettner, Dr. Biochem. Prof. Boettner is Principal of Colegio Goethe, a private school in Asunción.

León Cadogan. Mr. Cadogan is the son of Australian immigrants to Paraguay. His patient studies, based on many years of living among the Indians of Paraguay, have earned him the esteem of professional anthropologists in the Americas and Europe.

Teófilo Fariña Sánchez, D. Sc. Dr. Fariña is a Captain in the Paraguayan Navy and is Chief of the Meteorological Service of Paraguay.

John Richard Gorham, Ph.D. Dr. Gorham conducts research on biting flies at an Alaskan research center and teaches entomology at the University of Alaska. From 1961 to 1963 he served as malaria entomologist for the Pan American Health Organization in Paraguay.

Francisco H. Schade. After formal education in Vienna, Prof. Schade emigrated to Paraguay. He is Curator of the Zoological Museum of the Faculty of Agronomy and Veterinary Medicine, National University of Asunción, and Chief of the Plant Parasite Laboratory of the Ministry of Agriculture and Ranching.

Pabla Duarte de Storni, Dr. Biochem. Dr. de Storni is Chief of the Immunology and Nutrition Section of the Regional Institute of Pathology at Resistencia, Argentina. Until recently she served as Chief of the Bromatology and Nutrition Biochemistry Laboratory of the Ministry of Public Health and Social Welfare, Asunción, and as Assistant Professor of Materia Medica and Biochemistry in the Faculty of Medicine, National University of Asunción.

Branka J. Susnik, Ph.D. Dr. Susnik received her formal education in Poland. Since coming to Paraguay, she has studied the historical, cultural and linguistic anthropology of Paraguayan Indians. She is Curator of the Andrés Barbero Ethnographic Museum in Asunción.

Robert Unruh, B. Sc. Agr., M. Ed. Agr. Ed. Mr. Unruh served the Mennonite colonies of the Paraguayan Chaco for nearly ten years as Director of the Chaco Experimental Farm. After graduate work at Texas A & M, he returned to the Chaco where he is now doing agricultural extension work and vocational education for the colonists and their Indian neighbors.

Index

Published in association with Field Research Projects
Coconut Grove, Miami, Florida 33133